EVERY BI

Pat Thomas is a writer, lec
ing in pregnancy and chil
AIMS (Association for
Services), editor of the *AIM* , a contributing editor to
the newsletter *Mothers Know Best*, and has written extensively
in the field of women's health. She lives in London with her
son.

Also by Pat Thomas

Every Woman's BirthRights

EVERY BIRTH IS DIFFERENT

Women's Experiences in Their Own Words

Pat Thomas

HEADLINE

This book is dedicated to the women who contributed to it and to every other woman whose life has been shunted into a different orbit by pregnancy, birth and motherhood.

First published in 1997
by HEADLINE BOOK PUBLISHING

10 9 8 7 6 5 4 3 2 1

ISBN 0 7472 7737 0

Typeset by
Letterpart Limited, Reigate, Surrey

Printed and bound in Great Britain by
Mackays of Chatham PLC, Chatham, Kent

HEADLINE BOOK PUBLISHING
A division of Hodder Headline PLC
338 Euston Road
London NW1 3BH

Contents

Foreword

For many women the experience of birth is so intense and vivid that it remains with them for the rest of their lives. Don't believe it when people say that 'you soon forget it'. There is evidence that memories remain strong twenty and thirty years later.[1] Details are remembered with often microscopic accuracy. This is especially so concerning a woman's relationship with her care-givers. Kindness, consideration, friendship and emotional support form major themes in these memories. But so do coercion, authoritarian attitudes, emotional neglect and cruelty.

In this book women talk vividly about birth as it is, in a complex interplay of light and dark, achievement and frustration. Their stories can help a pregnant woman work out her priorities for birth and will enable any midwife to understand better how she can give woman-centred care. Pat Thomas's crisp comments put each account in context and explain why a particular obstetric intervention, for example, altered the course of labour and led to a series of events which took control away from a woman.

When a woman thinks how she wants to give birth – whether in hospital or at home, with an obstetric team or with a midwife whom she already knows, and whether she decides in advance that she wants an epidural or to learn the skills of handling pain that reduce the chances of needing pharmacological pain relief – she is making decisions about one of the most deeply personal and intimate experiences of her life. Only she can know the hopes, fears and inner meaning that lie at the root of the choices that she makes, or sometimes of her inability to choose. She should not have to explain herself, to justify her actions, or argue the case for the kind of birth she wants. This is as much so if she decides on an elective caesarean section as if she opts for labour without drugs and with no obstetric intervention.

Read the accounts in this book and you will see that for each woman the journey through birth is an odyssey. It is an adventure into the unknown. It is not just a question of trusting care-providers or of relaxing and having a baby. It involves skills of investigation and negotiation, and entails often demanding and stressful relationships and powerful emotions. Perhaps birth ought to be more simple. But in our complex, northern technocratic society it is not.

It is a paradox that at the same time that birth is an intimate personal experience, it is also a political act. A woman is either a conformist or a non-conformist. She slips into the role of a compliant patient or she takes an active part. She submits to whatever professional decisions are made on her behalf, or she seeks information, asks questions, thinks through her priorities, and tries to negotiate the kind of birth she wants. Birth is political because it entails interaction between the health service, hospital trusts and other organisations that embody expectations about how birth should be and how women should behave, the authority of professionals, and women who are actually having babies. It concerns everything that goes on between the relatively powerful and the relatively powerless. For even when care is kindly, compassionate and sensitive, professional care-providers possess information, authority and power which individual childbearing women do not have.

Woman-centred birth is a good deal more than being allowed choices between alternatives. We have choices when we go to a supermarket and choose between different brands of breakfast cereal. Yet the position and layout of the display, the selection provided, the lighting and store design, the relative prices, the 'free offers', special mark-downs and all the elements inherent in the marketing of products have been decided by the supermarket management long before we have set foot in the store. There is choice certainly, but choices are limited and controlled by those selling the products. A menu of choices is not the same as freedom.

Today women are encouraged to believe that they have free choice about childbirth. In reality, the medical system defines, frames and limits these choices. Gate-keepers direct patients onto particular pathways and present a limited number of options, if any at all are offered, often warning women of the dangers of resisting or neglecting the advice given. They control each pregnant woman's passage through ante-natal, intra-partum and post-natal care. In the UK the initial gate-keeper is the GP.

At each stage of the process the power of the medical system is reinforced through the agency of the ante-natal clinic, the rites of admission to hospital by medical and midwifery protocols and the interventions that aim to regulate labour and make it conform to the norm.

In 1993, following the report *Changing Childbirth*,[2] the Conservative government introduced a maternity care policy which was a striking advance on the previous authoritarian and paternalistic system. From now on women were to be treated as consumers, and consumer choice was to be the basis of care. Four years later it is evident that there is marked professional resistance to the introduction of this new philosophy and that obstetricians are seeking to maintain control of territory and reinforce the hospital as an obstetric power base.

To give one example, a booklet produced by a relatively enlightened NHS trust, *Community Based Antenatal Care*,[3] in 1996 instructs GPs and community midwives on criteria for ante-natal care. The very first ruling in this booklet is that 'Community ante-natal care should be offered to all women aged over seventeen years of age who do not have any past or current significant medical, gynaecological or obstetric problem.' Choice is completely ruled out for any women who have complicated pregnancies. This includes an 'abnormal glucose tolerance test'. Glycosuria is to be tested at each ante-natal visit and if detected on any occasion it must be followed by a timed random plasma glucose and a series of other tests which require hospital admission. Since most women have a trace of sugar in their urine at some time during pregnancy, even if only because they have eaten a banana, but above all, because gestational diabetes is not in itself a disease and means only that the baby is likely to be large, this medicalises the pregnancies of many women who are completely healthy. Thus any woman pregnant under the age of eighteen and any woman who has had previous gynaecological and obstetric difficulties is automatically denied choice. It is taken for granted that, whether she wants it or not, she must have consultant care. As a result, she is processed through the system, and the issue of choice is ignored. Indeed, if she raises any objections or seeks some autonomy, she may be warned that she is risking her baby's life.

Midwives are caught up in this system. They are supposed to make it work efficiently. Their jobs depend on it. This is why a woman who looks to a midwife to support her in making her own choices and expects her to understand her hopes and fears often feels let down and deserted. When midwives have to work in large teams, in the absence of a one-to-one relationship, both childbearing women and midwives themselves are programmed for frustration and disappointment.

'Control' is sometimes dismissed as impossible in childbirth because the experience is so powerful and overwhelming that the uterus cannot be controlled as a skilled rider does a horse. Each labour has its mountains and abysses, storms and tidal waves, and a woman often feels that she has 'lost control'. But the control that is important in childbirth is control over the environment in which birth takes place, being able to come to our own decisions about the best place in which to give birth, the people to have with us, and the kind of help we want at the time. With all the talk about 'choice' there are still far too many women who feel that they have been treated like lumps of meat and who afterwards feel not only cheated, but often as if in the act of giving birth to a new life, they have been raped. When this happens this disempowerment, the sense of guilt that is invariably associated with it and the loss of self-esteem may remain with a woman for months, years – and sometimes for the rest of her life.

This book is important because it takes us back to the roots of women's birth experiences. Until everyone in the health service listens to women, the care offered cannot serve women's needs. Listening sounds an easy and obvious thing to do. Yet it is often neglected. It is assumed that care-providers know best. With this book Pat Thomas enables us to increase the quality of care in childbirth.

Sheila Kitzinger, January 1997

---

[1] 'Just Another Day in a Woman's Life? Part II: Nature and Consistency of Women's Long-Term Memories of Their First Birth Experiences', Penny Simkin, P.T. *Birth Issues in Perinatal Care*, Vol 19, Number 2, June 1992, Blackwell Scientific Publications
[2] Oxford Radcliffe Hospital (NHS Trust) Women's Centre, Community Based Antenatal Care, Information Pack for GPs and Community Midwives, April 1996
[3] Department of Health, Report of the Expert Maternity Group, 1993

Acknowledgements

So many authors talk about their books in terms of team efforts. In this case it's really true. My first and most profound thanks go out to the mothers who contributed their stories, who chose to share their lives and experiences so openly and honestly and who did it so eloquently, often juxtaposing motherly tasks with the job at hand. This book was compiled and edited in much the same way, ironically in between helping my son with his own first attempts at reading and writing, so I understand how difficult it can be.

Thank you to everyone at AIMS, particularly Beverley Beech, Sandar Warshal, Nadine Edwards, Jean Robinson, Elizabeth Key and Leslie Batchelor. You have empowered me professionally, but more important is the way you have empowered me personally through your friendship, intelligence, wicked good humour and love.

I am grateful for the larger network of women and organisations whose like-mindedness helped draw mothers to this project: The Active Birth Centre, The South East London Midwifery Practice, The Wessex Maternity Centre and Caroline Flint Midwifery Services.

Christine Grabowska was, as always, a mine of useful information and contacts around the country, as were Gina Lowdon, Pauline Cook, and Lynne McTaggart and Bryan Hubbard at *Mothers Know Best*. Thanks also to Mary Cronk who cast a first critical midwife's eye over the text.

Like many other mothers I am grateful to Sheila Kitzinger for being 'there', albeit on the pages of books, when I was pregnant; also for taking the time from her busy schedule to read and comment on the text and for providing the foreword.

I am, once again, indebted to my agent, Laura Longrigg, for her tireless and good-humoured efforts on my behalf, for her longer-term view of things and for always being there on the end of the phone as my spirits rise and fall.

Thanks to everyone at Headline, especially my editor Lindsay Symons, for being so patient and on the ball and for having an intuitive feel for the project from the beginning.

Childcare arrangements are always problematical. Thanks again to Arlene Neckles and her family for the care and feeding of Alexander, and to Jay for working with me towards some measure of peace and flexibility through raising our son.

Finally, thanks to Alexander who tolerated this intrusion on our play time with rather less good grace than he did the last time around ('But Mummy, you've *already* written a book!'). This time we both had some hard lessons to learn about family co-operation – no doubt the first of many.

Introduction

This is a book about birth. The text grew out of a need to portray pregnant and birthing women as something other than victims of a medical process, or passive visitors in the nation's medical institutions. Today more and more women are becoming aware of their choices in childbirth and are making good use of them. They are fashioning ante-natal care and birth in a way that suits them instead of forcing themselves to fit in with the 'system'. At the same time, an increasing number of doctors and midwives are coming around to the idea that many of the routine procedures they have relied upon for years are unhelpful, unproductive and, in some cases, unproven. Inch by inch the maternity services are becoming less medically oriented and more 'mother-centred'. That was clear from the tone of the first stories which reached me and continued to be so right through to the end.

By the time this book was finished, however, it was apparent that this was also a book about things which were bigger than birth. By encouraging women to write, not just about the nuts and bolts of pregnancy and birth, but about what was important to them within that framework, bigger issues emerged and birth, so often the single focus of our endeavours ante-natally, is put into its proper context of a life event.

In the same way that I made the notes for this introduction – and indeed, have edited most of this book – in-between peeling the potatoes for dinner, or correcting school work, or bandaging a finger, or acting as referee between my son and his father (all the while muttering incongruously to myself that Martin Scorsese never has to work under these conditions!), women negotiate pregnancy and birth, and everything which comes before and after, according to the bigger picture of their lives. Many of the stories in this book were written with a small baby in one hand and a pen or keyboard in the other. Others were written in stolen moments on the office computer. Some were written negotiating the difficult boundaries between telling one's own truth and remaining silent for fear of hurting those closest to us. The fact that they are so articulate, so moving, and occasionally so startling, is all the more surprising because of this. After all, motherhood is supposed to addle the brain and dull the senses – isn't it?

Medical practitioners often throw their hands up in bewilderment when women decide to take responsibility for their maternity care: 'Why on earth do you want to give birth in water?'; 'What possesses you to want a home birth?'; 'What do you mean you don't want a scan?'; 'Do you understand the risk you are taking?' Because practitioners view birth as a medical process it never occurs to them that what motivates a woman could be something as deceptively simple as a poster on a wall, a sign on a building or an overheard conversation that moves them to want something more out of birth – or it could be something more profound like a death in the family, a failing relationship, an abusive past. Then again, it could be something practical like the demands of a busy career. In this respect, as in so many others, the idea of 'choices' is something of a fallacy. Life plays its hand, and we negotiate. What else can we do?

And so it is with birth. It is often an act of negotiation, but it is also an act of self-expression. In fact, the concept of self-expression and the sharing of information with other women is where this book began.

I first contacted the Association for Improvements in the Maternity Services (AIMS) when I was pregnant and having trouble finding the information I needed to move forward with my own choices. (See What is AIMS? on page 255.) Their help was invaluable, and some years later I was thrilled to be asked to edit the *AIMS Journal*.

For many years the *AIMS Journal* has published women's birth stories – and unlike many other publications it doesn't edit out those bits which challenge our soft focus perception of birth. Through my contact with other mothers over the years, I have come to realise that women have a deep need to tell their birth stories and that other mothers and mothers-to-be have just as profound a need to listen and learn from them.

I am always struck by how fluent women suddenly become when they are talking about birth. Equally, I have a strong belief that, in a world awash with medical information about birth, the voices of pregnant and birthing women so often get drowned out. This is such a shame because the views of women are one of the most potent resources that maternity services have to draw on – if only they would.

Although this book started out as a small collection of women's letters to AIMS, it soon became clear that there were many kindred spirits out there. So, in addition to letters to the journal and letters from AIMS' members written specifically for the book, there are many stories which have come via that very female way of doing things – networking with like-minded individuals.

As the stories came in there were some happy surprises as well as some nasty ones. On the plus side, I was intrigued to see that women's views of pregnancy and birth are rarely as sentimental as they are portrayed in the media. I was also interested to see how important detail is when recalling birth. Many medical practitioners think that birthing women are totally 'out of it' and therefore it doesn't matter what is said or done around them. Labouring women, however, are highly aware and sensitive to what goes on. Memories of being offered a banana, an alarm ringing, an offhand comment or the brush of someone's scarf against their naked bodies may be among the vignettes which women carry with them forever. If some of our practitioners could come to terms with this fact, they might be less reckless in the way they treat labouring women.

I was also very glad to see how many women were finding ways of making the maternity services work for them. There are lots of options out there – and when the women who have access to them don't exercise their right to choose, it drags the whole system down.

There were also things which shocked me. Firstly the rate of ARM – breaking a woman's waters – in these stories is frankly appalling. This is one of the most common procedures performed on labouring women and there is absolutely no evidence that it is necessary or desirable. Midwives do it because they've always done it – it's no more scientific than that. If it had a nasty taste like castor oil and milk or an anti-social effect like an enema or the result could be seen by the naked eye like pubic shaving, it would have been abandoned long ago, except in the most pressing cases.

It was alternately funny and depressing to hear that we still have so many birth cheerleaders, chanting 'Push! Push!' from the side-lines. As one mother put it: 'I wanted to tell him to shut up' – but she didn't, because she felt saying it made her husband feel better! If women never pushed in labour, their babies would still get born and their bodies would end up in much better shape.

Further to this point, I was amazed that there are still midwives out there who tell women not to make so much noise during labour. There are a lot of midwives who have never had children and haven't got the imagination to know what it must be like. Perhaps this explains this peculiar point of view? Like many of the mothers in this book, I advocate making whatever noise you need to make (during, as well as before, birth!).

Finally, a book of this nature can only ever reflect a proportion of the many different experiences of birth, but I hope in these stories readers will find enlightenment and entertainment, and perhaps also the encouragement to create a birth experience that suits them. I hope also that it will be a practical as well as an emotional resource, before and after birth.

Years ago AIMS stopped using the motto 'It is better to light one small candle, than to curse the darkness' on its published material. For the purposes of this book, however, I would like to resurrect it.

Here's hoping that the stories in this volume will serve as a handful of small candles passed on from mother to mother.

A Birthday Surprise

Donna Flower

Like so many other women, my personal experience of birth so far has been very narrow. In fact, it has been limited to my own birth and the birth of my daughter.

My mother was seventeen years old when she became pregnant with me. My mother's parents did not approve of my father, so my parents decided to have a baby in order to persuade their parents to allow them to marry. My mum left home to follow my dad to Wales where he was stationed in the army. She had lodgings in Pembroke-shire and was very much alone, without the support of family or friends, and although the family she lodged with were very kind, she felt very isolated. She registered with an old-fashioned doctor who sought her out when he realised that she had not been for a check-up for a while and insisted on checking her over there and then. She attended ante-natal classes and birth classes, at the hospital, where she was taught 'breathing practice'. They were very vague and pain or pain relief were never mentioned.

I was two weeks overdue and, as my dad was about to be posted to Germany, my mum kept asking the doctor to do something. He decided to induce her, and on April 14th 1964, she was booked into the hospital, shaved and given an enema, which was the 'procedure' then. She was then given a huge glass of castor oil and milk to get her going and thus escape the need for induction. The next few hours were spent on the toilet and at 10pm her waters broke. It had worked!

The other women in the ward were settling down for the night and as Mum was getting regular contractions, she was moved to a side ward and left on her own. She wanted to ring my dad, but a nurse told her to let him sleep. She tried the breathing exercises, but had no one to be brave for. When the contractions became stronger and more painful, she shouted. A nurse came in and told her off for making a noise and told her to stop disturbing other people. She felt

Although it was once a routine procedure, today's practitioners don't give mothers castor oil. It's not as attractive or fashionable an idea as sex or eating a curry, but castor oil can be a potent labour inducer and has none of the lasting side effects of more popular modern solutions such as prostaglandin pessaries. There's room for everything and it's worth a try if you feel the need to move things along. Like most of the methods of labour induction, it tends to work best when your cervix is very 'ripe' and you are nearly ready to go into labour anyway – but if it doesn't work, at least you won't have the stigma of 'failed induction' hanging over your head. See 'Birth Basics' for information on inductions.

very lonely, frightened and unsupported. No one offered to rub her back, or even sit with her. She felt a strong desire to push, so she lay on the bed pushing, then thought she ought to tell someone. She rang a bell and a nurse came, examined her, told her not to push and left. The nurse did not say why, and as the desire to push was so strong, Mum carried on pushing, alone. After some time she was examined again and judged ready to give birth, so was then wheeled off to a delivery room and lain on her back.

She remembers gripping the headboard when the pain came, but was told by the midwife not to. She was to push whilst holding her breath, in order to use the contraction to its full effect. I was born around 7am. My mum was very happy that I was a girl, which is what she had hoped for, but she felt very remorseful for having 'made a fuss', and even apologised to the nurses. I was taken to a nursery with the other babies and brought back at feeding time. A nurse asked her, 'Breast or bottle?' Looking round and seeing all the other mothers bottle-feeding, Mum said, 'Bottle?' and that was it. No encouragement or suggestion that she might try breast-feeding. The current trend was bottle-feeding. After five days in hospital my mum took me home.

On April 15th 1990, twenty-six years later, I woke up around 7.30am feeling 'funny'. Because it was twenty days until my estimated delivery date, I put it down to feeling excited about it being my birthday. I told my partner Paul and he immediately got out his guitar and started serenading me. I said, 'I really don't think it's anything. Don't get too excited.' But he knew something was happening and I think deep down inside, I did too. I was just refusing to get excited as we'd had a few practice contractions before. One of these episodes had resulted in me being taken to hospital and being monitored for several hours before I was sent home.

Since it was my birthday, we had planned a party and had invited a few friends. So I just busied myself with food preparation, occasionally acknowledging the 'mild period pains' I was having. This continued throughout most of the day.

My guest started arriving early in the evening and I calmly announced to each one that I thought that I may be in labour, which shocked them all. I remember feeling very detached from myself, and feeling that things were not real. I was very calm and relaxed and was enjoying myself, eating, drinking and chatting. A friend called Helen had come with her six-year-old daughter, Scarlett. She wanted to play dressing-up, so she and I went and raided my wardrobe and found some dressing-up clothes. We had lots of fun and it took my mind off the cramps I was having. I let my mum know every time I had one of these 'twinges' and she had started to jot the times down. Eventually she told me that they were a few minutes apart and that we should call the midwife for some advice. I still didn't think that it was proper labour. My friend Nikki, who was also pregnant, told me a few days later that it had taken her almost two hours to eat her fruit salad because she was just so stunned at how I was behaving.

Finally, around midnight, I was persuaded to call the midwife. I really thought that I would be wasting her time. A lovely midwife, called Estry, arrived. I had never met her before, as she had been off sick for some time during my ante-natal care. I had met all the other midwives on my Domino scheme and I had discussed my birth plan with all of them. At first, I was a bit disappointed she wasn't a familiar face, but Estry proved to be a marvel. She examined me as I lay on my bed, something I had vowed never to do, but I was still in denial. She told me that I was in fact two centimetres dilated. I remember saying something like, 'So it's really happening then. This is it?'

After being examined, the contractions started to hurt. I don't know if this was because I lay down, or just the fact that I had confirmation that I was really in labour, but I found myself less able to cope. Estry left saying that it would be a long time yet and I should really try to get some sleep. I was too excited to sleep, and the contractions had started to hurt. My mum and Paul, who were going to be my birth attendants, got things packed and were generally busying themselves in preparation. I decided to have a bath, but it just made me feel nauseous. I needed to go to the toilet often and had diarrhoea. I decided to re-position the living room, most of my guests having left rather hurriedly by now! I leant forward on to cushions with someone rubbing my back. The contractions were coming faster and were more painful now and I was making loud 'cow' type moaning noises. I felt uncomfortable about this as Paul had invited his brother, sister and his brother's girlfriend to stay and they were trying to sleep in the next room.

We thought we should call Estry again as I felt that things were progressing and maybe it was time to go to the hospital. It had only been a few hours since she had left. She came over and was rather surprised. I don't remember how dilated I was, but she said that it was definitely time to go to the hospital. She went on ahead to let them know I was coming. Paul, Mum and I followed behind. Since there was nowhere to park outside the hospital, my uncle drove our car so that he could take it home again. When we got to the delivery room, we pushed the bed out of the way and laid cushions on the floor. Unfortunately, we hadn't brought enough cushions and the hospital didn't have any so we had to telephone my uncle and ask him to come back with some more! We had an oil burner, with lavender oil burning, and had a tape recorder and some tapes. With the scene set, the serious business of labour started.

I was being very sick, but this didn't bother me at the time. I also had the runs, which was worse because the toilet was some distance from the delivery room, and usually meant several contractions on the way there, and on the way back. I remember some nurses, who were sitting at a desk, looking at me very disapprovingly, since I was making lots of noise. I felt slightly self-conscious – I seemed to be the only one doing this – but I just had to do it, because it helped.

I spent most of my time in between contractions leaning forward on to my cushions and having my back rubbed. I didn't like being spoken to during a contraction, or being touched, and remember asking Paul very politely if he could not speak words of encouragement during contractions! Because we weren't quite ready for labour, we had forgotten several things. One of these was the massage oil. I suddenly became aware of the skin on my back feeling sore. My wonderfully attentive attendants had rubbed my back raw!

After coming back from one of my trips to the toilet, I decided to stay standing. I was gently swaying my hips and put my arms around Paul's neck and he began swaying with me. We danced like this for some time. It felt good. Estry was very kind and didn't

Many women find being spoken to during contractions very distracting, and back rubs can sometimes hurt more than they help, unless they are delivered with skill and care. In fact, the ritual of back rubbing can sometimes disintegrate into a way of giving those around you something to do instead of something which is genuinely helpful for you. The people around you need to be sensitive to *your* needs, not the other way round. You should not have to play the hostess during labour. Let somebody else be responsible for the needs of the other adults in the room or, better still, let them be responsible for themselves.

interfere or speak unless she needed to. She just quietly made notes and gently made suggestions. She seemed a bit concerned that my waters hadn't broken and asked if I wanted her to break them. I declined, but after a while she said she really should. I asked her to wait for just a bit longer, and remember with the next few contractions really visualising 'opening', and suddenly my waters broke. It was such an exhilarating feeling.

There was meconium in the water so Estry monitored me standing up. While I was being monitored, the fire alarms went off! They were on for ages, but whilst Mum remembers this as quite distressing, it only seemed like a remote annoyance to me. I think she must have been wondering what would happen if there was a fire and we had to go outside, but I just didn't even think about that. I was too busy! Eventually the alarms stopped and I was taken off the monitor.

I remember having a wonderful transition period, which came soon afterwards. It was very peaceful and I felt almost asleep, although I could hear and was aware of things going on around me. I remember Paul asking Mum what was happening and her explaining to him about transition. They both seemed very far away.

Soon after transition, I felt the need to push. Estry examined me and said that I wasn't quite ready, she could see an anterior lip. I quickly and calmly organised my cushions and got into the knee-chest position. After a few contractions, I asked Estry if the lip had gone. It had, and Estry said that, considering there was meconium in the water, I should only push for about an hour as the baby may be in distress.

I squatted on Paul's knees as we had practised in our couples course but it hurt him too much, so we tried a hanging squat. This was much more comfortable and fifty-five minutes later, at 6.50am, Jasmine was born. She lay very still and very quiet, face down, in front of us. We just

When a lip of cervix remains it means that the cervix has not dilated evenly and some part of it is still covering the baby's head. In this case, a bit of cervix, towards the front of the mother's body, had not moved out of the way. Because the cervix is so close to being fully dilated you may feel an urge to bear down. You'll need to hold back, however, until you are fully dilated, in order to avoid tearing your cervix. The best way to do this is to get on all fours, with your bottom higher than your head, and maintain light, quick breathing through your contractions.

looked at her in amazement. I remember my mum saying, 'Oh, it's a baby!' and I thought, 'Well, of course it is, what did you expect?' After a short while, I picked her up and put her to the breast. Estry said something about 'her' and I realised that I hadn't asked what sex she was, nor was I bothered at that moment.

We waited until the cord had stopped pulsating and then cut it. Estry was going to pull on it to remove the placenta when Paul reminded her that I had specifically asked for this not to be done. I was too absorbed in Jasmine to realise what was happening at this time and was grateful that Paul had remembered. I soon felt the need to push again and in one contraction the placenta was born. The paediatrician came in to check Jasmine over and he looked quite aghast at the mess we had made of the delivery room.

After everything else had been done, I had to have stitches, which hurt a lot. After fifteen minutes or so, I asked Estry if she had finished yet. She had only just started and said that it would take another hour or so. I had ripped through three layers of tissue, and yet I hadn't felt a thing. Jasmine breast-fed during this time and Mum and I spoke about the labour.

Paul and Mum went home for some rest and refreshment and I had a bath. They took me to the labour ward to get some rest, but I was too excited to sleep. I had something to eat and looked at my new baby. An hour or so later, Paul and Mum came to collect me and we proudly took Jasmine home.

Looking at these two births, you can see how completely different they are. I had spoken to my mum about my birth when I was in my teens, and was determined that I would never go through that experience. When I became pregnant, I wanted to arm myself with as much information as possible, and this led me to an active birth. As a result, Jasmine's birth was a wonderful, positive experience.

Aravinda – Man of the Match

Natania Jansz

It was Thursday. The mangled lyrics of a Paul Simon song floated in
and out of my mind: 'Yesterday it was my due date, I hung a former
life on the line'. The last time I had allowed Paul Simon such
ascendancy I was in an A-line skirt and acrylic overknee socks, but
retro tunes have a habit of getting lodged in my unguarded brain.

For seven months a due date had been hanging in my firmament,
a mid-point around which this baby might rush or demur, and now it
had passed. Mark and I had been bandying around ideas of rightful
celebration, scratch'n'sniff prostaglandin cards or boxes of lobster
decked in ribbon, or Veeraswamy's by ambulance. Instead, I marked
it by setting the flat adrift with a bucket of tight orange roses
perched on the telly, a pot of freesias wafting their breezy scent
from our all-purpose table and three anthuriums, the colour of
lemon curd, snaking up from the windowsill, all gathered in an early
morning rush (or tottering lumber) around Covent Garden market. It
had come as a relief to be somewhere where the lights were on and
the atmosphere sociable, rather than lying huddled in bed making
the occasional petulant shove at Mark's sleeping bulk. Strange how
lumpen and huge his sleep became as mine began to vaporise. He'd
even taken up snoring which struck me as a deeply provocative, if
subconscious, form of gloating.

But that was the day before, and the flowers, though not exactly
flagging, already had an entrenched look. I lowered myself, spread-
kneed, on to my usual footstool and phoned Caroline, my independent midwife. I had a question to ask, a deceptively casual one: 'I just
wanted to know how long you'd be away this weekend at the
conference . . . just so I can keep the times in mind.' Caroline's
voice came back measured: 'I'll be leaving early Friday morning
and I'll be back late Monday night, and I'll see you again on
Tuesday.' It sounded brusque to my ears, at odds with the embracing

cheerfulness of her usual phone manner, as if she were steeling herself for a backlash. My tone remained light, this was OK, it had to be: 'Well, I hope it all goes well for you. I've decided I won't go into labour until you get back.' 'That's fine, I'm sure it won't be for some days yet,' she answered with a return of warmth.

We should have wished each other goodbye at this stage, but suddenly a trump card appeared on my pile: 'Just one more question, Caroline, I haven't felt the baby move this morning, is there anything I should do to help this along?'

I can't remember what the answer was. Its tone was reassuring, with some practical suggestions of some exercises to prod a bit of action, but I heard none of it. 'Yes, OK, I'll try that, goodbye,' and I hung up as tears sprang to my eyes and the panic crested. 'Move. Move! Just show me you're alive.' My murmured exhortations ricocheted off the silent mound of my body as I sat rocking on my footstool.

I had chosen Caroline's independent midwifery service, chosen to spend large amounts of money for what seemed, in my ignorance, to be a routine and simple service (after all anyone can take blood pressure and prod a lump), chosen privilege despite my fervent espousal of the NHS, for one reason only: to know that a midwife of my choice would be there and see me through. That such a simple requirement wasn't available with my local services – out of the three I'd met, one was leaving her job, one had blithely announced that she'd probably be away and one was just too over-committed to offer any guarantees – was a welfare state failure that I just didn't have the energy to rise to.

Most women go independent, if they have the means, in their determination to have a home birth against the odds of age, breech presentation, or other predicted medical complications. Not me. I was happy to be whisked to hospital, felt comforted by the thought of all the emergency services that would be available if my baby was endangered (my nephew's life was saved by intensive care), felt intrigued by, almost eager for, the various pain relief drugs on offer. Along with the midwifery care, it was a trusted advocate that I needed, someone to bridge, momentarily, the chasm that had opened in my third month of pregnancy when my mother suddenly died and left me to carry my child alone. My father, a retired doctor, had managed with sage gentleness to guide me beyond the point when I feared I would miscarry (my first pregnancy had been labelled

An *independent midwife* can attend you either in hospital or at home or in one of the few birth centres in the country. Unlike many other forms of private care, it is seldom a hankering for prestige which drives women to choose independent midwives. Often it is because there is no other way for a woman to get continuity of care or a particular type of skilled care such as for a breech delivery or birth in water.

Women who are denied choice within the hospital system for any other reason, such as past obstetric history, age, physical or mental disability or other factors can be reassured that they are probably in better hands with an experienced independent midwife than they are with a less experienced hospital or community midwife. The experience of women throughout the country has also shown that the post-natal care provided by independent midwives, which often goes well beyond the statutory ten days after birth, is also invaluable, providing them with consistent advice on caring for themselves and their babies and support while establishing breast-feeding, all of which can be lacking in a busy hospital environment. Women who choose independent midwives are not always 'rich' – which is why many independent midwives allow payments to be spread out over a number of months. They are also usually happy to talk to women, without obligation, and advise them about their various birth options.

To find an independent midwife in your area you can get in touch with your local Community Health Council or contact the Independent Midwives Association.

'blighted' – a strangely Victorian explanation that haunts me still) but he was struggling with crutches and a possible thrombosis after a recent leg operation.

It would be crass to conclude that Caroline was to be my mother substitute, although certainly her warmth and presence (ample, extrovert, undaunted) were on such a scale. She was also a midwife of repute, known to most of the nurses on the labour ward at the hospital, and with an easy grasp of all the latest research in obstetrics. I wanted her there at the birth.

I think Caroline sensed how deeply let down I would feel by her absence. For two weeks she had been urging me to meet her colleagues, Andrea, the midwife I had agreed as second string to Caroline, and Val, whose role I couldn't imagine. Surely two midwives were enough to cover most eventualities? I knew Andrea slightly, a highly competent woman, attractive in an understated way, with a manner that a new-ager might call spiritual. I found her a calm, reassuring presence, who reminded me more of myself than my mother, but she wasn't Caroline and I'd already made my choice. These things are important when you're hiding from grief.

When I announced that the baby had stopped moving it wasn't that it had only just occurred to me, but that I had become fearful about it at that point. I was used to having occasional outcrops of fear that I could quieten by meditating on the baby, or reading the foreign pages in the paper, or phoning some friend who might be idling at a desk. None of these worked this time. I had the insight to know that the baby probably was moving, hammering away no doubt, in the manner of avalanche survivors, but panic was clouding my senses. If only I could relax.

I delayed phoning Mark, knowing how infectious panic could be. Instead I rummaged around for a swimsuit. Forty minutes later, I lowered myself into the therapy pool of the health club I had joined in that former life of ours. Water always does me good and, kicking off

---

It is normal for a baby's movements to slow down as you approach labour, particularly if its head has engaged. Many women describe their babies as being more 'settled' during this time and energetic kicks give way to nudges from knees and elbows. If the baby's movements seem to slow down before then, it isn't necessarily a sign of growth retardation or some other problem.

There are a number of reasons why you may not feel the normal activity of your baby, including the fact that the baby has shifted position, or that you may simply be preoccupied with work and arrangements for the impending birth and haven't had time to stop and listen to your baby or your body. However, towards the end of pregnancy, most women have a keen awareness of their baby's own individual pattern of rest and wakefulness. So, if you are concerned that you have not felt your baby move for the last 12 hours or so, contact your midwife or GP. They may advise the following:

- Fetal monitoring to listen to the baby's heart rate.
- An ultrasound scan to look for signs of movement.
- Keeping track of fetal movement via a 'kick chart' – ten movements in a twelve-hour period is generally a sign that all is well, though on its own this is not a reliable method of assessment.

from the side, with my baby floating in my own floating body, I began again to harbour intimations that all would be well. They didn't stick. Within seconds a muscular body in swimming lycra bounced on to a platform beside the pool and began shouting out a rhythm above a pounding bassline. What seemed like the whole of corporate London chose this signal to leap into the water beside me and began churning it into milky froth, breaking and slapping the surface like some mass audition for *Flipper*. I had coincided with a high-NRG aqua aerobics session. A kindly woman in a skin-grafted Speedo towed me through the mêlée to the steps.

Later that afternoon, I arranged with Caroline to have the baby's heart monitored at the hospital. Mark sped back from work. As we sat together, watching the sun set over the Thames in a collage of tourist postcards, an unutterable calmness descended. Caroline explained that the sensations of movement had been lost because the baby had shifted slightly. We chatted on about work and life, while the baby nudged the monitor's printer along a perfectly normal trajectory of peaks and troughs.

Sunday was destined to be notable. It was Mother's Day, my eldest sister's birthday, and the Sri Lankan cricket team were about to march out on to the impossibly green wicket of Lahore stadium and take on Australia for the World Cup. As Sri Lankan Dutch Burgers by birth (a fussy sort of genealogy impossible to summarise, but with a sense of nationhood rooted amongst relatives in Colombo and Kandy) we knew which side we were on. None of my family, however – father, three sisters and brother – were passionate about cricket. That task had rested solely with my mother, who would whoop with delight at the virtuosity of West Indian or Pakistani batsmen, waiting for Sri Lanka to enter the world arena. She would have gloried in the team's appearance in this final. And so, in pride and respect, we planned to get together at my sister's house and glory too. Except my body was letting me down. All the previous night I had felt a pressure mounting on my lower back and a strained weakness that felt like constipation.

There was no pain, just a bolt-alert discomfort, and it didn't cross my mind that I was going into labour. I had barred my mind against the thought. Labour was for Monday night at the earliest – after Caroline had returned. No, this was constipation, chronic and uncomfortable. My odd mental state the night before, querulous arguments with my brother and an explicable, though in retrospect totally clichéd, impulse to bake jam tarts – I have never in my life baked a jam tart – should have come as a warning. And yet, for all my feigned ignorance, I must have known why I manoeuvred myself quietly to my feet that night and tiptoed to the toilet with a Jane Austen omnibus, rather than risk disturbing Mark. I wanted him to have all the sleep he would need.

As early as was decent, I phoned my father to ask some advice about dealing with constipation, dismissing his worries with wilful assurance. I'd see him at lunch. Breakfast passed and the dull pressure remained. My sister-in-law dropped by and we chatted nonchalantly of motherhood and epidurals, summoning images of darts practice and backstabbings (it was after all the ides of March), while I shifted from chair to chair, lurching back to bed the moment the door closed behind her. Mark had his suspicions, but no more wanted them confirmed than I did. Instead he cloaked his anxieties beneath a biddable tenderness. I lay taut, squirming from time to time with a dull undulation in my lower back, trying to fix my attention to the pre-match commentary that Mark had found for me on the bedside clock radio. Ranatunga had won the toss and was putting the Australians in to bat.

Suddenly I needed to eat a packet of Burton's potato puffs. Not just any crisps, but the particular cheap and vacuous snack that I had seen in one of the piled-up boxes at our local Indian grocer's. I gave my order to Mark, detailing where he was to scrummage around with the precision of a spy leader. He returned with Smith's salt and vinegar. In one fluid motion of disappointed fury, I hoisted up some leggings, shuffled into slippers, and went padding down the road with Mark in attendance, explaining for the umpteenth time that the box was not to be found. He was right. I returned deflated, clutching a newspaper, sloughed off my clothes, and crouched on the bed. It was Sanath Jayasuriya's turn to bowl.

There were phone calls to make, one to my twin sister, Litza, to say I was staying at home and no, of course I wasn't in labour; the other to Andrea, midwife number two, to say I was feeling odd, but I was certain these weren't contractions. 'I'm here for you,' Andrea said, choosing intuitively the only words that could help. 'I'll wait by the phone. Call me if anything changes or if you feel worried.' Her voice receded and a sadness flooded over me. I knew the time was coming, and allowed myself to admit that the routine I was working up – rocking on my bed only to roll off it to stagger to the toilet – was because any moment I expected my waters to burst.

They didn't in the dramatic sort of way I'd anticipated, but not long after phoning Andrea I had a show, a thick smear of bloodied mucus. Only a madwoman would imagine this was an early return to menstruation and although still deep in denial, I was not yet mad. By now it wasn't the Caroline-less labour I feared, epic and awful though I knew it could be. It was the relentless pressing forward of motherhood that was stalling me, that moment when I would be called upon to take responsibility for a tiny baby, utterly and abjectly mine, day and night for weeks, months, years. This was the burden I was trying to stave off, rocking to the rhythm of its pressure, on hands and knees.

My first reaction on finding the show, the undeniable evidence that we had passed the starting line, was to snivel – a pathetic, cowardly, snotty-nosed snivel. All sorts of trivial mitigations clouded my mind: I wasn't ready; I hadn't finished reading an interesting article in the *Independent on Sunday*; I wanted to sleep; but most of all, I wanted a quiet cigarette. Here was one of the most important moments of my life, yet my mind was preoccupied with a quick puff behind the bike shed, or the nearest equivalent, despite the fact that I'd given up many moons ago. Fortunately, the moment passed and a sense of purpose, visceral as much as mental, took over. I was about to take charge.

Mark could sense that I had shifted gear and wanted to hang about me. I dispatched him to the front room to keep the radio vigil there, needing quiet but also feeling comforted by the litany of Sri Lankan names and cricket incidents. Aravinda de Silva, another boundary, Sanath Jayasuriya, cheers from the Sri Lankans and Pakistanis. Without being aware of it, I had screamed. Mark rushed in, just as a wild cheer reverberated around the Lahore stadium. 'What happened? What happened?' we asked in unison.

The pains started to come more quickly now, a sudden weakening as my body contorted with the pressure, leaving me whimpering alongside, rocking in a circular motion. Mark dialled Andrea and handed me the phone. 'When can you get here?' I managed, before mashing my face into the duvet in a gasp of pain. 'Forty-five minutes. I'm on my way.'

Forty-five minutes, this was a blow, but it was OK, I told myself – take charge, take charge. We had a TENS machine that Caroline had lent us and, although our dress rehearsal with it hadn't been a success (no sooner had Mark taped me up than half of Kennington decided to drop by for a visit), I felt that the time had come to try it. Mark, eager for practical involvement, emptied the case out on the bed and started fiddling with electrodes, jelly and tape. 'Do it properly! Do it properly!' I urged through panting breath, sounding to all the world as if I expected him to stick the electrodes up my nose. The phone rang. On the ansaphone I heard Litza's voice, a voice eerily like my own on tape, telling me that she was a mile down the road in Camberwell, with my father, and that they were ready to come over whenever I wanted. But my world had been sucked into too small a space to allow anyone fresh in. Mark, confused by my exhortations, wound more and more tape tightly around my back and handed me the TENS controls as I once more rolled to the edge of the bed and stumbled towards the toilet. Instead of crumpling with the pain I was pinned upright in what felt like the strappings of a gentleman's corset and, to add insult to absurdity, the button of the machine suddenly pinged free of its holding and catapulted itself behind the bowl. And so it was that my one and only attempt at pain relief was spent gunning out expletives while crouched stiffly in a corner, groping behind a toilet. The TENS machine soon followed in the wake of its control button while I ran the gauntlet of tightening muscle back to the bed.

Time truncated in the ensuing hour. I have a memory of rocking and moaning, the words of an ante-natal yoga instructor playing on my mind: 'Find a rhythm, go with the wave of the contractions.' This wasn't an intellectual memory and it surprised me to recognise Jayne's soft Scottish accent behind the movements I was making. I was, after all, the dissenter in her group, the wimp who glazed over at the thought of natural birth and used the hour to meditate on the baby growing within and to get some handy tips about local services. And there I was thinking of waves. The word 'wave' is of course far too benign, but the image of an awesome swell of water looming up behind, waiting to crush you in a sinewy mangle of tendons, while you suffocate in brine, seemed to fit. If only I could keep my nerve and concentrate hard enough, I might be able to ride it: 'Here it comes, hereitcomes, here . . .' and I'd listen as if from a distance, while a long, guttural scream tore from my mouth, and then another, and then a moment's panting quiet.

It was a surprise when I looked up to find Andrea on her haunches at the corner of the bed watching me. She reached out to

TENS stands for transcutaneous electrical nerve stimulation. You can rent TENS machines privately or through your hospital or clinic. The theory behind TENS is that when patches with electrodes in them are placed on strategic places on your body, in this case your back, and an electric current is passed through them, it will stimulate your body to produce more endorphins – the body's natural pain killers. TENS has never been formally evaluated and opinion, in this book and elsewhere, is very divided on its usefulness. Certainly it does not take the pain away, and whether it produces endorphins or not is debatable, but it can provide a subtle distraction from early labour pains. It will not help in later, more established labour.

Your body's production of endorphins rises naturally in labour to meet your body's increasing demands. Certain routine procedures interfere with the production of endorphins, leaving you with less natural resources to cope with the pain. These include the use of oxytocic drugs which accelerate contractions so quickly that the body cannot produce endorphins fast enough and in sufficient quantity to help itself. The administration of an epidural shuts down your body's production of endorphins altogether, though pethidine and gas and air do not appear to inhibit their production.

massage my back, but withdrew when she realised I wasn't to be touched. Mark later told me of how he had panicked and run out on to the streets with no coherent thought but some adrenaline-fuelled notion of flagging down a midwife, only to find Andrea crossing the road outside, bag in hand. 'As if she had been blown in on a high wind,' he had commented, 'like Mary Poppins.'

'Would you like me to examine you?' Andrea asked in a calm and business-like manner. Yes, I would. I needed to know just how productive all this effort was, and, at the back of my mind, I knew that my decision to move or stay depended on it. She and Mark helped turn me over and, with the minimum of fuss (amazing how some people can conjure up emergency wards just by the way they twang on their rubber gloves; Andrea avoided such pretensions), she announced that I was doing brilliantly. The rest had to wait as I was squirming urgently and shouting to them to turn me back and allow me to rock through the next giant wave. After it had passed, Andrea announced, 'You're seven centimetres dilated.' This was what I had dared to hope. The finale was in sight.

It must have been around then that the crowds spilled out on to the streets of Colombo, lighting firecrackers and dancing beside roadblocks, while Ranatunga raised his trophy to the world's satellite dishes.

Andrea asked if I wanted to stay where I was, as she had all the equipment we would need for a home birth, and would only need to phone another midwife, then tactfully left us to make up our mind. I didn't need to think this over. Nothing would induce me to move off the bed. The sea was dangerous as hell, and I had to keep my eye on the swell on the horizon – 'Coming up, it's here' (pause) 'aaaargh.' Mark, remembering how strongly I had felt about epidurals and the nearby intensive care ward, took a bit more convincing. So the next time I drew breath I choked out the words: 'I'm staying, I can't go anywhere, it's OK, Andrea's here . . . aaaaaargh.'

Val arrived and placed herself in the opposite corner of the bedroom. This left only the cat unaccounted for, who, it transpired, was working off some of her chagrin by peeing on the sofa in the front room.

Val had a difficult role to play. Ebullient by nature and a confident participant in the drama of birth, she was left with little to do but watch. A third presence was too much for me to take in and I swatted away any comments she tried to make, forcing her to retreat behind hand signals to Andrea.

Seven hours had passed since my first batch of phone calls, but time had taken on a strange elastic quality. My blood sugar, however, was less flexible. Mark had been holding cartons of juice beneath my mouth with bendy straw poised (never underestimate the use of bendy straws in labour) but I was beginning to seriously flag, knees and wrists buckling under the weight of my swaying body. I remembered the dextrose tablets I had packed in my labour bag and gasped out instructions to Mark, who tried to pop a couple in my mouth, not easy through gritted teeth. The next contraction hit to a soundtrack of crunching glucose as a ravenous Mark and Andrea worked their way through the rest of the pack.

I didn't need to be told that I was entering the second stage. From rocking the pain round in a circle I suddenly began to strain outwards, tensing my legs and bearing down on my bowels. With a shock I recognised the sensation of the round solid mass of my baby's head cramming against my pelvis. The acerbic words of a character of some long-forgotten novel surged to mind. 'It's like shitting a melon,' she had said, answering a question about childbirth. But this head was not a melon, it was unknitted bone loosely held to a body, encasing the future potential of our baby, and I couldn't bear to think of the trauma it was suffering as it rammed against me. So I didn't, although I grasped at the theme of defecation with enthusiasm.

The baby was coming – it would be done – but how? An image of tearing flesh gained a hold and I felt my body sag. 'Push again,' came Andrea's voice. 'You're doing really well, but listen, Nat, try to cry out from the bass downwards – not up.' Odd to have a lesson in vocal technique at such a stage, but I knew what she meant, I was dissipating my efforts in squealing to the rafters. I needed to wait, to stall, it was happening too soon. 'Phone Litza and Dad,' I cried. 'Not you, Mark – Val.' Only then did I realise that I was gripping Mark's arm. If I lost him all would be lost. Val dialled and began talking, but the pace was conversational. 'Now, now, come now,' I screamed to my dad and sister, heaving forward on the bed. They heard.

Val passed Andrea a scribbled note. I needed to change position. 'Come to the edge of the bed,' she suggested, guiding me, 'and now squat down resting between Mark's legs.' I struggled for leverage, comforted by the warm drill covering Mark's thighs, and his hands clasping my shoulders. 'Push again,' said Andrea. It was too much for Mark. 'Come on, Nat, one last push,' he said. 'No. Don't say that!' I cried out in fury. 'You don't know.' Indeed, no one could know (another sobbing heave shook me). It was truth and certainty that I needed now, not wishful speculations. Mark understood and transferred his hopes to holding me.

Something was wrong. Andrea and Val were giving each other quizzical looks. 'It's your perineum,' reported Andrea, 'it just keeps stretching.' I don't know how these outbreaks of lucidity occur but I heard myself coolly suggest that Andrea got a mirror from the bathroom to have a closer look. She did and saw the baby's head. 'He's coming, but you really need to push as deeply as you can.' So I pushed. Then again, and in the instant it takes for one plane of your life to shear off into another, a moist, bloodied, slithering figure flopped into Andrea's hands.

Mark and I bowed down, his head above mine, to greet our child. Andrea's latex-covered fingers gave way to my naked ones and I held him, slightly away from me, in a charade of holding since he weighed almost nothing, so that we both could see him, our newborn baby. The words were clichés. 'Isn't he lovely, look, Mark, our beautiful little boy.' I had hoped to feel euphoric, but instead I felt quietly and profoundly impressed. There was a sound in the corridor and the bedroom door opened, framing my twin sister and father. Val had let them in fifteen minutes earlier. 'Isn't he just lovely,' I mouthed as if, once again, summing up some universal truth. They stood smiling down at the picture of Mark and me smiling down at the tiny blood-spattered figure of our son, before retreating to await their next audience amongst the feline devastation of our front room.

It seems cruel that birth is only safely over after you've returned to the business of labour. I had the afterbirth to expel and now that it had dawned on me that I had managed to give birth at home, to a healthy seven-and-a-half-pound boy, without the use of drugs, there was no way I was going to allow it all to become eclipsed by a late emergency admission. The problem was that I had no push left. I couldn't blow my nose, let alone heave again at my bowels. The endorphins I must have relied on had long since drained away, leaving my body a flaccid lump, befuddled by spent emotion. Why couldn't I be left alone to examine minutely the tiny body that Mark was cradling, instead of being hoisted into yet another position on newly plumped pillows?

The rest I remember through a cobweb gauze of exhaustion. Andrea holding the baby to my breast, forefinger and thumb squeezing his cupid lips to a pout, me starting up in bewilderment at the first vigorous pull. Litza leaning over with something metallic to clamp the cord, hand steered by Andrea, her woolly scarf brushing my breast, reckless of the flecks of blood. A bath (how did I get in there?), holding the baby against my knees, trickling water over him like a Ganges devotee, and back to bed to try once more to push. By now the mood was darkening. I had to produce the afterbirth. So I pushed and I screamed, a wild hollow scream that had less to do with pain than dissent. I'd had enough. At last it came in its sloppy mass of blood. Only Andrea was intent this time, inspecting it as carefully as you might an undiagnosed twin. 'It's wonderful, Nat, it's all there.' She must have examined me again at this point because both she and Val agreed that a small labial tear would heal itself.

It was time for celebration. Mark snapped back into the role of host and re-emerged bearing sparkling wine, herbal tea and a plate of peeled mangoes oozing ripeness. Litza was busy preparing a more substantial midnight snack.

Names, names, names. 'You tell me what you want to be called, my precious,' I whispered as I slipped a finger into my baby's determined grasp. How rough and gnarled my hand seemed by comparison, with spots spreading on its reptilian surface. Surely not liver spots? Mark was receiving a resumé of the cricket from Dad. Aravinda de Silva had knocked them all over the place – sha! – he was superb – man of the match.

Aravinda-man-of-the-match. That would do for now.

Natascha's Birth

Sarah Allen

I waited a long time to become pregnant. Despite periods of intense broodiness, I held back until I was in a stable relationship before taking the plunge, and my husband, Andy, was even more apprehensive. I think having divorced parents makes one cautious. When I did become pregnant, I was thrilled. I cleared the local library shelves of books on the subject, but soon found them rather daunting, if not frightening. Suddenly pregnancy and childbirth seemed to me to be a minefield of potential disasters. I put all the books away until I was about five months pregnant and able to face them again and bought cosy maternity magazines with lots of cute baby pictures instead.

This 'childbirth is a dangerous minefield which cannot be navigated without intervention at every stage' attitude prevailed at the teaching hospital where I was to give birth. Indeed, my consultant became somewhat irrational during discussions about my birth plan. She said that she could not understand why active birth plans sought to avoid routine pain relief ('We're not Hitlers here, you know. We're only trying to help. It would be far easier for me to pay my mortgage as a shop assistant!'), and that my desire not to have syntometrine administered to expel my placenta might lead to my bleeding to death. She was obviously getting rather emotional, so I didn't argue, but neither did I change my birth plan. After all, the only reason I was having my baby in hospital in the first place was as an insurance policy against possible dangers. The consultant *assumed* that intervention was essential; I *assumed* that I was perfectly capable of giving birth naturally. I think that some consultants don't like handing over power to women in labour because it reduces their role to that of a back-up facility.

I was keen to avoid back pain during pregnancy and having done some Alexander Technique as a student, checked out a book on the subject by Ilana Machover. The more I read, the more I began to realise that, not only would Alexander Technique help me during pregnancy, but it could also help me during labour. I was delighted to find that Ilana lived reasonably near me. I called her on the phone and knew instantly that this was a woman I could trust. Her classes proved very empowering, and I felt able and ready to face whatever labour might have in store for me.

My waters broke at midnight, in a great gush. Poor Andy, who had just dropped off to sleep after a terrible, long day at work, staggered out of bed, and went off to make cups of raspberry leaf tea, while I dripped my way to the bathroom. I had been feeling unaccountably ratty and restless all day, so it was a relief and rather exciting to think, *this is it!* I called my friend Jane (who is also an Alexander teacher and who had agreed to be my birth partner) to put her on 'standby', suggesting that we would call her from the hospital, as I wouldn't be able, as planned, to spend several hours at home. I wasn't too happy at the prospect of having to go to hospital pretty soon, so as the waters were clear, I decided after consultation with the hospital to have a bath at home first.

Knowing that I would not be allowed to eat at the hospital, I detailed Andy to make large quantities of banana-yoghurt milkshake, which

---

There has been little clinical evaluation of women's nutritional needs in labour. One thing is certain: it is totally unnecessary and cruel to deny women food and drink when they are doing the most physically demanding job of their lives. The uterus is a muscle and needs energy to do its job properly. In addition, women who do not eat during labour may experience hypoglycaemia (a sudden drop in blood sugar levels), which leaves them tired and vulnerable and ultimately too weak to give birth. If you are at home, you should continue to eat and drink as and when you need to.

If you are in hospital, you may well be told you cannot eat anything. However, you have the right to bring your own food, and often this is advisable. Try packing soft fruits like bananas or mangoes, yoghurt or fromage frais, pots of honey or honey sandwiches, dextrose tablets and plain biscuits for yourself and perhaps something more substantial for your birth partner(s). You will need to drink as well as eat, since it is essential to keep your body fluids up in order to keep your kidneys working well. Try fruit juices, flasks of herbal tea or clear broth.

would provide me with energy and also help me keep calm (I think there is a chemical in this mixture called serotonin which is soothing). After my bath I got dressed, but had to change a couple of times, as I kept leaking amniotic fluid. I started experiencing period-like pains of varying intensity, which were easy to cope with by bouncing on my gymnastic ball. I also listened to Prokofiev's second violin concerto.

The midwife at the hospital had told us not to hang around too long before coming in, so we arrived around 3am. There were some raised eyebrows at the sight of my gymnastic ball. One midwife said, 'I've seen a few things in my time, but what is that for?' 'It's going to help me get through labour,' I replied.

We were shown into a labour room, and left for what seemed a long time, before a midwife appeared, saying she was prepared to try to accommodate my birth plan, but that, if I hadn't reached full dilation within twelve hours of my waters breaking, it was 'hospital policy' to induce labour. This is apparently because of the risk of infection. I decided to fight that particular battle when I came to it.

The midwife persuaded me to lie back on the bed (the one and

The risk of infection is actually greater in hospital, where a mother is likely to encounter all sorts of foreign bacteria. What midwives and doctors are really worried about is cord prolapse, where the umbilical cord slips down and gets crushed between the baby's head (or bottom if it's a breech) and the mother's pelvis. This can be a risk when your waters break spontaneously and the baby's head is high in your womb – but it's just as much of a risk if someone breaks them artificially, so it seems hospital policy may serve to create the very problems it's trying to avoid.

Once your waters have broken and cord prolapse is ruled out, you should do everything you can to protect your baby and yourself from infection. Minimise the number of internal examinations you have or, better still, forget them altogether. An experienced midwife doesn't need to examine you to tell how far along you are – she can tell from the positions you take up and the noises you make. She can also provide you with the encouragement you need to trust that your body is doing what it needs to do, at the speed it needs to do it. It will be obvious to just about everyone when the baby is about to arrive! Unless there are indications, don't let anybody introduce a scalp monitor or other paraphernalia into your vagina as this also increases the risk of infection. See 'Birth Basics' for information on Artificial Rupture of the Membranes.

only time I consented) for an internal examination, which was *excruciating*. She pronounced me one centimetre dilated. She agreed to monitor the baby's heartbeat and my contractions while I bounced on the ball, and, having set this up, disappeared. The contractions were slowly but surely increasing in intensity and frequency, but I was able to do 'whispered ahs' all the way through. After about twenty minutes, the midwife reappeared, and decided that, as I was clearly coping with the contractions, I could not be in 'true' labour. I was to be sent to the ante-natal ward until such time as 'true' labour had started and Andy would not be permitted to join me there. I pointed out that, although manageable, the contractions were building up steadily, but she was unimpressed.

We gathered up all our equipment, and were led along the corridors to a room divided by curtains into four cubicles, each containing a bed and bedside table. There was not enough room to swing a cat, let alone crawl around, do 'pear' movements or whatever. Another midwife appeared, and suggested that I lie down and try and get some sleep, and that Andy should go home. I protested that I could not bear him to go, and that it would be a half-hour taxi-ride in each direction. She repeated that husbands were not allowed on the ante-natal ward, and that three other women were in the same boat – their husbands had dutifully disappeared home. One of these women was trying to get some sleep in the cubicle next door – she clearly was not having contractions of any kind. I pointed out that I was hardly going to sleep with contractions coming every two-and-a-half minutes, and

You don't actually have a legal right to have anyone with you in hospital. However, most hospitals now recognise the moral right of the father, or whomever the mother chooses as her birth partner, to be there. No woman should be left to cope alone in labour and 'hospital policy' is not a convincing argument. Under these circumstances the kind of stubborn refusal shown here is the best option.

that I did not wish to lie down, as this would increase the pain and slow down labour. 'Nothing can slow down labour. It's going to take a long time! Get some rest while you can!' she replied. Nobody was listening to me.

Andy held my hand and didn't budge. They were probably aware that he was still there, but left us to it. Things started hotting up and getting really painful. I started listening to the slow movement of Ravel's piano concerto, got Andy to massage my sacrum, put his warm hand on my belly, in fact anything to distract me. There was not even enough room for the ball to rotate properly. I wasn't sure I was going to be able to cope with the pain, and I was feeling self-conscious about the amount of noise I was making. I continued to leak amniotic fluid in copious amounts. Suddenly I started shaking with cold, and put some clothes back on.

We decided to escape the cramped conditions, and made our way to the day sitting room along the corridor. Much better! It was dark, with a nice, soft carpet, which I proceeded to crawl around on, as ever, leaving a trail of amniotic fluid wherever I went (serves them right for messing me around!). Although I was not able to do any fancy breathing during the contractions (I just tried to get through them somehow), I did manage to relax between them, which made all the difference. I tried to 'smile through the perineum' during a 'whispered ah', as Jane had practised with me only the day before, and actually felt my cervix dilating! That is to say, I distinctly felt pain and movement in that area, plus an opening movement. I excitedly communicated this to Andy, who said that he could also feel movement under his hand on my sacrum – 'I think she's going round the s-bend!' he said. In the meantime, a night-duty nurse appeared, presumably wondering what all the noise was about, and was astonished to find us there. I told her to tell them on the labour ward that things were definitely happening. She witnessed a particularly painful contraction and disappeared, muttering, 'I'll see what I can do.'

Time takes on a different dimension in labour, but I swear it was soon after this that I suddenly felt the urge to push. I immediately adopted the head down, bottom-in-the-air position, chanting 'Must not push!' through each contraction. Andy rushed off to get a midwife. He still hadn't found an opportunity to call Jane, which was a shame because I definitely could have done with her help, especially in the second stage, which was about to begin.

We made our way back to the labour ward, with me dropping down to the floor frequently with the contractions, finally reaching yet another room for me to mess up! The midwife seemed astonished that I could be in an advanced stage of labour. I refused to lie down, so she performed another excruciating internal, this time with me standing up (and screaming blue murder). Afterwards she said, 'In which position would you like to deliver? You're fully dilated!'

I wanted to squat, preferably supported by Jane and Andy, but Jane was still tucked up in bed at home and I had to get on with it. So I knelt on the bed, leaning forward into the pillow, which I hope somewhat muffled the animal noises I was making. Although the pain, at first, was bearable, and I felt excited that we were almost there, I suddenly felt I didn't know what to do next. I wasted a lot of energy pushing out my breath, instead of the baby. I was grateful for Andy's enthusiasm and support throughout, but at the same time found myself wishing that Jane were there to guide me through it.

The midwife did help, but I feel that, in a supported squat, I would probably not have torn at all, whereas on all fours – the *midwife*'s preferred position – I did tear slightly (the stitches healed in just over a week). The sensation of trying to push this enormous watermelon through me was extraordinary, and I wasn't at all sure I could do it. The midwife encouraged me to hold on to the baby at the end of each push, as she kept sliding back. As the head reached the perineum it felt like iodine poured on an open wound, but a couple of contractions later Natascha was born. I moved back slightly to see her, almost sat on her and splattered her with blood, but it didn't seem to faze her.

A second midwife had appeared and asked, 'Where's the syntometrine?' 'She's not having syntometrine!' replied the first. She seemed concerned that I had lost a lot of blood (400ml, though God knows how they measure it), but she knew I was determined to try. I tried putting the baby to my breast, but she didn't seem remotely interested. In fact, this seemed to distress her, so she was handed to her proud father. I felt a contraction, the midwife told me to push, and within ten minutes, the placenta slid out. Hallelujah!

An hour later, the day shift took over. A lot of midwives came in to inspect the gymnastic ball, as word had clearly got round that somebody had managed a natural childbirth without any intervention and no pain relief. I was clearly a curiosity. One quietly congratulated me on sticking to my guns, saying it was almost unheard of in a teaching hospital. Another (silly cow) suggested I get in a supply of paracetamol, as I would soon be racked with pain urinating and from the after-pains. In fact, I coped with the former by pouring warm water from a bottle over the area while peeing and the latter never did seem particularly painful.

Marianne, the senior midwife, whom I had always found sympathetic on my ante-natal visits, asked who I had prepared with. We told her that we had attended a seminar with Yvonne Moore, which was excellent, but that instead of yoga, I had used Alexander Technique with Ilana. She asked me for Yvonne *and* Ilana's telephone numbers.

Soon, the baby took to my breast, with a lot of inexpert fumbling on both sides, and spent most of the day on my chest – lots of luxurious skin contact. Marianne suggested that, as both of us were so well, we could contemplate going home that very day, subject to the paediatrician's check-up. It would be far more restful than sharing a room with three other mothers, and almost make it a homebirth. We jumped at it, and were home at nine o'clock that evening.

In retrospect, two elements were crucial to my managing to get through the birth process, and despite the pain, and the extraordinarily uncomfortable sensations, to look back on it as an essentially positive experience. One was the presence and unfailing support of my

---

Alexander Technique provides a way of integrating body and mind to help heighten awareness of the way in which we perform even the most mundane everyday tasks such as sitting or walking. It is a therapy which primarily addresses a person's posture and so is ideally suited to pregnancy, when altered posture can lead to back problems, tiredness and, in extreme cases, malpositioning of the baby. It does not concentrate on breathing as in yoga, since Alexander practitioners believe that when the body is properly aligned, proper breathing is a natural and automatic extension of this. Since many women approach pregnancy more or less disconnected from their bodies, Alexander Technique is a good way of re-establishing some sort of relationship with your body and its potential, particularly at a time when your body will be changing rapidly.

Instead of bean bags, Alexander Technique advises the use of a large, inflatable gymnastic ball to help before and during labour. Mothers can sit on it, bounce on it, rotate their hips and use it to support their bodies in a number of different ways. The gymnastic ball provides rather more substantial support than a bean bag or pillow. Alexander Technique also utilises visualisation, body movements, and, specifically for labour, ways of 'breathing the baby out' which can help a mother relax and avoid tearing.

For more information on Alexander Technique see 'Suggested Reading' and 'Useful Contacts'.

husband, Andy. Without him, I would have panicked during the first stage and transition, when we were effectively abandoned by the hospital staff. The other was the sense of empowerment that my careful preparations had given me, particularly the Alexander Technique classes. We never had the chance to unpack all the goodies in my labour bag, although I did take arnica after the birth for three doses.

Natascha and I got off to a good start, perhaps because we did leave hospital so quickly. I was very motivated to breast-feed her and, although it took about a month before it became easy, I persevered. I even returned to my ante-natal clinic to talk to other mothers about breast-feeding and encourage them not to give up too soon. The benefits, after all, were easy to see – a beautiful little baby girl who was a joy to be around.

I Have A Baby, But I've Never Given Birth

Gina Lowdon

I knew a few weeks before my due date that my baby was a breech; consequently I was offered an elective caesarean which I declined, preferring at least to have a go. I had desperately wanted to have as natural a labour as possible, and had stated this wish to maternity services personnel at every opportunity. Following X-rays, I was told that I had every chance of delivering 'normally'. In this case, 'normally' meant on my back with my legs in stirrups, large episiotomy and forceps, preferably under epidural anaesthetic. I have always had two nightmares regarding childbirth and here I was being asked which of the two I wished to endure. Despite nine months of pregnancy, I was not psychologically ready to give birth. I had no acceptable choices open to me.

My contractions began at 6.30am on a Monday morning, but by lunch time they had disappeared. They started again at 8pm. At around 10.30pm my waters started to leak with each contraction. Due to vague worry about cord prolapse and bearing in mind various horror stories of breech births, I decided to do what my

Doctors stopped routinely X-raying pregnant women thirty years ago when the link between childhood cancer and X-rays was established. Today, many hospitals have abandoned the ritual X-raying of mothers with breech babies – or babies in any kind of unusual position – in order to ascertain how big the mother's pelvis is. Pelvic X-rays, or pelvimetries, are known to be so inaccurate that the procedure is a complete waste of time, and may expose your baby to unnecessary risk. The best way to tell if your pelvis is big enough to pass a baby through it is to go into labour and see what happens. Thousands of years of birthing experience have produced these irrefutable facts – women's pelvises are purpose-built for birth and their bodies rarely make babies 'too big' to come out.

husband thought best and go to the hospital.

We arrived at hospital at 12.30am Tuesday morning. Admission was very relaxed, as it was obvious my labour was not 'established', and had it not been my first baby and in a breech position, I would have been sent home. I was monitored for two half-hour sessions: the first soon after admission, the second at around 6am, when my labour was officially deemed to have begun. The monitor also confirmed that the baby was strong and coping well with the contractions. I found this news a great comfort as I was disappointed in the performance of my own body! In fact, the baby was not in distress at any point during my labour.

By 11am I was extremely tired as I had been up all night. I was only three centimetres dilated and my contractions were still inefficient; they were strong but short and five or six minutes apart. I was advised that if I was to have my baby that day, labour would need to be accelerated and, since I didn't relish the thought of a second night like the last one, I readily agreed. I also asked to have an epidural as I felt I had tasted labour sufficiently to know I would not be able to cope with artificially accelerated contractions, and I knew from previous discussions that it was preferred I should have an epidural. Also, I had already declined the offer of an epidural twice since arriving at the hospital. All requests by medical staff were made in a very pleasant manner and being a good patient, concerned for the baby, I was hardly in the frame of mind or position to argue. I simply did as I was told, relinquishing all involvement in and responsibility for my labour without question, argument or comment.

I was moved from the labour room to the delivery room. The epidural was fitted, the oxytocin drip set up, and I was put back on the monitor. A clip was attached to the baby's bottom and again it was good to know that although I was knackered, the baby was still strong and coping well. With the epidural working it was such a relief to lie there quietly drowsing, it was so peaceful. My husband was able to go off for a cup of tea and something to eat while I dozed. By 3pm I was nearly fully dilated, but there was still a rim of cervix. It would have been unwise to start pushing too early with a breech, but by 5pm I was given the all clear and the hard work began. Pushing was difficult as my epidural was still working very well. However, I could still feel the contractions and was surprised at how much control over the pushing I did have.

One and a half hours of pushing later, the contractions, which had

---

Scalp electrodes are used to detect signs of fetal distress. They should never be used on a just-in-case basis since they can damage your baby's scalp and introduce infection into your womb and your baby. If your waters have not been broken, then your membranes will be artificially ruptured and the monitor – an electrode on the end of a spiral or s-shaped hook – will be screwed into your baby's scalp, or bottom if the baby is a breech (or anywhere else if the consultant is really determined). They are tricky to fit and often come loose. To get an accurate picture of how distressed your baby really is, fetal scalp monitoring should be used in conjunction with fetal blood sampling. Once the electrode is attached you will be discouraged from moving and this may further complicate your labour and cause further distress to your baby. Fetal distress is greatly over-diagnosed, making it difficult for mothers and practitioners to make rational decisions about how best to manage it.

---

been fading fast, packed their bags and deserted. I had no more strength left, and in any case could not have pushed my baby out without the help of contractions. It was obvious that my baby was not going to be born in the normal manner. A very emotional and tearful interlude followed as the inevitable was agreed – off I was wheeled to the theatre where a medical team was ready and waiting.

The operation was carried out under epidural so I was awake throughout. My baby arrived in the world about 20 minutes after the end of pushing as it took them no longer than about ten minutes to get her out. She was in perfect health.

My husband was present, music was playing (Simon and Garfunkel's Greatest Hits will never sound the same again!), the theatre was full of people and pleasant conversation, several jokes were made, and one of the theatre technicians took some photos of us with my camera. It took about an hour to sew me up, but the time passed quickly as our attention was on the baby, who was lying across my shoulder for most of the time. The experience was as good as the hospital staff were able to make it. It is a pity that I was in no state of mind to make the most of their efforts.

It certainly was an experience and, although I could not honestly say that it was 'pleasant', it was certainly 'interesting'. It was nowhere near as terrible as I had expected and I would not be frightened of repeating the experience (although there would have to be a cast iron reason).

It was not easy to decide whether to have the operation under epidural or general anaesthetic when I was given the choice. My epidural was already sited and working well so I opted for that, although I did wonder what I'd let myself in for. It was the right decision for me, as I was able to see my baby as soon as she was delivered, which I believe was crucial to the positive way I've felt about her ever since.

There were unpleasant moments though – I started to retch at one point. Trying to be sick while you're lying on your back with your stomach cut open is not pleasant. It didn't last long however and was soon under control. The surgeon removed the afterbirth and I was very uncomfortable while he swabbed the top of my uterus, as it was just above where the epidural was effective, but although it hurt, it wasn't too bad. The only really painful bit was while he put in a 'zip fastener', a form of stitching used in the nerve layer of skin. I had to concentrate and breathe my way through that bit which, although it took about five minutes, seemed a lot longer. It was even more painful some days later when it was taken out, because by then, by my own choice, I was no longer on any kind of pain killers.

Immediately after the operation we were left in peace in a quiet, dim side room and I put my baby successfully to the breast. Gordon was under no pressure to leave, although he did so soon after making a couple of phone calls on a portable telephone which was brought into the room for us.

I needed my baby with me because I needed to reassure myself, at a glance, that it had indeed all been worthwhile. I also received a lot of help breast-feeding and found the staff to be very helpful and pleasant at all times. I was able to take things very easily for the first two weeks at home, as my husband and my mother did all the housework and cleaning. The biggest relief of all was that I felt no animosity whatsoever towards my baby at any time. I had been worried that I might 'blame' her if my labour was long or difficult, and was surprised by my attachment to her right from the beginning.

In the days immediately following the operation the sense of relief that the worst was over was overwhelmingly enormous. I was in a state of euphoria because I had survived my worst nightmare. This feeling of euphoria lasted for three or four months, about the time it took for life to settle into the new version of 'normality'.

Then, one day, out of the blue, like a slap in the face, with absolutely no warning, the thought struck – *I have a baby, but I've never given birth*. Words cannot describe how deeply sad I felt. Nor can they adequately explain the sense of loss, of failure. Why me? Where did I go wrong? Over the months I cried and cried and cried. I thought perhaps if I cried enough I would not be able to cry any more, but the tears just kept coming.

It has taken me a long time just to make sense of my feelings, to explore what they are and why I feel them. Physically I am fit and healthy. I recovered well from the operation. My baby is perfect – you could not possibly find a better advertisement for 'caesarean section makes better babies'. I live in a reasonably modern house, equipped with TV, video, fridge, freezer, microwave. I have worked happily with computers. Modern technology is not a problem for

---

Breech babies are not medical emergencies. Up to about 32 weeks 15 per cent of babies are breech and only 3 or 4 per cent persist in this position up to labour. Some breeches turn in labour. Delivering a breech baby does require a different set of skills from delivering one in a cephalic, or head down, position. It also requires that the mother be a more active participant in her labour. It is even more important, for instance, that she is upright and on her feet and that she has birth partners who are able to hold her in a supported squat – to help open up her pelvis. Your midwife needs to be confident and experienced. If she is not, dismiss her and find one who is.

Doctors and midwives' main worry is that in a breech delivery the baby's head needs to be delivered quickly and may be born too fast to allow the gradual moulding which takes place during a head down delivery. With a skilled practitioner this should not be a problem. You can protect your baby by not accepting induction or acceleration of labour, since the more violent contractions produced will make a gradual delivery difficult, and by opening up your pelvis to its full extent by remaining upright and in a supported squat.

The only way to find out if you can deliver your breech baby vaginally is to go into labour and see what happens. This is what doctors call a 'trial of labour'. If the first stage progresses well, in other words if the baby is descending, then there is generally no reason why you cannot deliver your baby vaginally – avoiding all the unnecessary trauma, for mother and baby, which can be the result of a caesarean operation.

me. So why do I feel such a strong need to return to the 'Stone Age' to have my babies? Why wasn't I satisfied? After all, many women have had much worse experiences. For a long time, none of my feelings made logical sense, but I have come to realise that feelings are not always logical. Equally strong, genuine feelings can even seem contradictory. What I am acutely aware of is that there is a great deal more to birth than merely extracting a healthy baby from a healthy mother.

Basically, I feel as though I spent a long time baking a very special cake, only to have someone else come along, take it out of the oven, and ice it for me. Despite the fact that they did a beautiful job, I simply wanted to do it myself. I have been over and over my labour so many times. The 'perhaps ifs' crop up all over the place: *perhaps if* I had not gone into hospital so soon . . . *perhaps if* I had prepared myself better for feeling so tired . . . *perhaps if* I had refused the drip and insisted my labour be allowed to take its natural course . . . *perhaps if* I had not given into psychological pressure and agreed to have an epidural . . . Perhaps if, perhaps if, perhaps if. Why were my contractions so inefficient? Why did my labour end without achieving the birth of my baby? Why didn't I know what to do? Why did I give in so easily and do exactly what I was told without question?

Generally, I am an independent individual. I do not like to rely on others. I strongly dislike the hospital environment – it makes me uneasy. I don't know why. My husband and I are extensively renovating and extending our home ourselves. I knit and sew. I take particular pride and pleasure in producing beautiful things myself. It is therefore particularly hard for me to have had the experience of giving birth to my baby taken away from me. The only truly active part I could have had in bringing my child into the world was denied me. People used to ask me if I was proud of my baby and I used to think, 'What a strange question!' Of course I wasn't proud of her. Her arrival had nothing to do with any conscious thought or action on my part.

I have always seen her as lovable, beautiful and individual, but not much to do with me. She wasn't born, she was cut out. How strange that something so beautiful should exit the body in the same way as ugly tumours and malfunctioning organs. *There is a difference between a woman giving birth and a doctor getting the baby out*. I didn't give birth to her. I just happened to be there. She doesn't really feel mine. The surgeon cut the connection between my pregnancy and my baby when he cut into me. A regular nightmare was that she'd been stolen and I couldn't prove she was mine. Most mothers probably worry about their babies being stolen, but how many worry about proving their baby is theirs? It is almost as if my baby died and someone said, 'Never mind, dear, have this one, it's better than the one you had anyway.' And yet, I have no intellectual doubt that she is mine. I recognised her as soon as she was delivered, and anyway, she's so exactly like her father in looks there can be no possible doubt.

I was relieved at the time, and still am, that my extreme negative feelings about the arrival of my baby do not seem to have affected my feelings for her, except for the lack of pride in the early months. She was successfully breast-fed until she gave up of her own initiative at around nine months, and I have never, even for a second, blamed her for the nightmare of her birth.

I appreciate that I may have delved into this issue more deeply than some, but I cannot believe that I am totally alone in the feelings and emotions I have had to cope with, as a result of undergoing a caesarean. I personally believe there are three important issues in childbirth. The first two are the health of the baby and the mother, and the third is the quality of the experience of childbirth. The quality of my caesarean experience was good, the quality of my childbirth experience was nil. Nothing will ever convince me that my caesarean could not have been avoided, although, of course, it was necessary under the prevailing circumstances. However, I know I could have given birth naturally, without detriment to myself or my baby, had I felt confident and had I been in the hands of a midwife with the relevant experience. Unfortunately, I did not realise this at the time.

I have now completed my journey from the negative to a positive viewpoint. I now understand fully the reasons behind why my baby had to be delivered surgically. I have succeeded in finding my own answers and consequently I have learnt a great deal about myself. The baby that arrived in such an unnatural manner has grown into MY daughter – a bright, intelligent, beautiful little girl.

I shall always be very sad and regretful that her arrival should have been such a traumatic experience, but at least I have been able to gain from it and can see it now as a positive base on which to build the rest of my life.

Congratulations, You're Pregnant

Janis Wilson

I had been with my partner for about six years when the idea snuck up on me that it would be good if we had a baby. Richard was not quite as enthusiastic as me, but was eventually brought round to the idea. I thought that it would be a case of 'instant baby', but after two years with not even a hint of morning sickness it started to dawn on us that it was not going to be quite as easy as we had first thought.

Because I had two children from a previous relationship, everyone assumed that the reason must lie with Richard, but, following numerous tests, it turned out to be my fault. That's when we were referred for IVF treatment.

What should have been a loving act between two people was now a military-like operation involving a cast of many. The first hurdle we had to get over was the daily injections of various fertility drugs – a task at which I am now an expert and one for which, Richard says, he should be made an honorary doctor. Each stage of the procedure was looked upon as a test. We talked about everything, except what would happen if it failed. The staff at the hospital became our family. Regular scans monitored the growth of my eggs, until the day came for the egg collection. The emotion of the day was such that it felt as if this was the very start of the birth of our baby.

Seventeen eggs were collected. I didn't care – I'd had a tranquilliser and a local anaesthetic. Richard, however, didn't get off so lightly. Off he went, clutching his jar, as did another man, whose wife was sitting next to me. Her husband returned after a short while looking pleased with himself – and relieved. I waited, patiently at first, then with mounting panic. After all, it can't be that easy in the gents' loo! Eventually, my hero returned clutching his prize, looking a bit flustered, but otherwise OK.

We waited in a hospital corridor for news of the conception. Any romantic ideas we may have had left surrounding the making of a

IVF – in vitro fertilisation – is a process by which the eggs and sperm are brought together in a laboratory, outside the mother's body. If the sperm, which first go through a kind of 'washing' process to weed out the least motile amongst them, success-fully fertilise the eggs, several embryos are then implanted into the woman's womb.

IVF first hit the headlines in 1978 with the birth of Louise Brown, the first 'test tube' baby. It has been hailed by some as the most significant breakthrough in fertility treatment. The success rates quoted are usually between 20 and 30 per cent, but research has shown that actually they hover somewhere around the 10 per cent mark and depend greatly on the reason for infertility in the first place. For example, in couples where the male is infertile or where the cause of infertility is unexplained, the rate of success is considerably lower. Couples can be on the programme for years before conception is successful and there can be considerable stress involved. Mothers are usually put on a course of fertility drugs, in order to produce more eggs. Any extra embryos are frozen, and kept in storage in case the implanted embryos don't take. In addition to drugs, IVF also involves a lot of intensive ultrasound scanning, which has yet to be proven safe. See 'Suggested Reading' for more details.

baby had gone. In the minutes that followed I had a shocking thought. What if the other couple's sperm ended up with my eggs? But before I could play the scene out in my mind, I was brought back into reality by one of the nurses explaining that Richard's sperm had been washed wrong and that he would have to provide another sample. Good grief, I thought, he had enough trouble getting the first one! Eventually the meeting of my eggs and Richard's sperm took place. We were not in the room at the time and so played only a minor supporting role. At least that's what it felt like.

We returned to the hospital two days later for what were now being called the 'embryos' to be implanted. We were lucky – thirteen embryos had fertilised. Six were chosen and out of those the 'best' three were implanted. The other seven were frozen. The longest fourteen days of my life followed. It was Richard's birthday and I was convinced that I would be pregnant – but I was wrong. I was definitely not pregnant. The stress of the last few weeks had been enormous and now to have nothing – it was just too much.

I think I went through a kind of grieving period, but hope was still with us in the form of seven frozen embryos. This involved a much more natural process. No drugs, just the implanting of the embryos and let nature take its course. Only two survived the thawing process and we kissed as they were given back to us. It was the closest we got to a natural conception.

After five years of trying for a baby and two attempts at IVF, we heard the magic words – 'Congratulations, you're pregnant.' I was given scans at five and seven weeks pregnant and told one single embryo had started to develop. At twelve weeks we went for our first ante-natal appointment and were told by a nurse that I was at least seventeen weeks pregnant. Of course I knew that was impossible. I knew to the exact hour how pregnant I was. Fear set in. I imagined it was all about to go horribly wrong. Perhaps it was pregnancy diabetes, or too much amniotic fluid indicating an abnormality with the baby. I had to kick up a bit of a stink and, I think just to get rid of me, they agreed to do another scan.

Twenty minutes later we left clutching the first picture of our twins. The rest of my pregnancy followed in a blur of swollen ankles, swollen hands and, last but definitely not least, a very swollen tummy. Later scans indicated that both babies were of a comparative size to that of a singleton baby. I didn't take any notice, what did a scan prove?

Towards the very end of my pregnancy, panic began to set in again. I felt that all control had been taken away from me. The doctors were talking about epidurals, caesareans, twin two – fetal distress and, also, problems because twin two was a feet-first breech presentation. Thankfully, rescue was at hand in the shape of a group of local midwives, who offered to assist me and my partner during the birth. At 38 weeks plus, and after feeling thoroughly miserable for the last two weeks, I arrived at hospital on a Tuesday evening to be induced – or shot at dawn. I didn't care which by this stage!

By the next morning, I was petrified with fear. It made no odds that I had given birth before. My mind was full of 'what ifs' and 'maybes'. A doctor took advantage of the moment to inform me quite forcibly of all the things that could go wrong, in an attempt to get me to have an epidural. I refused and prayed that I was doing the right thing. By 11.30 I had no time to think about whether I was or wasn't doing the right thing. I was lucky enough to start labour with very little help. The agreement with the hospital was that they would leave us pretty much on our own, unless any problems occurred, providing both babies were monitored at all times, and that a doctor would assist in the delivery of twin two – the breech.

My midwives, Dorothy and Jill, had prepared the room to be as comforting as possible. Lavender was sprinkled about and the lights were dimmed. No one wore hospital gowns or masks. It was Richard's job to keep the monitors in place, which he said made him feel of some use. It kept him fairly busy as well since I refused to stay in one place for too long. The most comfortable position was kneeling whilst grabbing the headboard for support. Unfortunately, I couldn't maintain that position for too long due to my huge size. So, for part of the time, I shifted from side to side.

I didn't want to take any drugs. This had nothing to do with bravery on my part. Gas and air made me sick and pethidine sent me to sleep – so what else was there? Instead, Jill and Dorothy gave me herbal remedies – I have no idea what – for the pain. I trusted them so completely, it never occurred to me to ask.

At 1pm Dorothy asked me if I wanted her to break my waters. I knew from previous labours that this would speed things up. A niggling doubt at the back of my mind panicked me again, but, I argued with myself, I could hardly cross my legs and say I wanted to go home and forget the whole thing. I prayed again, 'Please don't let me die.' As soon as my waters were broken, I felt as if I had been hurled into a different dimension. Richard said afterwards that he felt I had withdrawn into myself. I was not aware of the time that had elapsed and I barely spoke, such was my concentration. I was conscious of being told how far dilated I was, but it was almost as if I had distanced myself from what was happening.

It was 3pm. I was sick anyway (even without the gas and air), so much so that I had to have a drip put in to replenish lost body fluids. It took several attempts to fit the drip in the back of my hand. What was I doing here? I don't like the sight of blood, especially my own. I can quite honestly say the drip was the worst thing about my labour. That and being sick. In order to move about, I had to manoeuvre my way around three monitor wires and now the drip. In the end, I didn't let it worry me. I let everyone else shuffle about when I got my next whim to move.

By 4pm there was no turning back. I had been trying desperately to withdraw from the pains, when it dawned on me that my body was doing the opposite. I asked Dorothy if I should push. She told me, 'If you want to.' I had been told that it was easier to give birth kneeling up and I was determined to try. So once again, I shuffled round. It appeared then as if everyone else was holding their breath. Time was on hold. I was aware only of Richard saying, 'Push! Push!' I wanted to tell him to shut up, but I had a feeling that he thought, by saying the word 'push', it would somehow assist the babies' passage, so I said nothing.

Richard was still saying, 'Push! Push!' at 4.42pm. Then I heard Dorothy say, 'Have a look and tell us what it is.' I said, 'It's a girl.' I held her briefly before she was whisked away. Richard was amazed. He said later he was expecting me to scream or shout and I'm not sure why I didn't. Maybe I was just too tired. As I turned around, the room which had been so quiet was suddenly buzzing with two paediatricians, two nurses and a doctor to assist the birth of twin two. At that moment, any control I had was gone and the doctor's ante-natal warning came back to haunt me – 'twin two – fetal distress'.

Twenty minutes passed. I had to give in. My legs were up in the stirrups and I was flat on my back. There had been no relief after giving birth to twin one – it just kept on going. Out of the corner of my eye, I spotted her. She was lying in a crib looking very sad, as if she was wondering why no one was paying her any attention. It flashed through my mind what the scans had shown about them being big babies and I asked for twin one to be weighed, since twin two was supposed to be the bigger (this in the middle of a contraction!). Everyone thought I had gone mad, but I just wanted to know what sort of size it would be. They didn't respond. Everyone was too concerned with twin two.

The doctor was talking to me: 'What do you think the next baby will be?' 'A girl,' I replied, then I realised what she was about to do. She was reaching for some sort of scissors. When I saw this, I pushed as hard as I could so she had to stop to assist the baby. Dorothy said that when she saw her feet, she knew it was a big baby. It felt like she was being dragged out of me. When I looked up, the baby was blue and lifeless. I clutched Richard's hand and we held our breath whilst a tube cleared her throat and she began to cry. It felt as if I had been deflated, like a balloon. After the weight of the last few months, I felt like I would float off the bed.

Exhaustion set in at 5.30pm, but I could not rest because I was having difficulty with my afterbirth. I was still determined not to have any injection to assist this and was feeling very scared (correction, petrified) as Dorothy gently manipulated my stomach

and pulled on the umbilical cord, whilst I pushed as if my life were
depending on it (which wasn't far from the truth of how I felt).
Following the births of my other children, I didn't see my placentas,
but, because it is easier to determine whether or not twins are
fraternal or identical by the placentas, I wanted to see this one. It
was huge, but somehow quite beautiful. One single placenta with
rainbow colours said that my twins, by an act of Nature and not
medicine, were identical.

I had torn slightly and the doctor wanted to stitch me, but
Dorothy and Jill said it would heal on its own. Instead they gave me
arnica (a homeopathic remedy) for any bruising.

By 6.30pm I was cleaned, washed and totally exhausted. We
looked at our two perfect little babies. Wait a minute! Did I say
little? Twin one, now Madison, weighed 7lb 1oz; twin two, now
Caprice, weighed 8lb 1oz. Well what do you know – the scan was
right!

Your placenta is your property and you have the right to
inspect it and say how it should be disposed of. Many
mothers have never seen this miraculous organ which has
kept their babies alive for the nine months of pregnancy. Many
more are unaware that hospitals make money from them in
many ways. There has been a widespread practice of selling
them to face cream and cosmetic manufacturers, though this
is slowly being phased out due to fears about blood disease
such as hepatitis and HIV. Today, hospitals drain the blood,
which is sterile and very pure, out of them and use it to treat
leukaemia patients. Sadly, this is one reason why some
practitioners are so keen to cut the cord as soon as possible.
The blood in your placenta belongs to your baby – it is
necessary to prevent jaundice, to expand the lungs and
ensure proper heart function. This is why it is so important to
wait until the cord stops pulsating before cutting it.

Some women like to create rituals with the placenta – burying
them in the garden under a tree to mark the baby's birth, or freezing
them and eating them to stave off depression. Some would simply
like to be consulted and feel unhappy with the other way of
disposing of them – putting them three to a bag and dumping them
in the hospital incinerator. You may wish to think about these
things before your baby is born and note them down in your birth
plan, since in the excitement and exhaustion which follows labour
it can be difficult to think clearly about these issues.

My Anger Woke Me Up
Maggie Godsland

I wanted to have my first baby at home, but allowed myself to be talked out of it. My GP went into panic at the very thought and coerced me with various forms of emotional blackmail and pressure. It seemed that the very suggestion was outrageous. First of all there was my age, thirty-four, which she had mistakenly written down as thirty-seven. When I corrected her, she then announced that it was out of the question for a first baby, although of course, a second baby would be no problem. I was quite shaken up by all this and refused to see her again until I was 28 weeks pregnant, by which time I had tried without success to contact an independent midwife and had reconciled myself to birth in Milton Keynes General. In retrospect I feel that, in many ways, I was very young at the time. It never occurred to me to ask for a second opinion, even though I knew another doctor at the practice did home deliveries. I had so little faith in my own authority that I accepted my doctor's judgement of me as irresponsible with resentment but without real challenge.

The hospital delivery was not a great success. I was out of favour from the moment I arrived because, although my waters had gone at nine that morning, I stayed at home with my husband until seven in the evening. I did not make this decision lightly. I consulted a friend who had been in the same situation and she advised me to trust my instincts and stay at home for the time being. When they examined me at the hospital, they grudgingly admitted that only part of my waters had gone and no harm had been done, even on their terms. I found further disfavour by my refusal to be monitored at two-hourly intervals. It was a long and painful labour and I could not bear to be immobile for any length of time. The midwife reluctantly accepted my decision, but bitched about it at every opportunity. Luckily she was out of the room most of the time. She and I did not exactly hit it off. She seemed to specialise in giving me orders disguised as suggestions and then grew impatient when I did not comply immediately. At one point she was replaced by a really lovely woman whom I begged to stay with me. My husband and my friend joined in my pleas, but she felt she had to refuse out of consideration for the feelings of the midwife assigned to me. So much for my right to dismiss a birth attendant and for any regard for my feelings!

I remember the whole labour as taking place in a huge, dark, unknown place where I grew increasingly disconnected from my body. To be fair, I think that my own ambivalence about having a baby in the first place was the root cause of my distancing myself from the event, but the hospital environment, the gas and air that I used as pain relief, the fact that I had four different midwives during the twelve hours I was there, and that the one I got stuck with for longest seemed completely indifferent to me, did not help. It culminated in a second stage of four hours without my managing to push the baby out. This was followed by an episiotomy and loss of so much blood that panic broke out, blood transfusions were being set up and the situation was only resolved by intravenous syntometrine.

My original intent had been to come straight home after the baby was born, a concession won from my GP, who was so relieved by my finally consenting to go to hospital that had I asked for my dog to be present at the birth I think she would have agreed. My

---

If you don't like your midwife you can dismiss her at any time – even during labour. The problem is that you cannot request a specific replacement; you can only say who you *don't* want. If you have booked a hospital birth, you will need to contact the Head of Midwifery and/or the Duty Officer and request that you not be attended by this particular midwife or midwives. If you have booked a home birth, contact the Supervisor of Midwives. You will then be allocated another practitioner. If you are in labour and you do not want a particular midwife there, you or your partner will have to be very firm. Insist, or better still, get your partner to, on seeing whomever is in charge on the ward and assert your rights. Research is on your side – a skilled midwife (that is to say, 'skilled' not simply in clinical aspects of birth, but also the emotional ones) can cut your labour time in half; an unskilled midwife can turn it into a catalogue of disasters through her own fear and apprehension.

husband, Ian, however, was shattered by the whole event and, being convinced when I began to haemorrhage that I would bleed to death, he fled home, deserting me. Thinking that I would be best looked after in hospital, I consented to stay. Here, I made my biggest mistake. I asked if I could have my own room, which I knew was possible, but was met with a puzzled refusal. There followed a nightmare two days, when all that kept me going was the knowledge that I needed to look after our baby, Holly, as best I could and shield her from the worst effects of the hospital. I was overwhelmed with a sense of failure, and felt totally and utterly alone.

It was just after Christmas and nobody knew I was there. I was not on good terms with my family at the time, and a lot of my friends were away. An increasing sense of utter desolation crept up on me. I alone, of all the women on the ward, did not seem to be special. I had no cards or flowers and my husband was not much help when he came to visit. Being depressed himself, he spent a lot of time rebuking God for the horror of childbirth. My naïveté at thinking I would be looked after in hospital was soon exposed. I could not sleep and lay on my bed tense and miserable. A midwife snapped at me for not moving quickly enough to attend to Holly and I burst into tears. It was only when a friend of mine came to visit that her strength and energy inspired me to insist on seeing the doctor who had delivered Holly and to beg him to discharge me. I left that afternoon.

From a distance, I can see that the feelings of isolation and despair that overwhelmed me may well have had as much to do with my own birth as they did with my giving birth to Holly. I learned from my mother that, after a difficult labour and forceps delivery, I was left on a side ward for two days, during which I was never given to her. This was done so that she could 'rest'. My guess

> You don't need anybody's permission – not the GP's, midwife's or consultant's – to discharge yourself from hospital. Often a practitioner will present the option of an early discharge as if he or she was making some kind of special concession, but in reality you can check yourself and your baby out any time you wish. Provided you and your baby are well, you can even leave within a few hours of having a caesarean section. If you have the right kind of practical and emotional support around you, you might even find you make a better recovery at home.

is that giving birth myself revived the feelings of painful isolation that I had felt as a baby. I do not think that if I had had Holly at home, or had gone straight home afterwards, I would have been spared these feelings, but I do feel, and feel strongly, that my husband and I would have been able to talk to each other and take better care of each other at home. However painful my emotions were, I would have been in an environment where I could have dealt with them by simply accepting them and allowing them to be, instead of having them both reinforced and then suppressed by the hospital environment. As it was, it took a good six months for us to work our way through what had happened. I felt entirely doomed.

Uncomfortable as it was, the feeling of doom did, at least, make me do some serious thinking about what had gone wrong. When I became pregnant again, four years later, I could not face seeing my GP and, on the advice of the community midwife, changed to another at the same practice – a really lovely man with a very gentle manner, who took my feelings seriously, reminded me that the decisions were mine, and supported me when I made unorthodox ones. Since I still considered myself a failure, I did not even dare to broach the subject of a home delivery with him, but endeavoured instead to find a way of making it possible for me to go to hospital with confidence. Initially, I chose to go to a different hospital, but a booking interview with the consultant left me shattered, fearful and in renewed despair. Autocratic and arrogant, she never once had the grace to ask me what *I* wanted. Instead she quoted every available statistic to prove that I was in for endless problems during pregnancy and delivery, and stated, unequivocally, her intended course of action for me. Her assumptions reminded me of the attitudes of those around me at Holly's birth and I spent most of the interview unable to stop crying.

She did do me one favour though. She really brought it home to me how vulnerable I had felt, and still felt, and reminded me of how horrible it is to encounter someone so entirely unsympathetic during labour. When I confessed, through my tears, that I had really wanted to have Holly at home she remarked, unexpectedly and in passing, that there was an independent midwife in Milton Keynes and asked if I had discussed the matter with her. I assumed that this midwife would sympathise with me but not wish to take on a woman with my appalling obstetric record. Nevertheless, I made an appointment to see her. To my amazement, Jane listened carefully to my story, said she was prepared to take me on, and that she had no objection to my having my baby at home. She recommended that my GP book me into Milton Keynes General, the only local hospital where Jane was allowed to practise, but that we considered home delivery an option and that I could make up my mind whenever it seemed appropriate.

My GP was initially impatient with my wishing to change to Milton Keynes, but when I pleaded that Jane's guarantee to be with me through the pregnancy and delivery was what I needed in order to feel safe, he reluctantly agreed. Subsequently he cheered up, agreed to meet Jane, and was entirely supportive of me thereafter.

I hardly dared admit how excited I was by the possibility of a home delivery. I also felt confident that, if necessary, Jane would take good care of me in hospital and I had her promise, and my husband's, that neither of them would abandon me on the post-natal ward and that they would aid me in an immediate discharge. Even so, I still felt slightly apprehensive about the uncertainties inherent in being on

A lot of women feel pressured to make up their minds quickly about the kind of care they want and where they want to give birth. There is no time pressure and you can, literally, wait until the last minute, even until you are in labour, to decide. Particularly if this is your first baby, it is important to take your time and get a sense of who the people are who are going to be around you, and the range of facilities available, before making a decision. It can be hard to know what you want at first and it is common to have misgivings about the type of care you have chosen. If you have made a decision early on, and you find that you are no longer happy with it, you are entitled to change your mind at any time and make other, more appropriate, arrangements.

Be aware, however, that it can be much harder to change at the eleventh hour from a hospital birth to a home birth – though if you were to change from home to hospital you would more than likely be greeted by cheers, balloons and hearty (if somewhat irrational) congratulations for 'coming to your senses'! Unless you are under the care of a named community or independent midwife, unplanned last minute changes are not always the best way to go about it, since you will be delivered by someone you do not know, who may feel resentful about being called out of the blue and whose skills you cannot be sure of.

someone else's territory and I knew that my vulnerability would prevent me from asserting myself. In addition to all this, I still could not understand why I had been unable to push my baby out the first time around. I knew it had not been exhaustion alone, nor had I given up easily. I re-read books on childbirth, pondered the question, and discussed it with my doctor, but without illumination.

Then, about a week before my baby was due, in that stage of pregnancy when your attention is wholly directed inwards, in preparation, the answer came to me. My ambivalence about having a baby in the first place had left me entirely out of touch with what I was really doing and had prevented me from doing it well. I saw, too, that had I not been so out of touch from the very beginning, I would have insisted on trusting my own instinct that home was the best place for me and would have been able to push Holly out. At that point I knew I would stay at home.

And so it was. When I went into labour at about three o'clock Sunday afternoon it never even occurred to me to go elsewhere. This was an entirely different labour. The contractions were strong and followed quickly one after each other. I knew what to do. I knelt on all fours over a bean bag, leaning forward at each contraction and breathing my way through them. I could scarcely dare believe that things were going so well. Jane arrived just before the transitional stage, which I spent kneeling on the bathroom floor, commenting on how much I was shaking. For a brief moment I lost my nerve when I needed to push, but I recovered and pushed with focus and determination at each contraction. Between contractions I complained repeatedly that I did not like the second stage and each time Jane patiently commented that I had said that already. I gave birth in a standing squat, supported by my husband, clasping the edge of the bath for support, and screaming in outrage at the sensation of being almost split in two by the baby in my birth canal. Amber Rosamond was born at ten past six, all nine pounds ten of her. She screamed in imitation of her mother. After she had cried herself to sleep and Jane had left we had whisky and chocolate cake and tried to sleep as well, though I lay wakeful for a while. I could hardly believe that all had gone so well, and at the same time was still shocked by the outrageous sensations of the second stage. Finally we all slept.

In the three years between Amber's birth and my final pregnancy I had four miscarriages. When I finally became successfully pregnant I had no qualms about the place of birth this time. Initially all went well. My GP and the community midwife gave me their support, the latter even agreeing to my hiring a birthing pool for pain relief should it be a very long labour. The only minor hitch was that Amber had been just over a weight limit for home deliveries which, according to the Luton and Dunstable guidelines, put me at risk of shoulder dystocia. The Midwifery Supervisor threatened to visit me to ensure that I fully understood this risk. Instinctively I was against this. I didn't want a representative of the system in my house, making me anxious. I found out as much as I could about shoulder dystocia, satisfied myself that there was no way that I could be said to be at any particular risk and wrote the Supervisor a letter, outlining the results of my research. To my surprise one of the consultants replied, with additional information, but nevertheless generally in agreement with my view. Then the community midwife resigned – unhappy with the current state of the NHS, though which specific aspect I do not know – only to be replaced by a person best described as the Midwife from Hell.

In our initial interview at 34 weeks pregnant she spent half an hour trying to manipulate me out of my birthing pool and my home delivery. She chastised me for not co-operating with her, and finally examined me in such a clumsy fashion that I was almost in tears. Then, as if to add insult to injury, she announced that my baby was a breech and that I should see a consultant immediately.

I refused utterly to see a consultant or make further plans until I had my GP's opinion. I know that I find other people's anxiety very infectious and did not want to be contaminated by any of her fears. My GP, in contrast, moves slowly and calmly. He too thought that the baby was a breech and arranged for a

> Upper weight limits for home deliveries are guidelines only. Guidelines do not supersede the law, and the law is that any woman can have her baby at home, regardless of any perceived risk factors. The irony is that half of babies who end up with shoulder dystocia are under 4,000g (8lb 13oz)! If your baby does get stuck at the shoulder, it can be a midwife's nightmare. The usual solution is to put you in the lithotomy position – on your back, with your feet in stirrups – and give you a large episiotomy. This is, however, avoidable. Midwives in America have discovered that the best position to put the mother in is on all fours, where the baby can be delivered more easily, often without tearing.

scan to confirm this. There was no way, he said, I was giving birth to a breech baby. I had heard that acupuncture had a remedy and contacted a practitioner who burnt little pyramids of ragwort on my toes. The idea is that it gives the baby an energy boost which encourages it to turn. She meant well, but unfortunately found it necessary to entertain me with stories of her own breech delivery and a general account of the obstetric horrors of the seventies. I was scared enough of hospitals – I did not need further reinforcement. I also did some crawling on all fours, as recommended by one of the books I read. On the third day the baby seemed especially active for some time in the evening and that night I had a dream that I was driving around in a Mini with my baby in a car seat, announcing that I was turning my baby around.

I had the scan at the Radiology Department of Stoke Mandeville. Within a couple of minutes the doctor told me that the baby was head down. Then there was silence. I asked if anything else was wrong. Apparently, of the four pools of amniotic fluid, only one was of normal depth, but he, not being an obstetrician, did not understand the significance of this. I was both relieved and irritated. By the time I saw my GP I was scared. He said this condition, ogliohydramnios, was beyond his knowledge and we agreed that he should refer me to the consultant who had written to me earlier. I tried to put the whole business out of my mind, but was summoned two days later, by a phone call, to his clinic. I was 36 weeks pregnant at this point. I cannot remember whether he explained the risks of the condition, but his proposed remedy was either immediate induction by syntocinon or to go to term but to attend the hospital twice daily for the baby to be monitored. I would need to be monitored during labour and there was a risk of emergency caesarean.

I was almost paralysed with terror. The spectre of endless, justified medical intervention was before me. I opted for induction to get the nightmare over with, but did have the sense to refuse the syntocinon drip, and opt, instead, for prostaglandin pessaries. After twenty-four hours on the ante-natal ward, two apparently unsuccessful pessaries and a night spent tense and wakeful, I found myself so totally demoralised that I lay on my bed and wept. When you have problems, that's the time when you most need to be surrounded by the people and things that reassure you, yet, for me, they were nowhere to be found. I knew the hospital was not exactly doing me good. At the evening ward round I begged the consultant

Amniotic fluid is necessary for the proper formation of the lungs and other internal organs. Ogliohydramnios is a lack of sufficient amniotic fluid and it can be diagnosed fairly accurately through ultrasound. As a result, more and more practitioners are looking for it and finding it, albeit in varying degrees (and sometimes even when it does not exist) and inducing panic in mothers unnecessarily.

There is really nothing which can be done about ogliohydramnios. Procedures which seek to boost amniotic fluid levels by pumping a sterile solution into the womb may be of some short-term benefit, but no matter how sterile the solution, there is still the risk of introducing foreign bacteria into the womb, endangering mother and baby. Nobody is sure how much amniotic fluid is 'normal' – every mother and baby is different. As a result, some mothers are told they may not have enough amniotic fluid when in fact everything is fine. Some mothers are even told they have polyhydramnios – too much amniotic fluid! It is worth getting a second opinion, on a different machine with a different operator, before deciding what action to take. Even then, the most positive 'action' may be to wait and see and, if the diagnosis is certain, possibly to induce the labour (though if labour is very premature this may cause unnecessary strain on the baby) or perform a caesarean operation, after a time when the baby is likely to have a good chance of survival outside the womb. This is another situation where the mother should be encouraged to trust her instincts about what is happening with her baby.

to let me go home for the night so that I could sleep and return the next day. We agreed that I was definitely not in labour and I fled home with my husband to collapse in tears.

I am sure that it was this emotional release which allowed me to go into labour, as about half an hour later the remainder of my waters went and I felt a first contraction, followed within a couple of minutes by another. This was identical to my second labour and gave me enormous confidence. Instead of being the fearful and demoralised person I had been on the hospital ward, I was my normal, stroppy self. I knew I could do it and that my confidence would carry me through, no matter what they attempted to do to me. We rushed back to the hospital in the car, with me bitching all the way about the bizarre custom of forcing labouring women to make long car journeys. When we got there however, my fury and disappointment at not being at home hit me. I was shown to a labour room where I slammed my bag down on the bed and pounded it with my fists, shouting that I did not wish to be there, I wanted to be at home.

My anger woke me up and gave me energy. I had been exhausted after the 24-hour hospital stay, but the anger put me in touch with my own strength. I calmed down, apologised to Caroline, the midwife, and told her that I knew I needed to be monitored but that I was not prepared to sit still or lie down. The atmosphere became quieter and I knelt on the bed, bending forward on to my bag during contractions, breathing gently and circling my hips to disperse the pain. Ian held the monitor in place when my movements dislodged it. To my horror Caroline suggested fetal scalp monitoring at one point, but at my repeated 'No' dropped that suggestion. At times the exhaustion would return and, strangely, the thought of the caesarean, of surrendering to sleep and anaesthesia, seemed positively seductive. Caroline took a more energetic view: 'I'm going to deliver this baby,' she declared.

And so she did. After two hours or so of gentle contractions the pain increased to a hot, sharp ring radiating around my body. I tried some gas and air, but threw it away preferring the pain to the sick, unpleasantly high feeling it gave me. Ian held my hand and smiled gently and encouragingly. Caroline asked me if I wanted the baby placed on my tummy when it arrived. This sounded good, but wouldn't the baby fall off? To give birth sitting or lying down had never entered my head. Reflecting on this, I jumped off the bed and stood upright, holding on to its side. An image of an empty shaft with the lift at the top came into my mind, and, knowing I needed to push, I tried to assume the standing squat that had done the trick last time. A second midwife had arrived by now and, misunderstanding my intent, said that I was not in a good position to push. At that point the whole business descended, rather literally, into a farce which I've only been able to piece together with the help of my husband's photos. The second midwife lowered the bed, with me still clutching it, until I collapsed in some sort of kneeling position on the floor. I screamed and pushed like crazy. She was still telling me I was not in a good position when I felt the burning sensation of the baby's head crowning and knew it was too late.

Caroline handed me our baby. He was covered in vernix, his arms splaying out in surprise, his eyes tightly shut. We didn't have a name. The four miscarriages prior to this pregnancy had meant that

If women never pushed in labour, their babies would still be born – a fact which is lost on many midwives and doctors. Whenever we think of labour it's easy to conjure up images from TV and the movies of women surrounded by hordes of people enthusiastically urging them to 'push'. In labour rooms across the country life is imitating art and women are being urged to 'push' without anybody bothering to ask whether the effort is really necessary, and whether it may be doing more harm than good. Labour is what your body does to push the baby out. Careful and appropriately directed pushing may help in some circumstances when your body needs a little extra help. Otherwise, the force of your contractions is phenomenally powerful and fully capable of pushing the baby out. Energetic pushing may lead to unnecessary perineal tears and sometimes can lead to excessive moulding of your baby's head. Trust your body, it's doing good work.

certainties, even choosing a name, seemed tempting fate. I was overwhelmed with happiness. Someone washed me and brought me tea and toast. The midwives sewed me up and I told Caroline that we would like to go straight home. I still felt that I wasn't really meant to be there. Our baby was fine and I wasn't risking my good feelings by spending unnecessary time on a post-natal ward. Before long, we were driving off into the night with our little boy.

Peace and Pain

Karen Palmer

It was Christmas Eve 1992 when we discovered that I was pregnant. We wrote 'to a prospective and proud grandfather' on the gift tag of my father-in-law's Christmas present. Both of our families were delighted, for this was to be the long awaited first grandchild.

At ten and a half weeks, the ultrasound scan showed a tiny form with arms and legs which waved. I declined blood sampling for alphafetoprotein and this first decision seemed easy. An equally pregnant friend and I celebrated reaching twelve weeks by buying portable nursery monitors. One night, just past eighteen weeks, away from home and unable to sleep, I felt the first 'tap, tap, tap' of the life inside me. At twenty weeks exactly my husband was able to feel kicking too. The following day, the Monday before Easter, I was off work with a bad cold. My midwife had said it was always better to telephone than to worry, so I telephoned and she arranged to meet us. Hearing the whooshing of our baby's heart was such a relief that we would have returned home there and then, completely reassured.

Concern at my modest bump, however, resulted in another ultrasound scan. This time it showed profound ogliohydramnios and multiple abnormalities. I remember feeling dazed and our kind obstetrician leaning forward at the end of the consultation which followed and saying, 'What I am telling you is very bad news,' as if afraid that we had not understood. He was unable to give us an accurate prognosis, although he thought it was unlikely that the pregnancy would continue to term. He did not mention the word termination in that conversation. He suggested chorionic villus sampling (CVS), but said he wanted no decisions yet and sent us away for three days to let the news settle.

We went home and cried – cried for our hoped-for normal baby that we had lost. My stomach hurt and I remember thinking: 'Oh

Women giving birth today are the first generation who have come under pressure to decide whether or not they will terminate wanted babies. In many respects the natural order of things has become very skewed. It is always best to make difficult decisions, such as whether or not to terminate a pregnancy, away from the hospital environment. Although some practitioners will urge a mother to hurry up and decide, you can take all the time you want. If your baby is very damaged there is really no rush and some mothers find a certain comfort in spending a little extra time with their babies inside them. If your baby is already dead, you may find, by waiting, that nature takes its course anyway and labour will begin of its own accord. It's important to talk it through with family and friends and, if you need to, with supportive organisations such as Support Around Termination for Abnormality (SATFA).

good – I'm going to lose it now.' We felt as if we were drowning. All our previously held principles faded with the initial horror of this 'thing' inside me. I felt that I was no longer pregnant. On the Tuesday morning I tried to get into a pair of jeans which had not fitted me for two months. Over the next three days, however, the piece of driftwood which we found and clung to was that even this tiny, damaged life was precious and should not be abandoned. As if conscious of the need to remind us of its importance, the baby kicked more energetically during these days than it had ever done before. By the Thursday we were certain that we did not want any investigations that would not be of direct benefit to this child. We returned to the obstetrician, scared of being talked round, but, to our relief, found our decision supported.

The months that followed were hard. We were learning to love this different and unexpected child and yet never knew when we would lose her. We had tremendous support from family, friends, church and colleagues – even people we had never met – and we needed every ounce of it. A scan at 25 weeks showed only a tiny rim of lung tissue and we were told that the prognosis was grim. It was agony to feel the lively kicks and head butts of a growing child inside and know that we would never care for her. Social encounters with strangers or acquaintances were stressful. We had to brave many kindly enquiries as to what we wanted and whether we were excited and how much I had knitted or bought in preparation. We were grateful for friends and colleagues who spread the word about our situation for us.

As the weeks rolled by our obstetrician encouraged us to think through what we wanted to happen at delivery. Our baby was breech but small. It was unlikely that there would be a mechanical problem with vaginal delivery, but the lack of amniotic fluid might result in compression of the umbilical cord. She was unlikely to live for long so he did not recommend a caesarean section as it carries a small risk and has implications for future childbearing. Our child was likely to be in distress during delivery. Would it make sense to monitor and not intervene with emergency surgery when distress was diagnosed? Would it make more sense not to monitor? After the previous decision, this one felt too difficult.

Our heads were spinning and I began to dread the future in a way I had not done until then. I wished we could just beam her out of me or that I could carry her inside me, alive and kicking, for ever. Again, we were left with the certainty that we could not abandon her. We hated the idea of going through labour, knowing all the time that she would be having a rough time. Not to monitor would seem uncaring, and if I was to have a caesarean section I wanted to be awake.

On the morning of August 3rd 1993 our obstetrician performed an elective caesarean section. Jennifer Grace was lifted out – a pink and squirming, beautiful baby. She was held over us to touch and then taken away by the paediatricians.

We tasted real joy. My husband was able to join her in the paediatric department and introduce both sets of grandparents to this 'real wee fighter'. I was able to visit her when she was 3½ hours old. A scan confirmed renal agenesis [no kidneys]. Because her lungs had barely developed, ventilation was of only short-term benefit. To prolong it would have risked pneumothorax [their possible collapse]. For her last five minutes or so she was given to us to hold and say goodbye. No one rushed us and eventually my mother came into the little room and helped us dress her and take some photographs. She had lived for five hours.

Why am I telling this story? It is simply to let you see what followed from the decisions that we took. Perhaps it will cause some to rethink whether termination of pregnancy is the best way to care for the parents of a severely handicapped fetus. Since Jennifer's death we have looked back on those months of pregnancy as special because she was with us. We can give thanks for her and grieve for her as a much wanted, and forever to be missed, member of our family. We were able to have a funeral to celebrate her life and pay tribute to her. We can visit her grave, leave flowers, plant bulbs. We can talk about her. If we have other children we will tell them about their older sister. We can do all these things which help soothe the pain of loss.

A Family Affair

Mary Lake

Our fifth child was conceived due to a combination of Christmas excess and exhaustion – in other words, we were careless. Having had increasingly awful periods during the previous three or four years, I mistakenly imagined that a pregnancy was unlikely, if not impossible – and where do you go to get the morning after pill on Boxing Day? Our older children were 16, 13, 11 and 8, so a baby at this stage would be noticeable as an afterthought (otherwise known as an accident).

The first three months were full of tiredness and mixed emotions. Having had two miscarriages in the past, I felt this pregnancy was unlikely to survive. I carried on cycling to work, spent a strenuous weekend with a group of children walking in the snowy Peak District in February, and, when twelve weeks came and went with the baby becoming a reality, I still did not know what to feel. I did consider termination, but, having talked to someone at British Pregnancy Advisory Service, realised I could not go through with it. My husband, Carl, understood this decision, although he was very negative about the idea of another child and the reorganisation of family life and budget that would inevitably happen. We both felt rather embarrassed by our contraceptive ineptitude and decided not to tell the children until the Easter holidays when I would be sixteen weeks.

Meanwhile, I had to consider what ante-natal care I would like. Our third and fourth children were born at home. The second had been planned as a home birth, but, due to suspected (but not actual) prolapsed cord, we went into hospital at the last minute. She was delivered by a male midwife who did what I felt to be a totally unnecessary episiotomy – so he could tick it off on a list? I wondered afterwards – and I suffered with poor stitching for ages after. Our first baby was born in hospital – a lift-out forceps delivery, perhaps avoidable if I had not been immobilised by monitors. The contrast between the hospital deliveries and the feeling of personal integrity and control that the lack of intervention brings when giving birth in your own place convinced me that, regardless of my age (43) and parity, I wanted this baby to be born at home.

Our local midwives have a wonderful tradition of delivering babies at home regardless of contraindicating factors, so I rang and asked for the midwife who had cared for me during my fourth pregnancy, although she had not actually delivered the baby. Meanwhile my GP, who was pushing for me to have various anomaly screening tests which she considered appropriate for someone of my advanced years, had written a letter to a consultant at my local hospital, asking her to see me soon to discuss Down's screening etc.

I duly received a letter from the hospital, giving me a date and time for a standard booking visit with a midwife at 15-plus weeks, with the following visit to be with the consultant, by which time it would be too late for the alphafetoprotein (AFP), double or triple tests etc. I decided that I would not have any blood screening tests. I had read enough about the double and triple test to know that it only identifies two-thirds of affected babies, and that, in any event, I was unwilling to have an amniocentesis, even if my test result were to indicate high risk of chromosomal or other abnormality. I did, however, opt to have a detailed scan at twenty weeks, if only to stop

Women over the age of thirty-five are automatically offered all sorts of tests, since the prevailing mythology is that they are the ones most likely to have problems. In some cases older mothers feel under a tremendous pressure to accept these tests. Certainly older mothers are more at risk of having a baby with abnormalities such as Down's Syndrome, but for the majority of older mothers the risk is still very small. Age in itself is not as significant a risk factor as your general level of health, hereditary factors and your obstetric history, if any. For instance, out of every 100 women over the age of thirty-five who have an amniocentesis, only one will have any problems with their baby. By contrast, as many as two out of every 100 women who have an amniocentesis will miscarry as a result of the procedure. The risks and benefits of tests such as this must be weighed up very carefully.

anyone from pestering me about the 1 in 49 chance of having a baby with Down's.

It also turned out that, due to reorganisation of contracts, if I were to use my local hospital, I would have to use their midwives, who were less experienced at home births and might consider me too high a risk. This was such a recent change that I was in the embarrassing position of informing my GP about it, and it meant that I would be referred to a different hospital in order to have my choice of midwife. The best solution seemed to be to have midwife-only care, a decision with which I was very happy.

As the midwife who had cared for me eight years earlier was on holiday, Margaret, a midwife I knew a little in person and well by repute, came to see me at about fourteen weeks. I felt a good rapport with her, and also knew that regardless of when I went into labour she would deliver this baby, which mattered to me because my fourth baby had been delivered by a midwife I had never met before.

From then on, until just before my due date when I met her partner who would also be present when I was in labour, all my care was with one person whom I trusted and got to know well. Another wonderful thing about our local home birth team is that ante-natal visits are also in the home, so there is plenty of opportunity to discuss, in an informal way, choices for all aspects of ante-natal care and birth. For us this also meant that quite often my children were there and could listen to the baby's heartbeat on the sonic aid and get to learn something about pregnancy and birth. They also got to know, and like, Margaret very much.

During this time there were a few notable juxtapositions of timing. I reached thirteen weeks the day before my daughter's thirteenth birthday. While I was deciding whether or not to have any anomaly tests our son was discussing his A-level choices with us. I think all of this kept a sense of perspective for me. With a full-time job and four older children I could not become totally caught up with the pregnancy. However, as this was definitely going to be our last child, it was important to me to have the right care for me – I had enough experience to know what I did not want, and enough knowledge and confidence to go for what I did want.

Forty weeks to the day after my last menstrual period I started to lose my mucous plug, and although several days went by with nothing definite happening, I was having increasingly strong contractions which, although not painful, were definitely more than the mild, early contractions of Braxton Hicks.

On Saturday evening we went to a concert, and as I sat on a hard church pew listening to Mozart's requiem, I had several contractions where I could feel the top of my bump really flattening. I had hot chocolate and toast before bed and several hours' sleep until about 4.30am, when I woke with more definite contractions, but still not really painful. I read for a while and at about 7am decided I would try to get back to sleep. At about 7.15 I had the first painful contraction, and felt a slight pop. I went to the loo and found that I had a pinkish show. Contractions started coming every ten or fifteen minutes. I had a shower, and some tea and toast. I went back up to the bedroom and sat on a bucket with a folded towel over as I had found how comfortable this was at an ante-natal class. Why, I wondered, did I not know about this for previous labours?

At about 8.25 I rang Margaret. She suggested I call back when labour was definitely underway. As I put the phone down I had another contraction and my waters went, so it was fortunate I was sitting on the bucket! I called Margaret back and she said she would be with us within the hour. I sat and sorted socks into pairs, which was about all I felt up to in the way of activity, and watched Carl put up a new lampshade in our bedroom, which I regretted asking him to do, as watching him up the ladder was not very soothing.

My elder daughter, Katie, had said as soon as she knew I was pregnant that she wanted to be there at the birth. Carl and I had some qualms about this, but after a big discussion a few days earlier we had made sure she understood that if she was asked to leave at any point, she would do so without argument. She came in shortly after my waters went, and very helpfully made sure her younger sister had breakfast and then

> Your cervix can start to dilate late in pregnancy as well as in early or pre-labour, and when it does you may lose your mucous plug. If you do, you will see a discharge or 'show' of blood-stained mucus. Labour may establish itself within a few hours, but equally it may be days or weeks away. Some women don't lose their mucous plug until they are in established labour. A show is a sign that something is happening around your cervix and is a perfectly normal part of the process – there is no need to rush off to hospital when it happens.

came back to the bedroom and made herself useful.

Contractions speeded up to between four and eight minutes apart and at about 9.30 I needed the loo. Getting up off the bucket and walking into our bathroom seemed to speed things up and I had about three contractions while I was on the loo. I managed to make it as far as the sink and had another contraction, so I knelt down and leant over the laundry basket, which was a convenient height. Katie put a towel over the top so I would not get wickerwork marks and there I stayed until the baby was born. I now feel I have a whole new relationship with my laundry basket!

Margaret had arrived just before I went to the loo and she joined us in the bathroom, with Carl on one side massaging my lower back, Katie the other side with me squeezing her hand and Margaret behind me, very quiet and just occasionally asking a relevant question, but fortunately not requiring an answer. By this time I was using a lot of blowing breathing, and then found that the noises I had tried during yoga for pregnancy classes seemed right, so started humming and moaning, with the volume increasing as the contractions came closer.

At some point Margaret asked if I felt any pushing urge, and although I could not reply I realised that this felt close and I was in that state of wondering if I could manage to finish off this difficult task I had begun, presumably transition. Shortly after, I became aware of the changing nature of the contractions, and I felt the movement in my back passage as the head came down. I put my hand down to feel. The baby was not quite crowning, but with another contraction I could feel the head. Margaret suggested I pant, and I felt the head come out and Margaret checked and took the cord from around the neck where it was, although not tightly. Then with a push and a lot of blood and meconium (which landed on my daughter's feet, but to her eternal credit she did not make a sound) the body emerged quite quickly. I put my hands down and caught our baby, turned him over and found he was a boy.

He was a bit mucousy but started to breathe freely very soon. I put him to the breast, and he nuzzled but did not latch on straight away. I felt I did not want to try to push the placenta out at once as I had no feeling of needing to. After a while, with the children all arriving to see him, and photos being taken, he did latch on and Margaret suggested I try to deliver the placenta and with a push and a bit of discomfort it came away complete. Carl cut the cord, which he said was surprisingly tough. My sister-in-law had been staying with us overnight, and had kept my younger daughter Emily company during the birth. Emily had been offered the option to come in to see the baby being born, but I think she was rather put off by the noise I was making, so came in with her aunt just after the birth.

Then I went to have a bath, and baby was brought in to join me. Our bathroom light is rather bright, and Margaret suggested using candles, so all the children rushed off to find nightlights, and put them all along the tiles on the wall side of the bath. This was a truly magical experience and will be remembered by us all.

The birth felt so much like a part of our family life, special but not removed from the usual sphere. Maxim Peter, as he eventually was called after much family discussion (aka disagreement) is a lovely, cheerful, smiley baby already at four weeks and is greatly loved by all his brothers and sisters who pick him up at the least excuse, sing and talk to him, change his nappy and are excited by his every facial expression, noise and gesture. For our family, the care given to Maxim and me before, during and after the birth was an enriching experience for us all.

It's Not Like Losing A Real Baby, Is It?

Katharyn Stewart

I know this feeling, click, clack, click on the typewriter. Thump, bang, wallop inside me. Is this baby number four, or number eleven? That I can't decide. Miscarrying is a bad habit of mine, and one that's affected my attitude to pregnancy since the first disaster so many years ago.

Baby one was confirmed at morning surgery, and gone before I could phone the family that evening. Baby two I kept quiet about and lost at twelve weeks – a miserable experience on a stormy January day. I cried on the way to a D&C, and the hospital staff told me to pull myself together.

D&C is short for dilation and curettage. It is a very common procedure after a miscarriage, though opinion is seriously divided as to its usefulness. A D&C is performed to remove any possible fragments of the placenta and fetus which may remain after a miscarriage and cause prolonged bleeding or infection. It involves dilating the cervix and scraping the contents of the womb out, and is done under either a general or a local anaesthetic. Policies vary from doctor to doctor and many women find the procedure distressing. If you feel otherwise well, you may derive considerable benefit from staying at home and letting things take their course.

As in menstruation and birth, your body is perfectly capable of completing the job by itself. You are under no obligation to go to hospital, though in some cases considerable pressure will be brought to bear to force you to do so. It is usually only indicated if the miscarriage is 'incomplete' or if you are experiencing side effects such as fever or excessive bleeding. You should only agree to a D&C if it is what *you* want and not to appease your doctor. Some women prefer to use herbs to help the process along. See 'Suggested Reading' for more information.

Baby three I ignored since I'd lose it anyway. I climbed on Ben Nevis, fell down a gully and gave birth at home to a 7lb boy, one week early. I'd cracked it, surely?

A year later we tried again, and baby four went at eight weeks, as did baby five, messily, somewhere on the Coniston Fells. By then, marriage number one was on the rocks. Our only success had a few problems, needed frequent hospital treatment and our too young marriage wasn't up to the strain. Pregnancy six was an accident, I suppose. She happened during a brief and unsuccessful reconciliation. I couldn't believe my luck when she stayed put, and I didn't bother going near a doctor until nearly six months. If I wasn't officially pregnant, I couldn't have a miscarriage, could I? My husband was gone, but friends and parents rallied round. Baby six was born at home in 1½ hours, and that was that. There's one thing to be said for divorce: you're usually fairly safe from miscarriages!

I learned how to be a single parent, eventually returning to full-time work, moving into the category where all my friends still belong – woman 30-plus, mother of two, second career under way. And then, on holiday with my kids, formerly babies three and six, I met my second husband.

Before we married, I thought it only fair to warn him that I wasn't much good at staying pregnant. Baby seven seemed to prove me wrong. Because of my age, 36, my then GP urged amniocentesis, talked about caesareans, and struck me off when I pressed for a home birth. She was born at home, in 2½ hours, and met her half brother and sister immediately. The baby, as my eldest pointed out, made us all properly related, not just a step-family. And everyone voted for one more little one.

It seemed reasonable enough. After all, I now had a history of two live births in succession. I became pregnant while still breast-feeding and we were delighted. Two little ones, close in age. Only nothing seemed to happen. My breasts shrank, no bump grew. The scan showed a missed abortion. If only they'd accepted my dates, we could have found out sooner, but my GP fouled up the case by giving my positive test as the date of my last period.

Baby eight gone, we waited a little and tried again. By now I was worrying about my age. If they had argued for amniocentesis at 36, they'd try to insist two years later. I couldn't. Lots of people can, but I couldn't go through with a late abortion, and there's all there is to it. And I miscarry so easily . . .

Amniocentesis is a diagnostic test performed between 16 and 22 weeks. It involves inserting a long, thin needle into the amniotic sac and drawing off a small amount of fluid to test for abnormalities such as spina bifida and Down's Syndrome. The test is performed so late in pregnancy because, before this time, there is not enough amniotic fluid surrounding the baby to spare and removing some could harm your baby. It is routinely offered to all 'older' mothers and to those who may have been given screening tests which indicate an elevated risk of having a baby with birth defects.

Amniocentesis can double the risk of miscarriage in women who are prone to it, and even in those who are not, the risk of miscarriage is as high as two out of every 100 procedures. Its use also poses a dilemma for older mothers because, while they are, statistically, at greater risk of having a Down's Syndrome baby, they are also at greater risk from the procedure.

Amniocentesis should always be performed with the aid of ultrasound to establish where the baby and the placenta are. Do not, *under any circumstances*, let a practitioner proceed without one. You can, and probably should, insist on being referred to a large regional centre where they perform many amniocenteses each year, since the risks of the procedure are greatly reduced according to how skilled your practitioner is.

After an amniocentesis you may experience quite strong contractions, leakage of amniotic fluid and some bleeding. If a miscarriage does occur, it is usually within the week after the procedure. Results of your test can take up to three weeks to come through, and for some this is a very agonising wait.

Baby nine was underway when we snatched a brief, miraculous autumn holiday in Venice with our three, or two plus one, kids. We make a good family. People forget the older two aren't my husband's. We dared to buy exquisite hand-embroidered clothes for our midsummer baby. Before Christmas, he or she was gone. I had another D&C, which seems inevitable if you go into hospital.

The new year dawned. We went to a family wedding. There were compliments about my same size eight figure. If only they knew. This year would be my watershed. Terror of Down's and other abnormalities gets to me several times a day – and yet, we wanted another baby. I even tried to remember the squirm, kick, punch sensation at the typewriter. Would I ever feel it again?

This time we waited barely a month and there I was, pregnant with baby ten, due in the season of mists and mellow fruitfulness. I liked the idea of ripening with the year, but this time I didn't waste my money on baby clothes. Just as well, for ten kicked the bucket one of those gruesome February days when the sun never shines on the frost.

That's it, I snarled. We'd tried just about everything, even celibacy. Anyone who's had even one miscarriage will recognise that sick, shaky wretchedness when one goes to the loo and discovers blood that shouldn't be there.

I weakened almost at once. Anyone would think I'd nothing better to do, no other children, but the lost babies never let go. I can remember exactly when each one was due. Once I kept quiet about a baby that would have been a dead heat with my sister's first.

Babies, babies, babies. Three or ten? It was easier for my husband. He had one child, and wanted another as much as any other man. Spring. Daffodils and new lambs in the greening valleys. I'd miscarry, of course, and then we'd call it a day.

No pregnancy test. Male doctors will never believe this, but most people can recognise a cold the second time around. I ovulated and three days later I knew I was pregnant. The nausea was, and is, relentless, just like baby six, my ten-year-old. I checked the EDD charts and giggled – March 20th takes us to December 25th. Christmas Day. Three miscarriages in a row, then a Christmas baby. It simplifies things beautifully. Usually I start bitching about Christmas in August. Nasty, tacky presents the kids play with once. Cards – from who? And that lumbering ostrich in the fridge. Bah! Humbug! This year would have its own momentum. It would either be the Christmas baby, or the Christmas without a baby. We'd tell no one, then no one could feel sorry for us.

Eight weeks, then twelve, then sixteen. I held my breath. Sure a hundred times every day, sure I was bleeding. Besides, at my age surely it was handicapped . . .

We took no precautions. On the contrary, I tramped the fells carrying a bouncing two-year-old. I did everything anyone asked – shifted weights, stacked logs, raced about the country like a mad thing with the eldest's heartbreaking treble. If not duffers, won't drown, I argued. Sixteen weeks, and then the incredible moving someone in there. Twenty weeks, and kicks anyone could feel. This was when we would have got an amnio result. I'm scared, but it's no use. I couldn't let anyone remove a living, moving baby. Twenty-four weeks, and I start to complain. Kick, thump, wallop all day and half the night. My husband, irreverent, calls the bump 'Jesus' or JC. The kicks are more violent every day, making our 2½-year-old jump off my lap, giggling. Twenty-eight weeks . . . I can't have a miscarriage now. So there.

This is baby four, but he, or she, is also baby eleven. I'm not even going to argue about having him or her at home. Only two miscarriages ended up as D&Cs, but hospital is a place I go to have dead babies. Nevertheless, the local NHS don't give in easily. They prattled about helicopters last time, for a baby due on March 28th. Fine, if we get a white Christmas, they can come in a helicopter – 800 feet up we can provide stables, sheep, cattle-a-lowing as well as a baby. Even this year, waiting for December 25th, I'll remember the baby I lost last December. I wanted the other seven too, starting with baby one. You're told it's for the best, there must have been something wrong . . . people say, casually, 'Oh really? Only twelve weeks? At least it's not like losing a real baby.'

The niggling fear is still there. Last week I read Sheila Kitzinger's *Freedom and Choice in Childbirth*. She records a woman who miscarried after amniocentesis: 'I'd rather have six miscarriages than one handicapped child.' At twenty-two or three, you don't feel consoled when told there's plenty of time. At thirty-seven, eight, nine, you feel even less comforted if a consultant says that 50 per cent of all pregnancies in older women miscarry. Why I've miscarried so often remains a mystery. All my full-term pregnancies have ended with easy labours of 1½ to 3½ hours, and the birth of live, healthy babies. But I've never had more than three in succession and this time reasoned we had no time to waste having tests. So far so good. To coin a phrase, 'Jesus is alive!'

Seven miscarriages, three, soon to be four, children. The baby won't really turn up on December 25th. Sometimes, even now, I'm scared, never happy until it's all over. Last December, I was discharged at 8.30am, ten hours after I'd been in theatre, as if I'd had a tooth out. This Christmas, strangers will see our Christmas baby and admire, maybe even envy. Perhaps the woman next to me, buying satsumas and mistletoe, has just lost her baby, quite early on, so it wasn't like losing a real baby.

Believe me, it was. Seven times, it was like losing a real baby.

Breaking Point
Razia Vitasta

When the sun streams into my bedroom, and my most urgent problem is lying on towels on the ground kicking his legs, it is hard to capture the events of the last few months – events that were so largely inside my head and which have so consumed me with despair and rage that recall is not only painful but nearly impossible. At night it is easier, fear and exhaustion open the abyss.

As far as I was concerned, my second baby was a very wanted child. Ashish and I already had a son whom we both delighted in, but Ashish, who was an only child, hadn't wanted another and, given the collapse of our sexual relationship after Danyal's birth, it seemed unlikely that we would conceive again. Ours was a passionate long-distance relationship, which, in some ways, was deepened by having a child together; but it had also collapsed into domesticity and parenthood. In fact, we only really began to live together just before our son was born, and because I lived in England we ended up living here by default.

Because we both work freelance, we were able to stay at home for long periods with our son, but we had no stable work and eventually ran into severe financial problems which put a huge strain on our relationship. We also argued about where we should live. I was reluctant to move to India for a number of reasons. We had no home in India, and I felt it was Ashish's responsibility to sort it out. It was only when Danyal was nearly three that I agreed that we should start moving to India, provided we could find somewhere to live. Ashish went ahead.

Danyal and I went to India over Christmas. When we came back to freezing Britain, I was pregnant and found that I was facing what amounted to the life of a single mother. I was broke and with no work. I was terrified of the future – of finding money to pay the bills, and of what would happen in India if I moved there. While

Ashish had established a life and new friends, I found that I was excluded from it and that tensions between us were considerable. I found myself alternating between crying uncontrollably, and forcing myself to be 'normal' for my son, who missed his father dreadfully.

During my first pregnancy, I was wholly concentrated on myself and the changes in my body. Now, unable to imagine the baby for long periods, I stopped feeling pregnant. In the exhaustion of the early months, I could barely bring myself to cook properly for Danyal, but eventually, his needs, rather than the demands of my body, pulled me into reality; I was nearly forty and having my second child.

To the few friends I met during this period, I appeared to be coping well with a slightly difficult phase of my life. I was trying to find work and at least appeared to be active and busy. Yet I was in the grip of a severe depression and feeling completely isolated. In some respects I'd had a rich working life, but I had not been successful in a conventional way and I had experienced periods of unemployment combined with jobs that were not really compatible with bringing up children. The depression brought with it introspection and the realisation that I should rethink my life, looking at where I'd gone wrong and how I could combine work and mothering.

By the time Ashish returned to England, I was six months pregnant and had been through all the anxiety of early ante-natal screening on my own. I had climbed through the worst of the depression into an uneasy equilibrium and was hoping to enjoy the rest of my pregnancy as I had the first time around. I was also hoping that we would be able to talk about and iron out the tensions that had long existed between us. I wanted us to find more space for each other, as well as work out competition over work time and child care. I also hoped to remove one of the main sources of argument between us by agreeing to make a life in India, on his territory, provided he could address my fears about bringing up two young children in a city where I had no support.

Ashish too, it seems, had been rethinking his life, but he'd come to very different conclusions. While I was in Delhi, he had been pursuing a young woman, and had started a relationship with her as soon as I left. His frenetic socialising, nights out dancing, reluctant bouts of child care, although he knew he was going to be separated from Danyal, all fell into place. So did his rubbishing of me as a professional and his irrational fury that I competed with him over areas of work.

The claustrophobia of domesticity and child rearing had led him to demand 'space' and a new beginning to our relationship and he was prepared to stay with me only on this new basis. He went on to tell me that he'd wanted to leave me many times and had made a failed attempt to revive the relationship, during which our second baby was conceived. He now regretted this and had certainly not imagined that I would get pregnant so quickly – though he accepted that in some way the baby was meant to happen. I wondered why he had told me that he thought we should have another child, and why he hadn't said that he wanted to leave me or that he was intending to start a serious relationship with someone else.

I wasn't particularly surprised when I heard about Ashish's new relationship, but what did alternately amuse and enrage me was the idea that by accepting his arrangement we were forging some sort of brave new world. As far as I was concerned, the demand, indeed the grabbing of 'space', whether with a mistress, prostitute or lover, was as old as time. At school, I had seen two teachers express their fear of impending fatherhood by starting affairs with students. Several friends of mine had experienced the same problem and, as my pregnancy progressed, I heard of at least three women whose partners had left them while they were pregnant.

Ashish would not have seen any resemblance to himself. He tried to reassure me by saying that the other relationship was not a replacement project. I had no doubt of that; for one thing the young woman continued to be involved with her steady partner who knew about Ashish. It was obvious that by starting a relationship which did not require monogamy, Ashish was trying to recapture the lost eroticism of other relationships. It was essential, in fact, that this should have no ordinariness or domesticity to it. After years of refusing to organise a holiday with me or our son, he'd found the time to go to Goa with his new girlfriend.

For Danyal and me was reserved an aspect which would have astonished those who knew Ashish as a party animal. He walked into our flat with a patriarchal air, criticised my parenting, tidied up the mess and, in order to discipline Danyal, shouted at him or smacked him. While we generally avoided arguing in front of him, Danyal still bore the brunt of our tensions. Having been a very patient mother, my own temper was now on a very short fuse and liable to explode regularly if unpredictably. It took several strained weeks for us to try and find some equilibrium in relation to our son – to step back from what we were doing to him and try to present a common front which would discipline him but also ease the passage to having a new baby. In part, it was the shock of seeing the other out of control which forced us to look at our own behaviour.

Even as we discussed and tried to resolve immediate problems, the news he had brought sent me crashing through to another phase of despair. My mind filled with rage and my body with a disgust so acute that I could neither eat nor sleep. The urgent appetite of pregnancy was switched off so decisively that for days I ate hardly anything. Instead, I found that I was retching and gasping, unable to breathe properly. 'So, this is hyperventilating,' I thought. By late pregnancy I had hardly gained any weight. 'You look wonderful,' said my friends, 'so slim, such a neat bump.' The midwife looked at my static weight chart and my growing stomach and said, 'It's all baby.'

My head was full of white noise with a brain racing so hard that I couldn't bring myself to go to bed. Some nights, I walked out of the house, wandering the streets, willing something to happen to me. The thought of suicide became a constant longing, a sort of nostalgia for what I couldn't do – not because of the baby in my belly, who was part of me and who had, I felt,

During pregnancy the nutrients you consume will be split between yourself, your baby and your placenta. The baby's demands are perhaps the greatest of the three and when a mother neglects herself during pregnancy, she is generally the first one to suffer. Her body will divert all necessary nutrients to her baby first and she may become anaemic and terribly run down and even depressed.

If her diet continues to be inadequate, eventually other things will start to go wrong. Pre-eclampsia, a condition where the placenta fails to provide the nutrients necessary to sustain the baby, can be the result of poor nutrition, and growth retardation becomes a real possibility as well. A varied wholefood diet, with the mother eating more or less what she pleases, is the best way to ensure a healthy baby. Certainly no woman should be put on a restrictive diet during pregnancy, nor should there be restrictions on how much weight she is 'allowed' to gain.

no independent existence, but for my son. And yet, I did protect the baby: I took no drink or drugs, I tried to eat when I could and I went to yoga classes. But I could find no stillness, no 'centre', no place to 'visualise the baby'. If I tried to empty my mind, the noise would rush in and the insistent questions and anger would start up again.

I don't know which was worse, that or the despair and self-hate. I had never understood why women turn in on themselves. Now the desire to make the pain manifest was acute. I became obsessed with buying razor blades. One day, I walked into a chemist and started looking at the bewildering racks of new-fangled razors. I walked up to the counter and asked the chemist for old-fashioned blades. He was Asian and understood immediately. 'You want them for an older man?' he asked. 'Yes,' I said, 'for my father.' I walked out of the shop with a packet of Wilkinson Sword, feeling much better.

I had, of course, wanted Ashish to end his new relationship and had demanded that he should at least suspend it while he was with me during my pregnancy, saying that I needed to feel safe. He was due to go back to India a couple of months after the baby was born, at which time we could end our relationship. In any case, I had no control over what he did then. He refused saying that he was 'safer' for me while he was still involved with her than if he was forced to stop. He said that I should accept that he was here for me now and had no intention of leaving me or his child. It all exploded one night when the phone bill arrived and I discovered that, although we were very broke, Ashish had been phoning his girlfriend at least once a week. I completely lost control over myself and lashed out, in anger and despair, trying to hit him and kick him in the groin. When he tried to restrain me, I started banging my head against the wall.

That episode brought to an end the tentative efforts we had made, in periods of relative calm and affection, to try and reconnect sexually. In any case, though it was evident that Ashish was trying very hard, he was completely freaked out by my pregnant body, saying that he felt there was a third person between us. By contrast, age and motherhood had deepened and intensified my sexuality, leaving the person I had been in my twenties and early thirties a brittle memory. While Ashish seemed to be trying to recapture that period of his life in an endless loop of romantic clichés, the transformation of my body brought with it a heightened sensuality and a surge of desire so powerful that I was shaken by it. In fact, my body was possessed by a rage of emotions so pure and entire in their grip that they would sweep over me, leading me from exhaustion to exhilaration and then back again. I felt intensely vulnerable, needing to feel 'safe', but also, paradoxically, I felt invincible.

Then there was this sense of my future having crashed, of its fantasies and possibilities having been shut down. The plan to move to India was shelved and with it the likelihood of family life and life as a couple that I had hoped for. I could not see how there could be space outside the relationship, with the intense demands of work, a young child and a baby. It would be hard enough to try and find some energy for each other. Nor could I accept that the space which Ashish was taking was separate and autonomous, nothing to do with me. It had already destroyed my peace of mind.

While I could see that Ashish would want to run away periodically, in order to be able to come back, I was completely tied down. I didn't want to sit in Delhi, feeding bile to my baby while he was out carousing, so I decided I would stay on in Britain. It was a decision which suited Ashish very well, once he realised that I wasn't going to co-operate. He wanted to be free to come and go whenever he pleased, so he left the responsibility of looking after the children and supporting them to me. He was blithely unbothered by the fact that I'd reversed a major decision to move, one which had been such a bitter source of conflict for so long. 'We'd only argue,' he said.

One evening, two older friends of mine took me out to dinner. One of them said that her husband had got involved with someone while she was pregnant, and like all good Bohemians was militantly justificatory. He didn't believe in private property, so why should he believe in private relationships? Like Ashish years later, he was quite bewildered that his wife was not happy for him, and that she didn't relish being trapped in this situation at a time when she herself had no choice at all. 'It isn't only pregnancy which makes men behave oddly,' said the other. 'I was adopting a child when my partner started an affair.'

Their wry humour was bracing, as was their advice on how to start trying to make sense of the future. They wasted no time in recriminations against Ashish, but instead told me to decide what I needed for myself and my child in the short and medium term. Make no hasty decisions with very long-term consequences, they advised, such as throwing him out immediately. If I felt I needed support to have the baby and to look after my son, I should accept his help, but also try and sort my life out step by step, a few months or a year at a time. They were right; a relationship may survive adversity or go into a slow decline, but either way it can take a long time to unravel.

One of them advised me to stop working from home and get a job: 'You need a structure and discipline imposed on you. You'll be forced to function normally.' But I didn't want to work immediately after the baby was born, at least not work that was incompatible with breast-feeding. The baby, I was told, will survive a child minder, you will not survive madness.

As the birth of the baby approached, the memory of my last pregnancy came back with greater and greater clarity. The first time around, I had a good labour and had coped with the pain by using a water pool. The baby was posterior and I had a backache labour. Ashish massaged me through the contractions, standing, as he put it, in a 'wicket keeper's position'. The day after the birth, I jumped out of bed feeling fantastic and phoned Ashish at home. 'I'm aching all over!' he said. While the water had protected me from a lot of pain, the forward bending semi-squat that Ashish was in left him in agony. I took about ten hours to reach full dilation, but then complications set in. The baby's head wouldn't crown, no matter how much I pushed, and whatever position I tried. After about four hours, with the baby's heartbeat tiring, we agreed to a forceps delivery. In the delighted aftermath of my son's birth, the memory of the episiotomy and the forceps faded.

When I became pregnant again, a sense of failure – that I had not been able to push my baby out – returned. I discussed it with my midwife who said that the same conditions would not necessarily recur, and asked me whether I had considered having a home birth. I had always hankered after one, but Ashish vetoed the idea because he was afraid of complications and full of trepidation about under-going, for the second time, an experience which he'd seen as a unique event from which we had miraculously emerged safely. Also, combined with the panic of the second stage, we both had anecdotes of the remembered pleasures of the water pool, so we decided to go, once again, for a hospital birth using a pool.

The baby was due at the end of September, and we had settled into a sort of exhausted truce, getting our room ready for the baby, trying to prepare our son for the transition to being a big brother. In my first pregnancy, I was obsessed with the labour and much of my pregnancy was devoted to preparation for it. This time, I was more preoccupied with arrangements for Danyal. We had no relatives to rely on and had to make a number of alternative arrangements, depending on when I went into labour. A close friend who said she'd support me during the labour was also the mother of Danyal's best friend. It seemed likely that, rather than being with me, she would look after Danyal, since that was where he was likely to feel most comfortable if he were separated from both of us.

For some months before I was due, I'd experienced Braxton Hicks contractions on and off. As I entered the ninth month, the contractions were coming more regularly, and were occasionally intense enough to stop me walking. Three weeks before the baby was due, all three of us went for a check-up with the midwife. In the

---

A *posterior* or *backache labour* is when the baby's back is towards the mother's spine. As the baby descends, its head presses against the mother's spine causing intense, gnawing pain during and in-between contractions. In addition to terrible back pain, many mothers also experience severe gastric upset.

Any position where the mother is leaning forward will help to ease the pain since it will tip the baby forward from her spine. Leaning forward will also help the baby tip into the more favourable anterior position during labour. Sometimes it can also be comfortable to lie on your side. You will need a lot more support and encouragement to get through a labour like this and it seems prudent, ante-natally, to do what you can to help your baby settle into the optimal position for labour.

There seem to be more and more posterior, or other unfavourable positions, at the start of labour these days. Some observers have put it down to our modern lifestyle. Low-slung sofas, cars with bucket seats, a more sedentary lifestyle and even labour-saving devices which mean women are doing less housework which requires them to get down on their hands and knees, all mean that pregnant women spend a lot of time in positions where their knees are higher than their hips.

When a woman is in this position her pelvic inlet narrows, making it difficult for the baby to rotate in the right position. If your baby is diagnosed as being in a posterior position, it is important that you spend as much time as you can in forward leaning positions. Late in pregnancy these may not always be the most comfortable positions but they are a darn sight more comfortable than a backache labour (or a caesarean)! See 'Suggested Reading' for more information.

waiting room, I felt that the contractions were getting slightly more intense and uncomfortable. The water pool I had ordered had not been collected yet, and I was afraid of facing labour without it. Even after discussing it, we reached no conclusions as to whether the contractions were a false alarm or were building up to the real thing. The midwife said that she wasn't sure whether the baby was due soon or in a few days; Ashish said, 'I think it's going to be very soon.'

As we left the surgery we began to time the contractions. They were about ten minutes apart and regular. Yet we were still caught up in dealing with domestic matters: Danyal needed a pair of new shoes for school, and we wandered around the area looking for them. Sensing that something big was about to happen, Danyal got into a very bad mood, refusing all bribes. Eventually, we bought him a toy, saying that it was his present for when the baby arrived.

At home by five that afternoon, we became very businesslike. We contacted the hospital who sent the community midwife. Ashish was timing the contractions while getting Danyal's supper. Every now and then Danyal would shout out, 'Mama's having a 'traction!'

When the midwife came there was a mess of kids running about. Danyal had declared that he wanted to go to his friend's house and he was being picked up. The midwife examined me and found I was hardly dilated. She advised me to have something to eat, while she returned to the hospital to get a battery for her sonicaid. 'You're doing very well . . .' she said. I was walking around constantly and stopping during each contraction to rotate my hips. Barbie, a friend who was staying with us, walked into this scene and could not believe that I had gone into labour, which she had imagined to be a matter of white gowns and stirrups. 'It seemed so calm and ordinary. There was Ashish cooking, the midwife drinking tea and you were rotating round a chair, in between chatting about this and that.' As the contractions got closer and more painful, I was groaning through them and shouting to Ashish to come and massage me. This time was a backache labour as well.

The midwife, who still hadn't left and was observing me, suggested that we should ring for an ambulance. As the contractions continued to come more rapidly, Ashish and Barbie were preparing to take my things to hospital, putting my bags by the door, but, although no words passed between us, the midwife and I began to make other plans.

She began to bring her equipment in, which she pointed out to Barbie, and instead of waiting for the ambulance, I suddenly said, 'I want to shit!' and fled upstairs. I knew I had to get into position in the bedroom and I got Barbie and Ashish to move aside an old rug so I could get down on my hands and knees. After that my memory blurs. I was about six centimetres dilated when I was next examined, but now I had to concentrate really hard to get through the contractions. The ambulance arrived and I was aware of two ambulance men tramping upstairs into the room. It seemed like hours since we had called them, but I was told afterwards that they arrived within seven minutes. It didn't matter anyway because, by then, I knew that I was not going anywhere. Ashish told the midwife my previous history – the forceps delivery – and I heard her reassuring him and saying that it would be very difficult to get me down the stairs and out into the ambulance. As people moved round me, preparing the room as quickly as they could, pulling towels out of the bathroom and improvising, I concentrated on the contractions.

At one stage, after an examination in which I was told I was nearly fully dilated, I found myself collapsed on the floor. I was leaning against Ashish trying to brace my legs against someone. The midwife looked at me critically, and said, 'That's a very unstable position; try and get out of it.' 'I can't,' I said in a panic, 'I can't move.' Ashish hauled me up. 'Yes, you can,' he said.

I was in a standing squat, with Ashish supporting me, as I began to push. I remember very little about it except that he was holding me and that at some point I had my teeth sunk in his shoulder. After a couple of pushes, when I thought the head might have crowned, I demanded a mirror so that I could see what was happening, and was annoyed when I couldn't see anything in it. The next contraction came soon after. I pushed with a huge

> It really is important to remember that history doesn't always repeat itself with pregnancy and birth. A previous forceps delivery does not indicate the need for forceps next time around. A previous caesarean doesn't indicate the need for a repeat caesarean. A previous long, slow labour doesn't mean all your labours will be long and slow. Give yourself a chance to gauge what the next labour is going to be like, before you start planning interventions which may not be appropriate.

effort and suddenly felt the baby shoot out. I turned and looked down to the floor to see a baby boy with his umbilical cord still attached. He was lying on the ground, looking immensely surprised, and I knelt down towards him.

That was three months ago. Since then my life has been occupied by the immediate concerns and tasks of early motherhood. Right now, I don't know what will happen to me or to us. But meanwhile it is a mellow autumn, the sun still streams in through my window and Danyal needs picking up from school . . .

And God is sometimes kind to atheists.

It Felt Like There Were Angels in the Room

Fiona Christopher

I conceived on a bright and beautiful Saturday morning on Lantau Island in Hong Kong, two days before I was due to leave. As we were making love, I knew something amazing was happening inside me. There was this incredible amount of feeling with an extra 'ping' added on at the end! Andy felt it too as he frantically pedalled down to the harbour to get to work on his boat. Our very passionate passion had made him late.

En route back to London, I stopped off for a week in Thailand, followed with a few days in India. While I was visiting New Delhi, I decided to find out whether my intuition was correct. So, in very typical Indian fashion, I found a 'baby' doctor to whom I explained what I wanted. He, in turn, called a nurse to escort me down the road, through an alleyway, past a group of cars and up some stairs to a clinic where another doctor was waiting. He gave me a tiny jar, pointed me in the direction of the toilet and that was the last I saw of him! A nurse collected my sample and told me to wait. Two hours passed. I was beginning to feel frantic and my patience was running out. Finally, the nurse arrived back, only to type my results on to a computer, run them off the printer and place them in an envelope, which was kept in another room. No blue windows, pink dots, piss on a stick and thirty seconds later results in this place! Finally, I got my envelope and, yes, I was pregnant.

I remember feeling shocked, delighted, numb and very special, like I had this amazing secret inside me. I didn't want to tell anyone for a while. Just me and my baby. Automatically, my hand went to my stomach in that protective gesture I've witnessed so many pregnant women perform before me. The nurse had worked out my EDD – January 3rd – and it seemed like a decade away.

The following night I phoned Andy and he seemed really delighted. He wanted the baby and wanted to be with both of us. I remember feeling so very content and happy. At that moment, I was sure everything would be OK.

Once back in the UK, however, I began to feel terribly confused. I was twenty-seven years old, slim, attractive, with no responsibilities. Whilst in Hong Kong I had set up some exciting business opportunities which I was sure would be very successful, yet this little thing growing inside me would stop all of that. All of a sudden, we had a lot to talk about so Andy took some time off and flew over.

The following weeks were very taxing and emotionally draining for both of us. Although we had known each other vaguely for a year or so, we were only together as lovers for a couple of months and most of that time had been spent partying. Over the years, I had developed a deep distrust of men and rejection was my biggest fear. I never knew my father and, very sadly, my mum is a chronic alcohol and Prozac abuser. Being aware of the family pattern and the tendency for repetition, I felt quite terrified of inflicting my own up-bringing on my child. I knew I had to work through a lot of issues if I were to continue with this pregnancy.

Since I had contracted dysentery in India to say I was 'shit scared' was not an exaggeration. Still, with all the fear, in my heart and soul I wanted this baby so very much. I have a lot of love to give and the thought of termination just didn't feel like the right choice for me.

Andy was so amazingly patient during those couple of weeks. He put up with an awful lot. I pushed him to the very limits and continuously tested him on every aspect of manhood/fatherhood I could think of. Yet he didn't leave me and continued to support and love me.

Once we had made the decision to go ahead with the pregnancy, I felt very positive about our future together. Both Andy and I had travelled extensively in the last few years and were reluctant to give up the travel bug now. We planned to go out to Australia to have the baby and start a new life out there. Unfortunately, Andy had to go back to Hong Kong to complete his contract and would be away until the end of August.

In the meantime, I began to read up about my various birth options, which are endless nowadays. I've always had a strong belief in women's ability to give birth to their babies naturally, without interference and medicine. Hospitals have always left me cold – I'd heard too many horror stories of high-tech births where women lose control of such a special event. The idea of a water birth has always been attractive to me and now that I was pregnant this seemed the most natural and appealing choice.

The more I researched, the more stories I discovered of women giving birth in the ocean and even giving birth with dolphins present. So I began contacting women working with dolphins in Australia. There are a couple of midwives in Oz who have attended ocean births. Of course, whether dolphins turn up is up to them, but to me that sounded like such a natural way to give birth that I was willing to give it a go.

Time was flying by like never before and soon I was due for my 12-week scan. I was living in Camden Town at the time so my local hospital was University College Hospital. I felt quite nervous in the waiting room. I remember pacing, mainly to keep myself from pissing myself since I had a full bladder. When I finally got to go in for my scan, I was so preoccupied trying to make myself more comfortable that it took me a while to focus on the screen.

When the nurse said, 'Are there twins in your family?' I just couldn't believe it. I was so very shocked. I think I would have been less amazed if there hadn't been a baby there at all. Seeing not one, but two, little people on that screen is a sight I'll never forget. I couldn't stop crying with delight, excitement and shock. My two little babies. How happy I was to have kept you. Even then, they seemed so different. Twin one was very active and looked like it was jiving. Twin two was rocking side to side slowly like in a hammock. It was a miracle.

By the time I saw the midwife, I was in a state of shock. In the space of ten minutes my plans had completely shifted into a different reality. I remember discussing my ante-natal care with her

---

You don't need to have a full bladder to have an ultrasound scan unless the scan takes place very early in pregnancy. Before twelve weeks a full bladder will help push your uterus, which is still relatively small at this stage, up into your abdomen, so the sonographer can get a better picture. From twelve weeks onwards, when your uterus is bigger, there is no reason to suffer the discomfort of a full bladder while you wait to be scanned and you can safely ignore the request. Often the instruction to have a full bladder will be made without reference to your records to see how far along you are. It is also made without any regard for the fact that a full bladder late in pregnancy can distort the ultrasound image, making the placenta appear to be lying lower than it actually is. See 'Birth Basics' for more information on ultrasound.

and saying, 'Does this mean my ocean birth is out of the question?' She looked at me as if I would be safer locked up in a ward somewhere for six months until it was time to let me out. As our discussion progressed, it was quite apparent that my only option at this hospital would be a high-tech hospital birth with a minimum of twelve people present in the room with me. I couldn't begin to deal with that, so I decided to move hospitals.

I phoned Andy at work to tell him the news. He was also shocked, but very happy, and said we would have 'one of each'. How I wished he could have been with me, instead of always receiving life-changing news down the phone. I had great fun with all my friends, showing both scan pictures and waiting for them to notice 'Twin I' and 'Twin II' on the top of the pictures.

I also felt a little lost about my various options. The midwife at UCH had been so pessimistic about my chances of a natural birth that I had begun to feel quite down. As luck would have it, though, I decided to go to a talk Michel Odent was giving. I asked him if it was possible to give birth to twins in water and although he hadn't seen it personally, a midwife from a private hospital, St John and Elizabeth, spoke up saying she had recently attended a twin water birth. However, in this particular case, both babies were facing head down and the mother left the pool after the birth of the first one, to check that everything was fine to continue, and then got back in.

This was fantastic news! Now that I knew it could be done, if everything was well, I felt I had more chance of giving birth the way I wanted on the NHS.

My pull towards water was getting stronger daily. I felt I had to go swimming at least every other day to keep calm and balanced. My night dreams were weird encounters with dolphins swimming in clear, warm oceans. I knew there was a wild dolphin living in Dingle Bay on the west coast of Ireland. I decided that I wanted to swim with him, so I went to visit my aunt and uncle in Dublin.

My Aunt Sheelagh and I drove the eight hours across the country to arrive in this very pretty fishing village. I was struck by how mixed up and cosmopolitan the place was. The dolphin seemed to have attracted many nationalities to come and make a permanent home there, as indeed he had done.

The following morning I squeezed myself into a wet suit with a lot of tugging and help from Sheelagh (my tummy was growing rapidly, even though I was throwing up several times a day) and boarded the boat to go swimming with Funghie the Dolphin. Once in the water, I began to drift off, away from the others, because I was having a lot of trouble putting my fins on (tummy too big again!). There was no sign of Funghie yet so I floated for a while, willing him to come along. I decided to try and join the others and began to clean my mask.

As I put my face in the water there, lying directly below me, not even half a metre away, was the most magnificent creature on earth staring right back up at me. I was mesmerised. I have often heard that when a dolphin looks at you it's looking into your soul and that's exactly how I felt. He swam underneath me in silence for ages, which was truly magical, and before he swam off he touched his head to my belly ever so gently. It was such a lovely experience to connect with a dolphin in that way, and I'm sure the babies felt it too because, later on that night, I felt the very first flutterings of movement inside me. I was now fourteen weeks pregnant and more determined than ever to give birth in the water.

At about sixteen weeks I finally stopped throwing up and began to feel better and eat more. I started to have some very strong cravings, firstly for lemons – I could eat pounds of lemons daily – then spinach and carrot juice followed by Dairylea cheese and ice pops! I had been a strict veggie for many years so it came as a big shock to find myself unable to resist barbecued chicken on a couple of occasions.

I had begun to contact various hospitals with regards to a water birth, but without much success. Always there were the stipulations: 'As long as everything is fine with the babies and yourself in the first stage'; 'As long as both babies are head down and you agree to getting out of the water for a check between births.'

I even spoke to someone from the NCT who believed that there hadn't been a natural birth of twins in a leading London teaching hospital for several years. I was beginning to get more and more stressed about having my wishes met, but I kept looking. Then, by chance, I heard of a doctor at St Mary's who had let a woman go to 44 weeks with a big breech baby and I thought maybe I'd found my man.

After speaking to the senior midwife there, I provisionally booked at St Mary's and, since the consultant was away on holiday, I made an appointment to see the registrar to discuss my birth options. He said that I would be able to labour in water for the first part of the first stage, but I would have to get out for the actual delivery. The senior head of midwifery had heard about my request and also wasn't very happy. 'What about if both heads are down, the babies aren't premature (that is, over 37 weeks), and everything else is well?' I asked. I stated that I was willing to get out after the first baby was born, since from what I had understood, the first twin birth is very similar to a singleton birth. Basically, I was asking if, by any miracle or chance, I had a perfect labour, medically speaking was it possible to have a water birth? It was a frustrating meeting. The registrar got upset at my suggestion of no natural twin births on the NHS, but couldn't give me any figures to prove otherwise, nor could he provide a reason for not considering my requests.

Meanwhile, Andy had come home to be with me on my birthday and we both found it weird. I was getting bigger and was a lot more emotional about the babies and our life together. For Andy, the responsibility of supporting three extra people was daunting and probably not helped by the fact that I was so up and down. One minute the world was my oyster and the next a dark, frightening place. I found that being pregnant was bringing up memories of my childhood, memories of abuse, and I was beginning to feel very protective of my babies. Once again Andy took the brunt of my pain and supported me through it. His understanding and patience seemed never ending. After speaking to the head of midwifery, I arranged to meet and discuss my requests with her.

My best friend Nadia and Andy came along. Nadia came because she's an excellent arbitrator and, as a social worker, is used to dealing with bureaucracy. Having spoken already on the telephone, I didn't expect this to be an easy meeting and, in fact, it was atrocious! The whole thing lasted less than five minutes. During this time we were told that water births were dangerous and that there was no medical evidence to prove otherwise. It was impossible to monitor babies underwater and they wouldn't be able to get me in and out of the water. 'Too much hard work!' she said. 'I've been a midwife for thirty years . . .' was constantly repeated.

The registrar couldn't produce any figures about natural twin births because there aren't any. If anything, recent research shows that the policy of routinely delivering both twins, or the second twin, by caesarean does not improve outcomes. It may be practitioners' fear, caused by their own lack of skill, which causes them to refuse to consider delivering twins vaginally. See 'Birth Basics' for information on *twins*.

I began to feel like a silly little girl for daring to challenge the norm, yet all I wanted was what seemed to me the smoothest transition from life in the womb to life outside. I felt so disillusioned. I also felt the fact that it would be 'too much trouble', that it might require too much manpower or effort, were the *real* reasons behind the midwife's refusal. That, and the fact that the only ones benefiting from this type of birth would be myself and the babies. In retrospect, I hope to God this midwife was lying to me. If she wasn't, then she was remarkably misinformed for someone who has been in their profession for thirty years.

See 'Birth Basics' for information on water birth.

I was beginning to feel desperate and depressed. Everything I felt intuitively, and everything I'd read, indicated privacy was important for a smoother, less complicated labour. Because of this, a birthing pool would be ideal since, with twins, birth can turn into a bit of a circus. I know myself and I honestly felt I wouldn't be able to cope with a lot of strangers around me.

Yet another meeting was arranged for the middle of September, this time with the obstetrician who had arrived back from holiday to this big controversy. He said he felt that trust on both sides had broken down. The medical team, he said, were worried that I wouldn't leave the pool if there were complications, an accusation which I found most upsetting. All I wanted was the nicest way possible for my babies to be born. The midwives said there was no way a water birth would happen and that was the end of it – and there was no way I could achieve my aims without the support of the midwives. I was 25 weeks pregnant and my only option was to move to another hospital, but I was tired. The constant fight was wearing me out and I was frightened of premature labour if I kept this up. I ended that meeting in tears, feeling more and more certain I was going to lose control to the routines and machines of the hospital system.

Andy and I discussed the option of going to St John and Elizabeth. We would have to borrow the money, but since it looked like the only place that I was going to get a chance of a water birth, we decided to go for it.

My pregnancy had been going very well. I was fit and swimming every day, but I was beginning to get very tired. I was lucky that my

profession (aromatherapy) didn't recommend working whilst pregnant – I don't think I would have had the energy anyway. I was very
weepy and experiencing big highs and lows. In addition to all this,
we had moved down to Brighton to be near the sea and friends. It
was also the first time I had lived with a man, so it was a time of lots
of new experiences. I also began to do Active Birth classes, which
involved gentle yoga-meditation and lots of positivity about the
forthcoming birth. I found these a tremendous help.

The babies were moving around a lot and responding to my voice
and Andy's. We spent hours staring at my huge belly, feeling our
babies come and respond to our touch. Sometimes, even now, I'm
blown away by the sheer miracle of pregnancy.

I felt quite nervous when I went to St John's. Andy was working,
so Nadia came with me. I felt a terrible pressure to come across as
rational and totally calm and I hoped to God I didn't lose the plot,
since I needed someone in the medical profession to understand me.

My prayers were answered when I met Yehudi Gordon, a very
special man who seemed to have the gift of listening to what people
say and hearing what they mean. We went over the fact that I would
have to be double booked with an NHS hospital in Brighton in case
of premature labour. I confirmed that I would be happy to leave the
pool if needed for any reason or complication. At one point I
remember saying that I really believed I could do this and have a

---

The *Active Birth* movement, founded by Janet Balaskas in 1969,
came about as a response to the 'active management' of labour
which predominated then. An actively managed birth is one
where the mother hands over control of the process to her
doctors and midwives. It assumes, from the word go, that the
female body is not capable of delivering a healthy baby without
the aid of drugs and technology. In some ways it even views the
mother as superfluous to the whole process and her body as an
unpredictable force which must be regulated.

With Active Birth, mothers are encouraged to work with their
bodies and with gravity. They are encouraged to understand the
way that their bodies function, what part the pelvis, the uterus,
the cervix and the baby all play in birth. Birth preparation
classes are yoga based, to promote greater flexibility, and also
centre around meditation and solid emotional support. There are
Active Birth teachers and groups throughout the country. See
'Useful Contacts' for an address and phone number.

natural birth and was delighted when he said he believed it too.

Thirty-six weeks was the magic figure I had to reach. Any start of labour before that would mean high-tech intervention to save the babies. We were living a few minutes away from the Royal Sussex County Hospital in Brighton, the hospital I would go to in an emergency, but I decided to keep my ante-natal care at St Mary's since I couldn't face another change of hospital. Until December 6th I would visit St Mary's every two weeks and St John's on alternate weeks.

At St John's I started to see a counsellor, Ann, who was marvellous at supporting me through some emotional issues coming up. My changing body, my changing needs, my family and abuse from my childhood, all these things had to be looked at, worked on and let go. One of the most important issues at the time was to do with the fact that my dear friend Nadia had started a relationship with an ex-lover of mine. It became a very emotional issue for me, touching on my biggest fears of rejection and of not being 'good enough'. With hindsight, the counselling sessions were a very safe way of allowing me to work through some of my biggest fears and hurts of the past. I felt I had to let go of these things because I sensed a direct link between my ability to let go and be at peace with the situation and my ability to carry my babies to 36 weeks. That's the way it was for me. I let go of a lot of anger, jealousy and self-loathing. Sadly, I also had to let go of the idea of having Nadia with me at the birth. A few months back I couldn't imagine the big event without my closest female friend, who I love dearly, being with me. This was a very challenging time, but it was also a good, positive time as well.

I didn't really enjoy the next few weeks. I was so very scared of starting labour too early. I felt exhausted and mad and tearful. Every morning I would thank my babies for staying with me another day. I would touch them, massage them a lot, will them to stay inside me a few more weeks. Sometimes I thought I sensed them starting to come and I would feel scared. I was scared, also, of the smallness of premature babies, of whether I would be able to bond with them, feed them or hold them properly.

I continued my Active Birth classes and swimming every day. I used to wear this stretchy pinky-orange swimsuit and I reminded myself of a giant nectarine. I was so huge that every time I came up from the swimming pool steps, I had a vision of them separating from the wall from the sheer weight of me.

I couldn't really believe it when December arrived: 1st, 2nd, 3rd, 4th, 5th and then I was there. I had made the magic number! December 6th!

I planned to stay with my Aunt Maeve in North London for a couple of days before the babies were born and I was now in a state of real excitement. I would have my babies soon. I could look at them, touch and feel them, see what sex they were. Day after day nothing happened, apart from the fact that I got bigger and bigger. I got to 37 weeks, then 38. The scans I had showed they were both growing well and were big, bouncy babies. I had no high blood pressure and was fit. My Aunt Sheelagh came over for Christmas and left again for New Year, by which time I was willing the babies to come out.

I couldn't believe I was still pregnant. I had convinced myself I would have my babies by Christmas and the waiting was getting to me. I began to feel pressure from a lot of people. I questioned myself constantly on why my babies didn't want to come out. Was it because I was going to be such a bad mother? Throughout my pregnancy I always worried one baby wouldn't be OK. One was always quieter than the other. Was something wrong?

We had decided to try a course of acupuncture sessions to stimulate labour. I had become very uncomfortable and wasn't getting a lot of sleep. I was emotionally drained and weepy much of the time. As I write this, I feel so lucky to have had such tremendous support from Andy. He was a tower of strength: deeply understanding and loving at all times. I must have been hell to live with most of the time and I acknowledge him for staying, and love him truly for still being able to see me behind my fear and my rage.

The hospital had put me in touch with Meredith Churchill, a midwife/acupuncturist who ever so kindly performed four sessions on me over the holiday period. She told us how very effective and popular this treatment is in the former Soviet Union to start labour. After every session I felt mild contractions, like mild period pains, but once the session had stopped so did all the movement.

The 3rd of January birth date came and went and I found it very hard to understand why I was still pregnant. Everybody seemed amazed and I was feeling very weepy and frustrated. Was it because I just couldn't let go?

We came to the hospital the next day for a scan and then to see

Yehudi. The babies were absolutely fine and getting very big. From measurements taken the first twin weighed about 7lb 5oz (3.4 kg), the second 7lb 9oz (3.6 kg). Both babies were head down.

Since my cervix hadn't begun to dilate yet, it was agreed we would start inducing labour early the next morning. Nobody knows when term is for twins and the danger was that if the placentas started failing, the babies could become distressed and my chances of a normal delivery would vanish.

Andy and I left the hospital and went out for the day. I was finding it difficult comprehending that tomorrow I would start labour and, God willing, twenty-four hours later we would be a family. I remember feeling as if all the spontaneity of birth had been taken away and replaced with something altogether more clinical.

I didn't get much sleep that night. My fears kept me awake. Would I be a good mother? Would Andy be a good dad? Were my babies healthy? Would I have a natural birth? Could I cope with the pain?

Andy and I arrived slightly late that morning, so I had my first prostaglandin pessary inserted around 7.30am. From that point I was due to have a pessary inserted every six hours or until labour had begun. I felt a mild stinging around my vagina for a few minutes and was monitored for about an hour. My overriding feeling at this time was tiredness, so we ate breakfast and went to bed. It was so nice to have Andy sleeping next to me while I was going through my birth experience, and knowing that he would be able to be with me until I was discharged was comforting.

I awoke about 1.30pm with very slight pains in my tummy and lower back. The next pessary stung a little bit more. The babies were fine on the monitor and I was feeling excited and positive now that it wouldn't be long before I saw them. I asked Andy to go and get me a tape of ocean sounds. While he was gone I walked up and down the corridor, trying to keep the labour going. The mild period pains were getting more intense now and I had a slight show around 5.30pm. Every time I sat down the contractions stopped so I kept moving. By early evening my labour appeared to be more established, but I kept moving. Pat, my midwife at the time, suggested seeing if Meredith would come in and give a concentrated session of acupuncture.

Andy arrived back and I was moved into the labour room. Meredith came and was sticking needles into me. At the same time the babies were being monitored and a cannula was put into my vein in case I needed it later. I sat rocking in a chair. I was in pain but I had to laugh, because I absolutely hate the sight of needles and there I was, looking like a pin cushion.

At my next examination, at 9pm, I felt very disheartened that I hadn't begun to open up. Another pessary was inserted. I ate a little something and listened to a woman moaning with such power in the next room. She was pushing her baby out and I wondered would I be making noises like that?

With the acupuncture finished, the next few hours became a bit of a blur. I paced around continuously, throwing myself to the floor and moving my pelvis, trying to ease the pain. I know from my notes that Cathy, the night midwife, gave me a massage, but I have no recollection of it. I couldn't stop moving and moaning and rocking my hips. I was sipping Rescue Remedy in water and had some arnica which I believe helped. Cathy ran the water for the birthing pool and I continued to dance around the room. I remember not making any eye contact with Andy or Cathy.

It was wonderful to get into the pool and feel weightless and floaty. My contractions were coming very frequently without much of a break. My uterus and tummy were solid. It felt like the waves were building up inside me, crashing inside me and then subsiding – like a fantastic sea storm. Andy had put on the ocean tape, so water was everywhere, surrounding me in all of my senses. I lost any sense of time and being. I couldn't focus and my eyes felt wild. The contractions were very powerful. I felt I couldn't go on for much longer. I needed to know I was opening up and letting go. I remember asking Cathy was it possible to have a small, 'little bit' of an epidural?!

I also asked her to examine me to see how dilated I was, but found it too unbearably painful. The babies had been monitored very regularly throughout and were in great shape. I didn't think that much about them during labour – I was concentrated on the waves. At one point I started singing through contractions. I was given the homeopathic remedy natrum mur which relaxed me so well that I actually fell asleep during contractions.

I got out of the pool around 4am to see what was happening with my cervix. The examination was very uncomfortable, I couldn't bear it. Cathy wasn't sure of her findings and couldn't feel whether my cervix had dilated, so Debbie came in for a second opinion.

I couldn't believe it, I felt so bloody angry and such a failure. Why couldn't I open up like everyone else? Why couldn't I let go?

What was wrong with me? I felt like I needed to go and see a shrink because clearly my head was completely fucked.

I had some gas and air while Debbie examined me and she found the forewaters were bulging very lightly through my cervix and asked could she break my waters to see what was going on. With my waters broken I will always remember her saying that I was eight centimetres dilated and almost through!

Andy said I had the biggest smile on my face then. From that moment, everything changed. I knew I could do it and kept on saying, 'I can do this. I can do this, I *can* do this.' I stayed on the bed with the gas and air which was helpful for a while, but at some point I found screaming to be more beneficial. Yehudi and Pat arrived. Suddenly all my pain stopped and I wanted to start pushing.

I was back in the pool. Andy was holding me from behind, Pat was holding my hands in front and I was squatting down with each expulsive contraction. I didn't find the contractions at all painful, more amazing. The force coming through my body was incredible and getting stronger each time.

After about forty minutes of pushing, Yehudi suggested I might need gravity to help the babies out. He asked if I would leave the pool. I'll be honest, all I could think was 'shit, shit, shit' and I asked if I could try pushing one more time, after which I got out. The urge to push was becoming stronger and more powerful now and with each push the baby was moving well. Andy was still supporting me from behind and I was deep squatting with Pat balancing me by holding my hands. After one push, Cathy said she could see lots of dark hair, another push and I could feel soft downy hair.

Finally with another push, our first baby came sliding out of me and was placed between my legs. It felt like there were angels in the room. It was the most spiritual, magical, profound feeling of my life. Our Baby! No crying, just a little gentle cough. That touch of her skin, how sweet she smelled, how perfect she was. Her cord pulsated for seven minutes and when it stopped her daddy cut it and held her.

I got on to the bed for a quick scan to see what baby number two was doing. Thankfully still head down, but very high up in my womb, so my waters were broken again. As I got off the bed, a powerful contraction began. I felt this whoosh and the baby flew down my pelvis and began to pop out. After another push we were looking at our perfect baby boy. Once again no crying, just a couple of yawns. A miracle had happened.

They were both so very beautiful, our perfect little babies. How protective I felt. How much love I felt and how very privileged and blessed I felt.

I couldn't have been given better support. Cathy (along with Pat, Yehudi and Debbie) couldn't have supported me better. She was always 'present' and 'there', yet never intrusive. Every consideration was given to make the birth as smooth as such a big transition can ever be. Low lighting, silence and respect. The back-up team waited outside. In the end, having got out of the pool to give birth didn't bother me in the slightest. What was so important to me was that I was trusted enough to give it a go. I was able to see if I could do it the way I wanted.

Andy was brilliant – obviously a midwife in a previous life – and is a fantastic, caring father. Both my babies were over 7lb and perfectly healthy. I had no injuries, no stitches and pelvic-floor-wise everything toned up quickly.

It *is* possible to have a natural twin delivery. With the right kind of support and attitude, anybody can do it. Once the babies were home it was madness, very hard work and extremely tiring at times, but my birth experience kept me going and helped me to avoid the postnatal depression which can be the direct result of high-tech births.

I would love to do it again, and will do it again. Maybe somewhere hot and sunny in the ocean. If I'm really lucky, maybe a dolphin will pass by!

A point which many practitioners miss is that women, regardless of what kind of pregnancy they have, simply want to 'have a go'. You would be hard pressed to find any mother who would persist in her ideas about birth to the detriment of her baby or babies. In spite of this, many practitioners simply do not know how to 'wait and see'. Some actively set out to alter a mother's plans. If you have a midwife or doctor who can't see this point, you don't have that many options. You can change practitioners as this mother did, or you can make sure you have lots of strong support around you from family and friends. Make sure your partner knows what you want and is able to come with you and reinforce your preferences at any medical appointments.

Every Birth Is Different

Amanda Rayment

I have given birth three times and our children are called Tom, Rosie and Felix. Each birth has been so very different and I have experienced so many different emotions at each one. Recollecting Tom's birth can still make me feel angry at the thought of how he was welcomed into the world. His birth was so full of unnecessary intervention. We had the wonderful joy of our first child being born healthy, alert and so beautiful (as are all babies), but this did not alter the fact that we felt anger towards the hospital for the way we were treated.

Tom was an undiagnosed breech, which we did not find out about until I was in labour. At this time the hospital's policy was to follow strict criteria for breech babies. This meant a lot of pressure was put upon us to have X-rays and continual monitoring, both internal and external, throughout my labour.

Just as I was pushing Tom's bottom out, the monitor broke down. The doctor present told us he was not prepared to go on without a monitoring machine and no other machine could be found. My husband, Martin, and I were bewildered. One moment the doctor was showing us Tom's bottom – the next moment I was being wheeled away for an emergency caesarean. There was no discussion, no choice. After spending seven hours journeying down the birth canal, Tom was pushed back inside me and delivered by caesarean.

Because of the experience of Tom's birth, when I became pregnant with our second child, Rosie, we decided we would opt for a home birth. At my first ante-natal appointment I was shocked by the reaction I received. When I said I wanted a home birth I was told that I was 'foolish' and it was 'dangerous'. I tried over and over again to explain that Tom had been born by caesarean because the monitor had broken and not because he was in distress or because I was unable to give birth to him. In the end I was told I would need a 'trial of labour'. Immediately thoughts of this baby being born in an atmosphere of monitoring machines and doctors watching and checking throughout the labour brought back all the angry feelings and fears from Tom's birth. I left the clinic feeling very low and trapped in a system I didn't know how to challenge.

I spent the time leading up to my next appointment reading and gathering information and statistics on vaginal birth after a bikini line caesarean operation. The more I read the more I was convinced I should follow my instincts as a woman and a mother. At my next visit to the clinic I went prepared with all this information, ready to have an informed discussion. The reply I received was: 'I do not know anything about statistics and I will not discuss home birth with you any further.' Discouraged, I carried on with the appointment and ended up with all the usual check-ups, not bothering to mention the birth of our baby again. I left feeling even lower than last time. The same day I remembered seeing a poster about an independent midwife. I rang her and it was wonderful to talk to someone who listened to what I had to say and understood how I felt about pregnancy and birth.

To my great relief, Sue, the midwife, did have experience of delivering a woman with a previous caesarean section at a home birth. We arranged for Martin and myself to meet her and in the meantime she would obtain my case notes from the hospital. My notes confirmed that Tom's birth happened just as I described. After our meeting, she agreed to deliver our baby at home. From that point on I had all my ante-natal check-ups at home with our

It is important to take someone with you if you are going to enter into a dialogue with your doctor or midwife about the kind of care you wish to receive. A woman on her own has the air of someone who is unsupported. The presence of your husband or a friend sends a clear message that you have discussed the options with others, that they are on your side and that you are unwilling to back down. Of course, you don't have to enter into this kind of dialogue at all. Lots of women feel under tremendous pressure to appear calm, informed and level headed at these kinds of meetings, but you can just say, 'This is what I want,' and leave it at that. Your doctor or midwife is under a legal obligation to provide whatever level of care you wish to receive. You may want to consider whether a big confrontation is worth the effort.

midwife, although I did have a routine scan at the hospital. We took the decision to have the scan after treating a small blood loss with emotional support from our midwife and herbal treatment from a medical herbalist. We were well informed about the use of scans and felt quite clear that we were using this technology for a good purpose – in our case to check that the placenta was healthy.

We began to look forward to the birth of our second child. We enjoyed the pregnancy and we were so pleased to have found a midwife who was very wise, experienced and loving. Unfortunately, we did not know at any time during my pregnancy that our daughter, Rosie, had Edward's Syndrome. As a result she had severe abnormalities and three days after my expected date of delivery we were told our baby had died *in utero*.

> Edwards Syndrome, also known as Trisomy 18, is a rare chromosomal abnormality. It affects around 1 in 3,000 babies, producing multiple abnormalities. It affects females more than males and few live more than a month after birth.

We decided to induce labour and, with an enormous amount of support from Sue, Rosie was born in hospital. Her birth was loving, gentle, silent and quick. I got through those first few hours of grief with the love and strength of Martin and Sue and by knowing that our baby had been born with love and dignity.

The hospital staff were very supportive towards Martin and myself and continued to be so for weeks after Rosie's birth. Even now, I hold on to how close I felt to Rosie while I was pregnant and that there was so much love at her birth. The pain and grief does not go away, but I have learned to enjoy life again with the help of people I love and my friends.

Our third child, Felix, was born at home after a two-hour labour. He is happy, healthy and wonderful. We asked Sue to be our midwife again, since, once again, the hospital did not support us in wanting a home birth. In the end we decided to wait until I went into labour before deciding where to give birth – this left the options open for all three of us. The pregnancy went very well. As with my other pregnancies, I exercised every day, meditated, ate healthily and, most important, kept my mind clear at all times ready to listen to my body and our baby. I went into labour a week early and we all felt the birth should be at home. This turned out to be the right decision for us and Felix was welcomed into the world with a wonderful birth, free from intervention, technology or drugs – just the magic of birth.

Because of my experience, I have come to feel that it is important that women know that having a vaginal birth after a caesarean (VBAC) is not simply a matter of finding an obstetrician who is willing to 'let' them 'have a go', or, if they want a home birth as well, of arming themselves with a load of statistics. I did a lot of preparation for a home VBAC – and most of it was on myself. I once read that VBAC women are not high risk medically, but are high risk emotionally, mentally and spiritually. I believe this is true. For me, the first step was to let go of the experience of Tom's birth. That meant letting the anger as well as all the other difficult emotions come to the surface. Once they had, I was finally able to let go.

> See 'Birth Basics' for information on *Vaginal Birth After Caesarean* (VBAC).

The other important part of preparing for a VBAC was to look at the part I played in ending up with a caesarean in the first place. This may sound strange, but for me it meant learning to take responsibility for my own life and the lives of my babies. It meant getting informed – not just from books but by learning to listen to my body as well. With this knowledge, I wouldn't need anybody's permission to give birth, nor would I have to accept anybody else's version of how birth should be. I can see now that my own fear and lack of confidence were contributing factors – both crazy reasons for a baby to be born by caesarean! I was very lucky to have a husband and a midwife who supported me while I discovered my own innate ability to give birth without the aid of obstetricians, monitoring machines and other interventions.

Every birth is different and I believe every woman and each pregnancy should be treated individually. I hope that one day, in a kinder and more well-informed world, women like myself won't have to struggle to have the kind of birth they want.

Past Imperfect
Jil Rickards

I fell pregnant with my first son in November 1990, which was a complete shock to me. At the time I was having therapy sessions to work through the violent, mental and sexual abuse by my father during my childhood. Thankfully, I was in a stable relationship with someone that I truly loved, although my initial thoughts were that I didn't want him anywhere near the birth. At first, we wanted a completely hospital-directed birth, being convinced that they would know best what to do, and we duly embarked on that course. However, over the months, we became more and more disillusioned with the process and, having gleaned sound information from the Active Birth Centre, we opted for a home delivery instead.

When I was pregnant, I remember being terrified that during the birth I would recall some ghastly hidden secret that had eluded me throughout my therapy. I was very lonely, as I had never been able to make substantial friendships. I was scared that I wouldn't be able to cope with bringing up an infant and convinced it would only be a matter of time before I was violent to my own child. I went from being a totally independent – and proud of it – working woman, with my own source of income, my own car and possessions, to someone who relied completely on one man, both financially and emotionally. I remember feeling vulnerable and scared that I would be attacked. There was a lack of family support from my parents and I felt so totally alone. Paradoxically, I also felt extremely well.

The birth did take place at home. I remember being so excited after such a long, long wait for the baby to come (nearly two weeks late). The first twinges of labour started at about 11am and it was a beautiful, balmy, sunny August day. Simon came home from work straight away, we had lunch and went for a walk to encourage the contractions. Even so, strong contractions didn't establish them-selves until about 6pm and an hour later the midwife arrived. I

For a woman who has been abused, the issues of security, continuity of care, privacy and control in labour are even more urgent. If her first experience of sexuality was an abusive one, it will be important to surround herself with people who can help her to feel as if her choices are being respected. Unfortunately, some practitioners only end up reinforcing, rather than breaking, the cycle of abuse.

Women who know they have been abused are often fearful that during labour they will have flashbacks to abusive incidents in their childhood, and indeed this does sometimes happen. One way to reduce the risk of this is to start working through some of these issues during pregnancy, with a counsellor whom you trust. Although there is no simplistic formula, some women who come from abused backgrounds have found that a positive birth experience is a fair-sized step towards redeeming and healing the past.

remember the pain of the contractions like nothing on earth I could have imagined. I clung to Simon and spent most of my time sitting on a wooden chair, screaming. The midwife did try and get me to walk around, but this was far too painful. I remember getting into a wonderful, warm bath surrounded by candles and lovely smells and for a little while the pain had gone. I cried. I felt that it would never end, and each contraction was more painful than the last. There seemed to be no time involved, but then, finally, I felt a strong urge to push. By this time, I was on all fours. The second midwife had arrived and it was very dark outside. Unfortunately, she decided to see if she could see the baby's head just as my waters broke. There was much slipping around on plastic ground sheets and trying to find a suitable position to deliver, and then the baby's head finally emerged.

Simon was virtually jumping up and down and the midwife grabbed my hand and said for me to touch the baby's head. I looked down to see this tiny head sticking out from between my legs and it was the most bizarre thing that I had ever seen. Two more pushes and my not so tiny 9½lb baby shot across the floor. They handed him to me and as I gazed into his eyes, I was overcome with shock and had to ask Simon to take him. It was now 6.45am and, while I was being helped down the long corridor of the flat and into bed, my baby was busy getting examined.

I felt relaxed and proud. I had given birth the way that I had determined and I had coped really well. I didn't have any terrible memories emerge and, in fact, nothing at all went wrong. It seemed to me the perfect birth.

The next ten months were very difficult. I didn't know much about looking after babies and my mother gave me little advice. I had mastitis. We were also trying to buy a place to live and I was working from home as well. I felt that if the baby didn't stop crying I would throw him out of the window and I often felt violent towards him. I feared I was turning into my father and this scared me so much I shot off to the doctor as I had nowhere else to turn. However, I also decided to go back to therapy and work through some more issues regarding the role models I had and how I was as a parent.

Twenty months later I was pregnant again with my second son. The contrast in pregnancies was astonishing. This time I knew what to expect and felt even more strongly that I would not be put on the hospital conveyor belt. This pregnancy was fraught with difficulties. I felt sick all the time, every day of the entire pregnancy. I was so tired, but I couldn't sleep during the day because I had my son, Joe, to cope with. During this time Joe went through a difficult phase of getting up at about 5.30am, not wanting to sleep in the day time and also waking at night. I was so exhausted. There was just me, Joe and Simon. I didn't have any family nearby to help and I felt awful. I felt I couldn't cope either with Joe or being pregnant and sometimes I resented them both. The second baby was much smaller too, probably because I was so run down. He remained breech for a long time and I had to accept that a caesarean might have to be done against my wishes. I had wanted another home birth in a birthing pool and the thought of going to hospital was frightening for me.

Throughout the pregnancy I stayed in therapy and this took me to the point of needing to confront my parents with what they had done. I felt that if I did this, I could stop the abusive behavioural pattern and not let it carry on through another generation with my children. My sister had also reached a similar point and we went together to see them. I was four months pregnant then and knew if I didn't do this at that time, then I never would. My mother was very good about listening to what we had to say, but put a lot of it down to my therapist putting ideas in my head. My father denied everything.

I tried very hard, through the next few months, to establish a truthful relationship with my mother and I never felt so much like I needed a mother. However, she found it too difficult and we now simply exchange pleasant letters. I felt tremendously let down.

My waters broke one Monday morning at 9.30am, just as the delivery men were due to arrive with chairs and sofas. Simon arrived at work, only to come straight back home. Contractions were not happening, however, and round about lunch time one of the midwives found old meconium in my waters and advised me to go to hospital. I spoke with the midwife who was to deliver my baby and she said she was not too concerned, that probably this happened when the baby turned a week or so before – but she also advised going to hospital to monitor the baby's heartbeat. This was devastating news to me and I burst into tears. I felt that if I went to hospital, I would not be allowed out and I would have to give birth there. In fact, my midwife told me that they would try to keep me in, but if I wanted to discharge myself she would still do the delivery.

I had to leave Joe with my brother-in-law which was terribly difficult. He had never stayed overnight anywhere before and although he was being brave I knew he was bewildered and upset. I duly went off to the hospital at about 5pm. The staff were not very pleasant at all and I was sent to have the baby's heartbeat monitored. Any hint of a contraction had disappeared completely in reaction to my distress. I stayed on the monitor for an hour and the heartbeat was regular and strong. However, the hospital staff were using frightening words such as induction around me, so I asked to leave. The registrar laughed and told me I wasn't going anywhere, but, after quite a long and unpleasant battle with the staff, I discharged myself. As I left, the registrar was still cautioning that I didn't understand the gravity of the situation, that my baby might die during delivery.

Simon and I went home. I think we had curry to eat and some wine. Then I had a bath and went to bed. I felt totally miserable and hoped desperately that I had done the right thing. The house felt so empty without little Joe.

During the night my contractions started to increase again. Poor Simon was made to fill the pool at about 3am. However, this turned out to be a false alarm and we slept in until 7am. We went for an early morning walk, had breakfast in a café, went to choose some

Contractions can come and go during labour and vary in their intensity and frequency throughout. Certain things can affect them, making them stronger or causing them to stop altogether. It is very common for a woman's contractions to slow down or disappear altogether when she enters the unfamiliar atmosphere of a hospital. Natural birth pioneer Michel Odent believes that, like all animals, we instinctively seek the places we feel are the most safe in order to give birth. If a woman feels frightened or under stress her body literally 'shuts down' until the 'danger' is past. Also, if you are very tired, your contractions may slow down, simply because your body needs to rest. Take the hint and try to rest if you can. Your midwife can monitor your baby's heartbeat while you rest and as long as everything is fine, there is no rush to move things along.

curtains and my contractions definitely started to increase. By lunch time the midwives had been called again, but progress was long, slow and extremely painful, especially in my back. In retrospect this may have been due to the baby being in a posterior position and trying to turn round. Simon and I were left alone in our sitting room and four hours later I agreed to an internal examination, only to find that I was only five centimetres dilated. This threw me into despair. I had been in the wonderful pool for hours and this helped a lot, especially in finding comfortable positions. I was in agony and had been for hours, and worst of all I was sick several times. The contractions were so painful I didn't know what to do, so I screamed and screamed and screamed. The midwife did another examination and half an hour later said she was going home for a while. Luckily, before she went, I felt a sudden urge to push.

By this stage I was losing any kind of control. My midwife was brilliant and managed to get me to do what was necessary without much dialogue. My little baby was pushed out in ten minutes. He was born under water and then helped to the surface and given to me. He was wonderful, but the midwives were getting concerned about him. They said he was a bit 'flat', meaning that he had trouble getting going I think. Simon was really worried. They slapped his feet and made him warm by the fire and they may have given him oxygen. I don't remember because I was left stranded in the pool, struggling with very painful contractions and a placenta that wouldn't shift. Thankfully they found my baby was all right, though perhaps a bit in shock from being pushed out so fast. Meanwhile, I continued to struggle until the midwife helped me to get the placenta out.

> When a baby doesn't breathe immediately it is described as being 'flat'. If the umbilical cord is still attached and pulsating there is no need to panic as your baby will still be getting plenty of oxygen – some babies just don't breathe immediately. Some can take as long as twenty minutes to breathe steadily. Some have a bit of sticky mucus in their respiratory tracts and this can be encouraged to drain out by placing the baby on its front with its head lower than its hips. Some babies sneeze this mucus out. If you are giving birth in an upright position, the mucus will drain out as a matter of course and your baby is less likely to have breathing problems.
>
> Babies are remarkably robust, especially if they are not premature or have not been exposed to pain killing drugs or other routine procedures. A baby can be gently encouraged to breathe without the aid of oxygen masks or suctioning, by wrapping it up warmly, especially the head since this is where most of its body heat will be lost. Lots of skin to skin contact will also help, as will gently talking to your baby.

My baby, Ben, was weighed – 7lb 1oz – and wrapped up warmly. He didn't want to feed for quite some time, and I was too exhausted anyway, but all things considered it was a very happy ending to a lousy pregnancy and worrying start to labour.

Ben was terrible at sleeping, worse even than his brother. He woke every hour or so for much too long and I was so very tired. I felt I could achieve anything if only I had some sleep. Poor Joe was suffering as well. I had little energy for him. I did not know how to handle his problems over the arrival of a new baby and all I can say is that I did my best, although I know it wasn't enough. There just wasn't enough of me to deal with a baby who woke all night, an older brother who got up at the crack of dawn and a house that needed decorating. We let this situation go on for nine months before trying the controlled crying technique. I had always been so totally opposed to this, but it did work and a week later he finally started to sleep.

Two and a half years later, I

feel I have still not quite recovered. A good night's sleep is never to be relied upon. However, I do feel that some of my old self may be returning. None of my worries about abusive behaviour have materialised. I still feel eternally let down by my mother, as I so much needed a mother to support me through all this, but life goes on and I continue to do the best by my children. I am exhausted by the emotions of my older son, and exasperated by the slowness and clumsiness of the younger one, but exhaustion and exasperation seem a small price to pay when I see such wonderful children growing up. What's more, I feel I have the power and confidence to provide them with the substantial family background which I so sadly lacked.

The Thin Blue Line
Joanna Elias

I had grown up never wanting children. For some inexplicable reason, I had always been terrified of the physical process of giving birth. It was not that my mother had put me off with tales of blood and gore. Nor, I believe, did she have a particularly difficult time – she is no longer alive, so I cannot ask her. I was just negative about every aspect of pregnancy, from getting fat to giving birth, and the aftermath of having a squawking baby to care for. I felt that a baby would diminish my professional life and force me into the domestic role that I had always eschewed. My husband and I had always travelled adventurously, and frequently. It was not unusual for us to pop over to New York for a couple of days to see friends, or go to a party. We rarely ate at home, and had a very interesting, lively social life. Philip had always wanted children, but when we first met, some fourteen years ago, I told him, categorically, that motherhood was not for me. He had the grace and decency not to pressurise me, but I guess he hoped that one day I would come round.

What changed my mind was the death of my parents, first my mother and then, eighteen months later, my father. At thirty-six I was an orphan and this strange, limbo-like state forced me into a major reappraisal of my life. I became actively interested in my Jewish heritage, about which I knew nothing, and over the next few years embarked upon a journey that introduced me to my own religion, culture and the Hebrew language. All my questioning and flirting with exotic cultures suddenly seemed irrelevant. The more I learned about Judaism, the more I wanted to pass on its beauties and its deep, rich meanings to someone else. At the age of forty-one I wanted to become pregnant. Philip, who is not Jewish, but who had encouraged me in my Jewish studies, was thrilled by the turn of events, but was slightly wary at this volte-face. I needed to convince him that my change of heart was for real. Fortunately, I became pregnant quickly – within a few months. When I saw the thin blue line of the pregnancy test emerge, it was literally like a new divide, a new life for me and, for us all, a new beginning. I felt blessed, and very aware of the miraculous.

I was also very frightened. None of my physical fears had vanished, and I knew that forty-one was fairly late for a first baby. I quickly took the decision to treat pregnancy like a journalistic job, and to research the market as exhaustively as possible. I wanted to avail myself of expert help wherever possible. I have always been very fit and healthy, so I had never got to know any of the doctors at our local surgery, and had no relationship with any doctor who I felt would help. My instant reaction was to go privately, and pay for the best help available. I spoke to all my friends about their birth experiences, and the more information I gathered, the more I realised the National Health system was brilliant for pregnancy. We were fortunate in that we lived a stone's throw from Queen Charlotte's, so I registered there, but with the feeling that I might change hospitals if I was not satisfied.

What surprised me about pregnancy was that you do not get to see anyone until you are sixteen weeks. I felt that at forty-one, I should have been offered various tests earlier. I knew from friends that a chorionic villus sampling (CVS) is performed around 11 to 13 weeks and if I had not had good personal contacts, I might have waited for my first hospital appointment at QC's at sixteen weeks, when it would have been too late.

As it happened, I made my own appointment to go to the Harris Birthright Trust at King's College, to have a CVS performed by Kypros Nikolaides, who was highly recommended. A nuchal fold scan indicated that my risk of having a Down's Syndrome baby was equivalent to that of a 31- rather than a 41-year-old. I decided it was still too much risk and, although terrified of needles, I opted for the CVS. Kypros was absolutely wonderful, totally reassuring, and so skilled that, even though it looked like an eighteen-inch-long knitting needle was probing my being, I did not feel any discomfort or pain. The CVS came back with a good result, and I learned that I was having a boy. I chose to have a CVS, rather than an amniocentesis, because amnios are performed later, the results take longer to come through, and I did not like the idea of a possible abortion at twenty weeks.

At sixteen weeks, I had my first appointment at Queen Charlotte's.

CVS, or chorionic villus sampling, is a diagnostic test performed between 9 and 11 weeks of pregnancy. During this procedure, a long, thin needle is inserted, either through the abdomen or through the cervix (the route depends on where the placenta is lying), and a small part of what will eventually develop into the placenta – known at this stage as the chorion – is withdrawn and taken to a laboratory for analysis. Results can be obtained within a day or two.

This particular procedure has double the risk of miscarriage, compared to amniocentesis, and can also result in other alarming side effects such as bleeding, infection and fetal blood leaking into the mother's system (a potentially serious complication for a mother who is Rh-negative, since her body may start to produce antibodies to her baby). Research also shows that there is an increased risk for babies of breathing difficulties, growth retardation and, if performed before 9 weeks, limb deformities. There is also a 6 per cent chance that the results will be inconclusive. Although many women choose CVS because it is performed earlier and produces results more quickly, some 10 per cent of those who have CVS will eventually go on to have amniocentesis.

Much of the accuracy of the test depends on who is performing it. This mother was right to go to a large centre where they specialise in screening and diagnostic procedures. She could have insisted on being referred through the NHS, instead of going private. In fact, any woman who wants to undergo diagnostic procedures like this should insist on being referred to a large regional centre where the doctors have more experience of these procedures. Unfortunately, when women want something which does not fit in with NHS timetables they are quite often denied it, which is why a number of women opt for diagnostic testing privately.

As with all tests for abnormality you should seek out *all* the facts before embarking on the test and insist on being counselled about the implications of the results, both positive and negative, of the test.

It was more of a routine check-up than anything else, but I left feeling that I was just one of a number, and resolved to find out what else was available. Being older, and neurotic, I wanted to be coaxed gently into this new world of pregnancy, doctors and babies.

Through a friend who lived locally, I learned that Queen Charlotte's offered a 'One to One' midwife scheme. Although we live outside the catchment area for the scheme, I rang to enquire and managed to get through to Pauline Cooke, the midwife who runs it. She kindly agreed to take me on. At twenty weeks, she came to my home for the first time, and from then on I felt like I was in safe hands. It is a fantastic feeling of relief, to have someone kind and knowledgeable who you feel is on your side. I explained to her all my negative feelings and emotions about pregnancy. She felt that a lot of my fears were based on ignorance and over the coming months helped to dispel my anxieties. She was so generous with her knowledge that I began to feel like I was doing a crash course in childbirth. The more I learned, the more positive and confident I became.

The One to One midwife scheme is brilliant and should be available to all women, all over the country. It is lovely to have the same person come to you in the privacy of your home. I never again had to hang around a hospital waiting room, and I never saw a doctor again. It gave me great confidence to know that Pauline was always just a telephone call away. Throughout, she was entirely professional, but I also felt we had become friends. I was lucky in that I was having a good pregnancy. Apart from feeling sick from eight to sixteen weeks, I felt absolutely well, and had no problems at all with blood pressure or water retention, or any of the other discomforts often associated with pregnancy. I have been a vegetarian for twenty-three years, and am also teetotal and a non-smoker, so I suppose that all helps. I carried on eating my usual diet, which is mainly raw food, but with more milk and cereal products. Until six and a half months, I did not look pregnant, and right at the end, I had gone from seven stone to just over eight stone.

At about 28 weeks the ante-natal classes started. Again, I wanted to get as much information as possible, so I took a three-pronged approach – the intellectual, the practical and the physical. I had been recommended to Christine Hill, an obstetric physiotherapist, who runs private classes aimed at neurotic, older first-time mothers. I signed up, and to my delight met about twelve other women, all 30 to 40+, most of whom were career women who, for varying reasons, needed extra reassurance. Christine's classes were wonderful. She gave us the facts straight, about what was going on in our bodies, how we could choose the various options when it came to delivery time, the advantages and disadvantages of certain drugs, how we needed to assert ourselves if things went wrong and, very importantly, how to look after a baby.

The One to One scheme, which originated in London, is also available in Leicester and Shropshire and will be put into operation in other hospitals in the country over the coming year. With One to One, hospital midwives practise in much the same way as community midwives – in other words one named midwife is responsible for your care and will, as far as possible, see you through your ante-natal care, labour and birth and the post-natal period. Often ante-natal care is in your own home and you and your midwife have a chance to get to know each other well throughout your pregnancy. There are no guarantees, unfortunately, that your named midwife will be with you in labour, and you will be encouraged to get to know her partner as well, just in case, but initial evaluations of the scheme show that the vast majority of women will have their named midwife with them in labour. Because of this, the One to One scheme has proved very popular with both midwives and mothers. If this kind of care appeals to you but is not available in your local hospital, you might consider transferring to the care of your community midwives, who tend to operate in much the same way, or booking a Domino delivery. Your GP or Community Health Council will be able to advise you about the different schemes in operation in your area.

It was surprising how many of us in that class had little or no experience of babies. She circulated us with everyone's telephone numbers. I made friends, and a whole new support system came into being which, sixteen months later, is still of enormous value. I also did the hospital's ante-natal classes. The course was less high-powered and less personal – there were about fifty of us – but it was useful because I learned the orientation of the hospital, and saw the various bits of medical equipment. However, I was glad that I was getting the bulk of my information from Christine, and of course Pauline. Finally, I did yoga classes aimed at people wanting a natural birth. Although it was my intention to use every pain-relieving drug possible, I still felt the need to be as supple and relaxed as I could.

The combination of doing three sets of ante-natal classes, plus having the luxury of a One to One midwife, meant that I approached my due date with a fair feeling of confidence. The last week, when I suddenly ballooned out, I panicked that the baby might be so huge it would never get out. At the very beginning of my pregnancy, my hope was to request a caesarean. I wanted to be put to sleep, and for the birth to be over as quickly as possible. My thinking had since changed, but I still wanted to make maximum use of modern medicine and drugs. I still cannot understand why some women want to go through long and painful births. I feel that the natural birth lobby is a bit of a conspiracy against women, especially when I hear women say that their husbands wanted them to have their babies without any 'help'.

Five days after my due date, Philip and I went out for a meal, and I managed to force down some minestrone – I felt decidedly off colour, and could not work out why! That night I had the most violent attack of sickness and diarrhoea that I have ever experienced – worse than anything in Turkey or India. In the morning we called Pauline, who rushed over to see me, and thought it was food poisoning. She said that I definitely was not in labour, and that it was quite common to have a fragile stomach when one is so heavily pregnant. She advised bed rest, and staying quiet. At about 4pm that afternoon, I noticed a slight tightening of my stomach muscles. It was not painful, but was a definite and different feeling. I told Philip, and we began to time them. They came at 30-minute intervals, and after two hours or so of regular 'feelings' we rang Pauline again. This time, she confirmed that the first stage of labour had started.

To my amazement, I felt very calm. I had a TENS machine ready and waiting, and at about 8pm, when the contractions were becoming longer, and a little more noticeable, Philip wired me up. The tingly feeling of the TENS helped to soothe the slight pain I was experiencing. My favourite music was

It is very easy (too easy) to polarise opinions about birth. The issue is not actually natural birth versus technological birth, nor is it home birth versus hospital birth. The issue is *appropriate care*, chosen by women to suit their individual needs. Not all women need or want lots of intervention; others feel more secure knowing intervention is available. The other important issue is *support*. There is a great deal of support for women who want 'everything going' because they fit so well into the hospital system. Women who make less popular choices are much less likely to find support within the system, even though their choices are as reasonable and safe as any others. If women can't get together on these issues, how can they possibly expect their doctors and midwives to?

playing and we were sitting in the bedroom – Philip, me and our two cats, who seemed to sense what was going on. At one point I had a hot bath, which felt delicious. Pauline came over to check me again at about 10pm, said that I was three centimetres dilated, and that we should meet her at the hospital at 11.30pm.

It was only on the way to the hospital that I felt I needed some pain relief. When I arrived, I requested an epidural, which was administered almost immediately. It was unpleasant having the epidural put in because for some reason I could not arch my back in the correct way – either due to nerves, or physical dyslexia – but anyway, they managed and twenty minutes later, when the epidural took effect, I suddenly began to feel fantastic. I had a mobile epidural, so I could walk around. I felt perfectly normal, except that I could no longer feel my contractions, which I gathered from the monitor were coming every 5 minutes or so. My waters did not break, so Pauline had to do it for me. She was with me the entire time, in a large room comfortably darkened so that Philip and I could rest. In fact we both dropped off, and when I woke up, some four hours later, I was eight centimetres dilated.

My memory is now a bit hazy, but I can honestly say that I never felt a second's pain after the epidural was administered. I was so relieved that the drug was working that I felt quite euphoric. In total I had three top-ups. Throughout, Pauline kept me informed of my and the baby's progress. Philip and I were cracking jokes, and at times I had to pinch myself. I just could not believe that having a baby could be so relaxed, and yes, so enjoyable. At ten centimetres, Pauline told me to walk around, as the gravity would help to get the baby out. We walked around the corridors, arm in arm, gently chatting away. It was far removed from all the TV films I had seen, with women shrieking in fear and pain.

Eventually, it was pushing time. I could not feel my contractions so Pauline had to tell

This birth went so well because she had an attentive and skilled midwife who worked with her, and because the mother was willing to listen to and trust her midwife's reassurance that many of her fears were based in ignorance. With a less knowledgeable midwife things could have gone very differently. It's only worth putting your total trust in someone whose skill you are sure of, who is willing to get to know you and pursue *your* aims and not their own, or the hospital's agenda.

me when to push, and where to direct my efforts – it was as though she could see every hidden nook in my birth canal, and guided the baby out with all-knowing hands. I had no idea a midwife could work with such selflessness and devotion. It was hard work pushing, but not unpleasant. I could not quite get the baby out, so after forty minutes, I had an episiotomy (which I did not feel), followed by a ventouse. About two minutes later, at 9.12am on Sunday June 11th, Elijah Marley was born. He was plonked on to my stomach, and I looked at this tiny scrap of humanity with amazement. At the age of forty-two I had just given birth to a totally perfect baby boy. He scored 10 out of 10 for each of his AGPAR tests, and was not stressed in any way. He weighed 6lb 8oz, and looked surprisingly long and alert. I was thrilled to notice that he resembled my late father, a fact which Philip commented upon as soon as he saw him. Soon after he was born I was stitched up, with Pauline urging the sewer to do a good job. I had very few stitches and again was relieved that it did not hurt.

For information on assisted labour see 'Birth Basics'.

Half an hour later, after admiring the baby, taking photographs, and going through all the various rituals, including telephoning my sister in Hong Kong on Philip's mobile, I wandered down the corridor, on the arm of a nurse, to have a bath. It seemed very surreal to go through the momentous process of birth, and so soon after to be having something as mundane as a bath. I kept wondering when I would feel pain. I just could not believe that my pregnancy, and delivery, had all gone so smoothly. I thanked God for his compassion.

After my bath, I was shown to my room – which was private, but on the NHS ward. It cost a mere £65. I had hardly got into bed when a nurse bustled in and ripped open my nightdress. Before I knew it, the baby had been attached to my breast, and was feeding away merrily. I had been in two minds whether to breastfeed. It was slightly too earth-mothery for me, but, as it happened, Elijah seemed to know exactly what to do, and it was easier than I had anticipated. I shall never forget Philip's face when he walked in, carrying my overnight bag, and saw the baby guzzling away. It was the antithesis of everything I had ever stood for in my previous, baby-phobic life.

I can only say that having a baby at forty-two is a total joy. Elijah is hard work. He is extremely lively and very self-willed, but every morning when I go in to wake him, I look at him with wonder. To me, he is incandescent with loveliness. He is still so close to source, an angel without wings, that I marvel at the potential for perfection that exists in all human beings.

On a practical note, I feel that having a baby in my forties will help to keep me young, whereas for twenty-somethings, I fear it is an ageing process. Of course, my day to day life has changed. I am not doing any writing or sculpture, and even though I have a live-in nanny, I still have little time for myself. I take Elijah for at least half of every day, because there is so much of the world that I want to introduce him to, and in my few hours off, time evaporates into a blur of seeing friends and household administration. Philip and I have less time together, and our trips to Africa or India have been replaced with tame jaunts to nearer places, but we are so enthralled with Elijah that it does not matter. These days life has a fresh and all-absorbing new dimension.

On My Own

Jessica Stanley

In the last three years I have had two babies and each time I felt thrilled to be carrying life inside me. From the very beginning I did not feel that I wanted the medical profession involved in any way, and my partner supported this position fully throughout my pregnancies, labours and births.

I wanted to give birth at home. I felt fit, healthy and in touch with the baby and at no time was I examined by a midwife or doctor during either pregnancy. I had heard the idea that birth is a body process and that it could be to a woman's advantage to keep her head and mind out of it. When I first became pregnant, I took this on board and made the decision not to read any books or gather any information on the subject. To be honest, the idea that books or someone else could tell me directly about my experience of myself or my baby seemed ludicrous.

It was only after my first birth, when I started talking to other women about their birth experiences, that I realised mine had been essentially different. Later, when I became pregnant for the second time, I began to read and explore the consensus opinion. The main difference in my attitude this time was the effect which all the information I had absorbed had on my psyche and my emotions. It took me away from that inner place and into my head, into a space that was based on ideas and abstract theories, rather than what was actually going on inside me. Sometimes I had to make a real effort to stop and return to the inner place and allow my instincts and feelings to tell me how my baby and I were.

For many years, I have taken responsibility for my own health and sought to address any problems which come up by exercising my right to make alternative choices about any kind of treatment I might have. Some of the things I did during pregnancy were to oil my belly and, for the last three months, drink raspberry leaf tea. I also booked a water pool for the birth. I worked out the due dates for both my pregnancies from reading an article which reviewed a number of studies in which women knew the date of conception. The duration of pregnancy was on average 266 days from that date and *not* from the last menstrual period. The studies showed that the idea of post-maturity did not really exist as no one exceeded 287 days. In my case, I had been unsure of the date of my first conception and consequently the birth was three weeks earlier than I had expected. With the second conception, I had a precise date and the baby was born after 269 days.

I think it's important to mention my social context during these pregnancies because, in retrospect, I can see how it affected me positively. My mother had died and I found myself in conflict with the rest of my family. I felt isolated from them. Because of the position I found myself in, my friends started to disappear and I was beginning to sense a new life ahead. I decided to move out of my local area. Although this was a difficult time in many ways, with respect to my pregnancies, I was very much in my own space and so managed to miss all the fears and inappropriate advice which often accompany pregnancy and birth.

The births themselves were incredible experiences and fairly straightforward. The first one began at 12.30am with a pain in my lower back. I did not think I was in labour, but within half an hour the contractions were coming every two minutes. I got into the bath – our birth pool was not due for another three weeks! I remember feeling frightened, not because I was without medical attention, but by the intensity of the contractions and the imminent responsibility of motherhood.

Within an hour I had found a way of breathing with the contractions which made them bearable. This continued for a few hours, some of it in the bath and some lying on the bed on my side, pushing my feet against the wall and squeezing my partner's hand. Then my waters broke. The baby had moved. The contractions changed and became less frequent and we even fell asleep for a short time.

This next phase passed very quickly; soon I felt the need to push and was sure the birth was imminent. My partner, however, wasn't so sure. I knelt on the floor for a while then returned to the bath, kneeling again, where, after three more contractions, the baby's head was delivered with a yell. I checked to see if the cord was

It is not illegal to give birth alone, although it is illegal for a labouring woman to be attended by anyone other than a doctor or midwife, except under emergency conditions. What this means is that any doctor can legally deliver a baby – even if he or she has no relevant experience in doing so; a lay person, however experienced, cannot. Strictly speaking, this mother was breaking the law by having her husband attend the birth. The problem is that there are women who feel cornered into choosing birth alone as a means of getting the kind of low intervention care they want. There are no figures to show how safe or unsafe birth alone is for a healthy woman. Those figures which do exist are mostly a reflection of concealed pregnancies (teenagers, illegal immigrants, etc) where the woman has then gone on to give birth alone and unsupported. Under these circumstances there is an understandably high rate of fetal death. In theory, it is unlikely that a healthy woman giving birth alone is going to have any problems, but in practice it is probably unwise. Much better to find a practitioner who is on your side, either within or outside the hospital system, if you can.

As far as ante-natal check-ups are concerned, there is no law which requires you to attend them if you do not wish to. Some areas are even operating schemes where they reduce the number of ante-natal visits or where mothers choose how many visits they want to have. From a psychological point of view ante-natal appointments rarely turn up anything earth shattering or useful. From an emotional perspective, some women find the regular visits to hospital or clinic, or in their own homes, reassuring. Of course, the amount of reassurance you get depends largely on the practitioner you have!

Wherever you give birth, you are legally obliged to register the birth of your baby.

around the baby's neck, which it was. We released it, but the cord broke and moments later I caught the baby as she came out. It was such a shocking, exciting, emotional happening. I put her to my breast where she suckled happily and my placenta was delivered within about ten minutes. The whole thing had taken six and a half hours.

With an accurate conception date for my next pregnancy, the birth pool was in place when my labour began at 2am. This labour was shorter, but much more intense. There seemed to be no build up. Instead, I went straight into full blown contractions. We had barely half-filled the pool by the time I felt the baby's head and the need to push. My daughter had awakened at the beginning of my labour and, once reassured, she enjoyed getting in and out of the pool and being a part of it all. Again, the pain of it frightened me, although the water helped enormously – as did lying down, standing up, kneeling, and getting out of the water for short periods of time. After three and a half hours, the baby's head came out as I knelt in the water.

I checked her neck and, once again, the cord was wrapped around it. This time I did not have enough time to release it before the next contraction and her body came shooting out. I caught her and lifted her gently to the surface where we unwound the cord and she took her first breath. Once again, she suckled immediately and the placenta followed shortly after. We tied the cord with sterilised string and then cut it. By 8am, all four of us were back in bed asleep.

I had not wanted to be touched during either labour, and I was glad that I had managed to direct the course of birth without being interfered with. Had I felt that something was wrong, I would not have hesitated to use whatever assistance I believed necessary in the circumstances, including going to hospital. I do not think I was 'lucky'. The fact that I was in touch with my own body process, and that I had a deep emotional commitment from my partner, brought about the positive outcomes which speak for themselves: two bonded, well adjusted and physically healthy babies.

Informed, Not Irresponsible

Deanne Pearson

The day I found out I was pregnant I stopped smoking. I remember lighting a cigarette, inhaling and imagining a huge carcinogenic cloud swirling down towards this new life growing inside me. I stubbed out my cigarette and that was that. I knew I didn't have the right to jeopardise my child's health and well-being.

I decided to take control of my health, and that of my baby, turning to complementary medicine as a safe and gentle means of looking after us both through pregnancy. When I had to go abroad, I opted for homeopathic prophylactics in place of the standard inoculations. My GP told me I was being irresponsible. It was something I was to hear from the medical profession on a number of occasions over the ensuing years.

After finding out everything I possibly could about labour, birth and the pros and cons of interventionist techniques, I was left in no doubt that a natural, active birth, with the freedom to move around and deliver in the upright position, was not only desirable but perfectly feasible. However, I also accepted that giving birth is not always straightforward and that the drugs and apparatus in the hospital delivery rooms could, and did, save lives. I just didn't want them used routinely.

So I drew up a birth plan, outlining how, ideally, I would like my labour to be managed, whilst at the same time making it clear that this was in no way intended to undermine the skill, experience and authority of the obstetric team. If there were any problems, I asked simply that we be kept informed and that we be consulted with regard to any proposed action.

I enjoyed my pregnancy immensely. I was fascinated by the changes my body underwent, enthralled by the sheer wonder of nature, and I took my new-found responsibility very seriously. I learned to tune in to my body and really listen to it. I took up yoga and learned to meditate, made sure I got enough rest and ate a healthy diet. I can honestly say I had never felt so well, or so special, in my entire life. I even looked forward to labour, considering the ability to give birth a great privilege which women were so lucky to have bestowed on them. I didn't kid myself that it wouldn't be painful, but reasoned that millions of women gave birth more than once, so the positive aspects had to outweigh the negative. And for me they did.

My waters broke at 6am on Saturday, August 11th, and I was summoned to the hospital where I spent all day having mild, intermittent contractions. By the end of the day they'd stopped. I started taking a homeopathic remedy called caulophyllum, which my homeopath had told me would help re-establish, or speed up, contractions. The consultant obstetrician laughed. I only wish he'd still been on duty two hours later when I was admitted to the delivery room in full-blown labour.

The midwife on duty – whom I'd never met before – was superb. She took careful note of my birth plan, dragged huge mats and pillows in for me to crawl around and lean on, and made me feel quite comfortable about screaming and yelling my head off, which I found was a great emotional release. The pain was much more intense than I'd expected, and the consultant suggested I try pethidine. Garry, my partner, explained that this was the last thing I would take, due to the possible effects on the baby, and, although the consultant tried to convince me these were minimal, the midwife gave me the thumbs-up behind his back. That did me far more good than any shot of opiates.

There was a reason, however, for the extraordinarily high level of pain. Although head down, my baby was poised to emerge facing up – 'face-to-pubes' as the midwife put it – instead of down, which would make the delivery more difficult. When the contractions slowed down and the baby started showing signs of distress, the consultant told me I needed an epidural and caesarean if I weren't to risk losing the baby. As I watched its heart rate steadily rising on the monitor, I knew this was the point where I had to hand over to modern medicine.

For information on *fetal distress* see 'Birth Basics'.

Once I'd had the epidural, the doctor told me to stay on my back while they prepared to take me to theatre, but I insisted on staying upright, hanging round Garry's neck as my legs could obviously no longer support me. Garry was great, keeping quiet and out of the way when I was coping (I'm not the sort of person who appreciates having their hand held and their brow mopped) and taking over when it looked like I wasn't. He knew as much as I did about the birthing process and the interventions which get used routinely and was in total agreement with everything in my birth plan.

The baby's head suddenly crowned and, although I wasn't able to push him out due to the effects of the epidural and had to have an episiotomy and forceps, I didn't need a caesarean.

As I gazed at my slightly bruised, but vigorous, 8lb 4oz baby boy, I felt a tremendous amount of satisfaction, along with that never-before-experienced surge of pure, all-encompassing love, joy and protectiveness that I don't believe anyone can fully appreciate until they become a parent. I wasn't disappointed that I hadn't been able to have a natural birth, because I knew I'd done the best I could under the circumstances.

The medical team left the three of us alone for a while, as we'd requested, and then tried to persuade me to allow them to inject our son, whom we named Finn, with vitamin K, the blood-clotting agent routinely administered to all newborn babies. But I knew there was evidence linking the intravenous method of administration with childhood leukaemia, and asked that it be given orally. I was told it was difficult to ensure the baby got the full dosage that way. I insisted, and they complied, although when they told me I was being irresponsible and that if my baby started haemorrhaging it would be too late and he would probably die, I nearly gave in.

I was, however, vindicated three years later when I returned to the same hospital, pregnant with my second child, to be handed a circular in the ante-natal waiting room informing me that, due to possible links with childhood leukaemia, vitamin K was now administered orally rather than intravenously.

I stayed in hospital for a couple of days after I'd had Finn, and kept being offered pain killers, but I was in no discomfort whatsoever. I used the homeopathic remedy arnica (for shock and bruising) after the birth, and poured water containing essential oils of tea tree and lavender over my genital area every time I peed, to help it heal – which it did beautifully.

I breast-fed Finn, but he lost more than the usual 10 per cent of his body weight following the birth, and the health visitor who called daily for the first ten days suggested I give him supplementary formula bottle-feeds. When I refused – arguing that he seemed very content and was sleeping well – she actually told me I was

Vitamin K is routinely given to newborns to prevent a rare bleeding disease called haemorrhagic disease of the newborn (HDN). The occurrence of this disease is measured in fractions of a per cent, 1.62 per 100,000 babies (or 0.00162 per cent). For years, all babies were given intramuscular injections of vitamin K to prevent HDN. Then panic ensued when a probable link was discovered between the injections and childhood cancer. So, to prevent this, hospitals began giving babies their doses of vitamin K orally. The link with cancer has now been refuted and the bigger issue is that the preventative qualities of synthetic vitamin K preparations have not been conclusively proven. So we may be giving our new babies something which does them no good and may even do them harm, since an overdose of vitamin K can have toxic effects.

Vitamin K is naturally present in breast-milk and highly concentrated in colostrum and the 'hind milk' which comes in at the end of a feed – so it's easy to see how restrictive breast-feeding policies in hospitals can deprive babies of their full complement of this vitamin. If the mother eats a good selection of foods which are high in vitamin K, she can pass all her baby needs on in her breast-milk. These foods include green vegetables, eggs, potatoes, soy bean products, rice bran, cow's milk and liver (preferably organic). For more information on vitamin K see 'Suggested Reading'.

starving him. Those words almost destroyed me. All I could think was that, because of my pigheadedness, my absolute conviction that I knew what was best for my child (after all, my experience of child-rearing consisted of a mere ten days compared to my health visitor's more than ten years), I was actually harming this tiny person whom I loved so much and who relied on me for his every need. The memory of how I felt chokes me even now, six years later. I felt I'd let Garry down too. After all, he'd trusted me with the well-being of our child.

He came with me to our local clinic, where the paediatrician reassured me that although Finn had lost more weight than was normal, he was fine and if I wanted to carry on breast-feeding I should. Finn started putting on weight, but very slowly. For the next few weeks various health visitors at the clinic, plus my GP, kept encouraging me to supplement his feeds with formula. I was told I didn't have enough milk, that it was of poor quality and nutritional value, and I became so anxious I almost gave in. I even began to

If a health visitor says something like this to you, you should report her to the United Kingdom Central Council for Nursing, Midwifery and Health Visitors (UKCC). She can be disciplined for passing on damaging and inaccurate information. There has never been a case of a breast-feeding mother starving her child to death and very few women do not have enough milk for their babies. The phrase 'Insufficient Milk Syndrome', which is often thrown at mothers, is not a recognised medical condition. It was invented by an American formula manufacturer in the 1970s to boost sales.

doubt the paediatrician's constant reassurances that all babies are individual and Finn had probably inherited both Garry's and my slight build and tendency not to put on weight.

Three months later, Finn's height and weight were average for his age, and although I'm glad I followed my instincts, I still feel angry at the trauma and distress I was put through.

I went through a similar scenario with my second child, Ryland. Weighing in at 9lb 10oz when he was born, he lost a lot of weight in the first couple of weeks and then started to pick up slowly. Yet again, I came under pressure to supplement with bottle-feeds, and felt stressed and anxious, but he too was a contented baby, and second time around I was much more confident about sticking to my guns.

Ryland's birth was comparatively straightforward – although, once again, only because I insisted on being in control. He was two weeks overdue when the hospital announced they wanted to induce me. I wanted to wait a little longer, and they told me I had to sign something saying I took full responsibility for going against their recommendations. They told me there was a danger the placenta would fail, my baby would be deprived of oxygen and could even die. I did some research and found there were risks involved, and that these appeared to be greater than those associated with induc-tion – so I agreed to go in the next day.

I was already three centimetres dilated and, rather than using prostaglandin suppositories to bring on labour, I asked the midwife to break my waters. Contractions started almost immediately. The doctor nevertheless started issuing instructions for a syntocinon drip to be set up to speed up the labour. When I said I would rather let the contractions gather momentum naturally, he expressed surprise, and irritation, that I didn't want to get it all over with as quickly as possible. 'I'll probably have to come back and put you on the drip anyway,' he huffed. After he'd gone, the midwife opined that she rather thought she'd be delivering the baby by the time he returned.

She was right. Two hours later I gave birth to my second son, in an upright position, without the use of any drugs or other interventions. It was an exhilarating experience, actually feeling him pop out as my abdomen suddenly deflated. He'd stuck one of his arms out with his head and I'd torn badly (not that I felt a thing), so although I'd also wanted to deliver the placenta naturally, my midwife explained that the longer I waited to be stitched up, the more difficult it would become due to swelling. This made sense, so I agreed to let her inject me with syntometrine to help the process along.

I was shown the placenta after delivery, and it was dull and grey in places, which, I was told, showed it was beginning to fail as a result of the baby being overdue. Ryland and I returned home a few hours later.

> See 'Birth Basics' for information on being *overdue*.

The battles with the establishment continued. I'd had reservations about childhood inoculations when I'd had Finn, but, because I hadn't done enough research, I didn't feel confident enough to stand up to charges that I was being an irresponsible mother if I didn't have my child vaccinated. Garry too was unsure, and I wasn't prepared to shoulder that amount of responsibility on my own.

By the time it was Ryland's turn to be vaccinated, however, we'd both thoroughly explored and considered both sides of the argument and decided to opt for polio and later, once Ry was walking, tetanus. Neither child has had MMR.

Our decision was based on a wealth of research we wish we'd done before Finn's birth, and would advise all parents to investigate, just as we would advise all would-be parents to familiarise themselves with the pros and cons of various routine birthing procedures and interventionist techniques. I believe modern technology has its place – the most important thing is ensuring it's not used routinely, and for convenience's sake. And that is quite a challenge . . .

When A Baby Dies

Lesley Brown

When I discovered that I was pregnant with Charlotte I was terrified. Even though we had planned and hoped to have another baby, I now worried about every possible thing: my age, money, and the gap between our three boys, ages 8, 10 and 12, and this baby. However, when I discovered that this baby was a girl, and seemed from the scan at seventeen weeks to be healthy and well, I was very excited. I went very quickly from thinking that I was so glad that I never had any girls because how would I raise a girl? to feeling that we were being given the greatest gift and blessing – a girl! I began to look forward with all my heart to holding this baby in my arms and in our family. I hoped for a lovely attachment between this baby and her three older brothers. I couldn't wait to see Brian, my husband, with a new baby in his arms.

For myself, I had two deep wishes: one was to breast-feed for as long as possible, and the other was to try this time to have our baby at home. I spent a long time deliberating about the decision – dithering even! I decided to go to hospital. Then I decided not to. I read constantly, in a pile of books about alternative birth that I kept beside my bed, about statistics for home births, for hospital births, for home birth practices, for hospital practices, for interventions, for different pregnancy managements. I looked at the 'homely' birthing room in my local hospital. It wasn't very homely – just a hospital room with wallpaper and a wooden headboard on the hospital bed. There was no bath available and the midwives, though they promised to do 'whatever you want', weren't trained particularly in active birth techniques. I decided that, based on the sort of labour I wanted – an active labour and active help with it, based on my research on the relative safety of home births where they are indicated, based on my good health and previous history of three speedy, uncomplicated labours, and based on the existence of a good local midwife – I would have a home birth.

My consultant wasn't in favour of the idea, but he didn't refuse to work with it. We agreed that, unless there were medical indications to the contrary, I would pursue my home birth. Whenever he discovered a potential problem in pregnancy, he would say, 'If this continues, you aren't having a home birth!' to which I would reply that if he told me not to have a home birth, I wouldn't have one.

So my pregnancy was managed in this way, with frequent visits to my GP, consultant and midwife, and all looked well. My due date came and went, with a few alarming contractions and loss of my

Many hospitals now have 'homely' rooms – but the homely quality varies from place to place. Some hospitals have called in interior decorators to make things look nice for birthing women – others just throw a few pillows on the bed and slap some paint on the walls. Of course, none of these things will make any difference to a woman who wants a home birth. A hospital room, no matter how nicely decorated, is not a home. Nor can wooden headboards and flowery bedspreads guarantee a 'normal' or 'low-tech' delivery. If you are taking the hospital tour and come across one of these rooms, ask yourself a few questions like: 'Where is the bed?' If it is right in the middle of the room, chances are it reflects the hospital's inflexible attitudes about how and where women should give birth. Check out those nice cabinets – all the high-tech equipment is usually hidden inside them. Don't rely on appearances. If you want to know how often your hospital intervenes in labour – get their statistics.

Many, but not all, hospitals keep records of how often certain procedures like forceps, caesareans, episiotomies and inductions are used. You can obtain these by writing to the Supervisor of Midwives. Your Community Health Council, in order to fulfil its brief as a watchdog for the community's health, should also have copies of these figures. If your local hospital is using any procedure more often than 10 per cent of the time, they are intervening more often than is indicated. You may also get useful information from mothers who have given birth in your chosen hospital. For instance, your consultant may say he never performs an episiotomy unnecessarily, but you may find that every single mother you talk to has had one. This should start the alarm bells ringing in your head. If neither the hospital or the CHC are helpful, you can try your local NCT or send an SAE to AIMS for a copy of their Maternity Statistics questionnaire, which you can send directly to your local unit(s).

mucous plug. One night, two weeks later, twelve days post-term, I went to bed knowing that the next day I would more than likely have my baby. When I woke up the next morning I had mild and regular contractions. I made arrangements for my children and dog to be minded. I called Lesley, my midwife, and while I waited for her to arrive, I tidied the house.

By the time she arrived the contractions were quite hard and I was ready to get down to serious business.

Despite all the reading I had done about squatting and all-fours and supported standing during labour, I found I was happiest lying on my side, where I could completely relax during my contractions. My husband lay beside me on one side and held me, and my midwife, on the other side, monitored the heartbeat, set things up for the birth, and supported me through contractions. As they grew stronger, I remember thinking, you can read all the books you want, and remain active in labour and try different positions and relax and breathe calmly and even have your baths, but at the end of the day, this still hurts – a lot!

Lesley's help in this labour, and indeed throughout the whole pregnancy, was of a completely different order from the help I have had from hospital midwives. She was in tune with the hopes and wishes I had for this labour and birth and was able to work with me and support me. Things like electronic fetal monitoring (EFM), enemas and episiotomies were deemed unnecessary. She monitored and recorded the baby's heartbeat with the hand-held monitor. About episiotomy she said, 'You will not need to be cut. You will breathe this baby out.'

To manage the pain she gave me Bach Flower Essences Rescue Remedy, which took that last searing edge off each of those final, worst contractions and made them manageable. So did praying, incidentally, and I mean the most straightforward prayer on earth – 'God, please help me!' She encouraged me to stay on top of the breathing with every contraction, which made me feel as if I could manage myself in the middle of the powerful process that had taken over my body. I found all these more useful than the gas and air offered during previous labours, which in my memory only increased the feelings of helplessness and panic in labour and dulled my concentration. When it came time to push, she was able to coach me in exactly which part of my perineum to be pushing. 'No. Not there, *here*.' And when I pushed *there*, with deep groans instead of tense yells, I could feel a power in my pushing. So much so that, for the first time in my labours, I didn't have that awful feeling of pushing a football through a pinhole, which results not only in terrible feelings of panic and helplessness, but also burst blood vessels all over your face.

In what my husband tells me was a shorter time than ever before, Charlotte was pushed out all at once. I felt surprised but suspended – what was it? Had I done it? Was all well? I sat up to see her properly and Lesley gave her to me and I held her right on my chest. What I remember so much about that moment is the way her small head, so beautiful, flopped and lolled on my chest, with just enough life to show that she was alive, but not any more hint of tone or response than that. Lesley began to flick her heels and then she took Charlotte to syringe her mouth and nose. Charlotte never snapped into that contented, alert life that most babies do. Very soon Lesley was saying, 'How could this happen . . . how could this happen?' And then, 'Brian, call an ambulance!' I held Charlotte and flicked her heels while Lesley quickly set up the ventilating bag. She took Charlotte from me and I noticed that her hands were shaking and I remember thinking, 'She is scared. Oh.'

At some point during all this, Lesley injected me with syntometrine to be sure I wouldn't, on top of everything else, start to haemorrhage, and told me to push the placenta out with the next contraction.

The ambulance arrived and set Charlotte up with oxygen. I jumped up from the bed, stuffed wads of muslin nappies between my legs, pulled on underwear with a track suit and got into the ambulance with Lesley, the ambulance attendant, the driver and my dear baby. Brian followed in our car. I sat in the ambulance, bracing my foot against the opposite wall as we careened around corners and down the road to the hospital. I kept my hands on her so that she would feel me near her. I stroked her head and touched and talked to her as much as I could. Just as we were nearing the hospital, the ambulance attendant, Paul, took the oxygen tube out of the plastic mouthpiece she was wearing and said, 'There, Mum, you give her the kiss of life.' How did he know what a precious thing that would be for me? As I breathed into the mouthpiece for her, for a few breaths, I felt a sort of last, tenuous, but deep connection with her – a sort of parting ritual before the hospital took her into its hands.

In the emergency room there were paediatricians, nurses – one of whom sat and held my hand all the while Charlotte was being resuscitated – and a registrar. Eventually, Charlotte was transferred to the neonatal unit in the maternity ward and I was given a room opposite, although Brian and I spent most of the day with her in the neonatal unit, stroking her chest and head and watching her gasp for breath.

We called my friend Geraldine who came immediately to the hospital and I told her how afraid I was that Charlotte was already so damaged that she would never be at all well. I talked about my fears about raising such a handicapped child. She said, 'What you know for now is that Charlotte knows you, and that she recognises the sound of your voice.' I found these words so helpful in focusing on the moment at hand. If she lived it was so important to her, and to me, that she felt surrounded by love and goodness in her earliest hours. If she died, it was important to be with her as wholly as we could be for now. Later, after she died, one of the most comforting things people wrote me in the letters that came was, 'I know she knew how much you loved her.'

She had been born at 1.30pm, just after lunch time. At around 9pm, after a series of false threats and false hopes, her heart rate started to drop in a final way. I asked the nurses to unhook her from the monitors and tubes, so that I could hold her close to me and so that our boys could hold her close to them. I can still remember the blessed feeling of being able to hold her right next to my skin, at last, for the first time that day. I also remember my eldest son holding her and looking with panic and fear at the falling numbers on the heart monitor, which was the last monitor to be removed. We reminded him to look at Charlotte, not the machine. In a way this expressed my hopes and feelings about the whole pregnancy and the whole day with her – I hoped to focus on our baby and not on the medical paraphernalia.

Finally the nurse listened for her heartbeat and, finding none, asked me to listen too. I couldn't hear her heartbeat either. She had died and we all cried and sobbed with the finality and the relief and the momentousness and the sadness of it all. We spent a long time holding her, passing her around our children and neighbours and looking at her and being with her. Everyone went home and Brian and I bathed her and put a nappy on her (she was still discharging meconium) and wrapped her up in a blanket. We stayed with her together in my hospital room over the night, awaiting the post-mortem.

It was a source of comfort to me later to recall that we never left her alone, struggling with life, for a single minute. We felt comforted by the fact that at one point during the day, when Brian and I were sitting alone together with her, we had baptised her – not in any sense to protect her, but in order to give her a name and to acknowledge her being among us – to welcome her into the world. Brian is a minister and it was lovely to hear him say the comforting and beautiful words of baptism quietly over our baby.

The neonatal nurses were so good to us, giving us our privacy, helping where they could, photographing the baby, accommodating the needs of our children to be with Charlotte, and the wishes of our closest friends to see her and be with us. It was a great comfort to sleep with her all the night after she died – Brian and I and Charlotte together in one narrow hospital bed all night long. I felt so happy to have her. She was so soft and still so warm that she was nearly alive and could have been asleep. Sometimes, with anxiety and fatigue, I would find myself staring at a corner in the hospital room, or the curtains there, and then I would remind myself how lucky I was to have her with me still and to gulp in every sensation of her beauty and our closeness while I could.

We felt comforted by the deep involvement of the hospital staff. My husband saw our consultant paediatrician brushing away tears at one point. Throughout the day, the registrar, who had been waiting to look after me when the ambulance came to the hospital, kept coming to the neonatal unit to see whether I needed him. He also ate his lunch with my midwife and got her a cup of coffee when we arrived and reassured her that these things happen and have happened to him. The ambulance attendant came up to see us that evening, after he was off work. The pathologist spent a lot of time with us, explaining the legal necessity of the post-mortem and the feelings of the whole staff when a baby dies. The pathologist's assistant was careful and loving with Charlotte when he took her away for the post-mortem, and when he brought her back. The hospital chaplain sat with her while we went to speak to the pathologist, so that we wouldn't feel we were leaving her alone. Between our neighbours looking after the children, the neonatal nurses and the whole hospital staff, we felt cushioned and held in love.

Eventually, I had to face the question of whether a different management of the pregnancy and a different birth would have saved Charlotte's life. My first overwhelming feelings about this, after Charlotte was born and failing, were something like: 'Well, what did you expect?' I began to file home birth in my heart in the same place that I had already filed other idealistic notions – like keeping goats to mow the lawn – good and pure in ideal, but disappointing in practice and not something within the reach of someone not good or

pure, like me. I felt it was well-deserved come-uppance for flying in
the face of all that authority, and I felt that if I had been a better
person I would have been able to hold on to that dear baby, instead
of letting her slip from my grasp. If I had been better, she would
have wanted to stay near me.

I did feel these things, but I didn't articulate them. They
expressed themselves in a sort of numb disappointment, until my
post-natal visit with the consultant. On that day he affirmed my
deepest fears in a most heartless way. His general argument was that
he followed my wishes because that's what he tends to do, but that
if he had managed the pregnancy and birth his way, with more scans
and a hospital birth, Charlotte very possibly would have lived. A
scan might have shown that the placenta was deteriorating, he said,
and this would have indicated that it was time to induce labour. In
another pregnancy, he said, he would induce me at thirty-eight
weeks, and there would be no argument. I left his office drained and
shaking. Had I killed my baby? Were my decisions arrogant and
foolhardy? Should I have trusted him completely? Why was this
man needing to blame me?

> There is no way this consult-
> ant can say with any accuracy
> that, if he had been managing
> the case, the baby would have
> lived. While it is unlikely that
> many parents in this situation
> would feel up to it, you have a
> right to complain about com-
> ments such as these which
> are inaccurate and only serve
> to add to a bereaved parent's
> distress.

I looked and looked for the
real answers to these questions
in all the books I had read
during pregnancy. Those books
which suggested and supported
home birth were strangely
silent and unreassuring now.
Where pages had been devoted
to labour and to the early days
of life with a baby, very little
was said about the early days
of bereavement. I was disappointed that there was no alter-
native advice on dealing with ever increasing supplies of milk and
ever more painful breasts, or information on how and whether the
uterus would contract down, without the breast-feeding contractions
to reduce it. I would have loved advice about looking after myself
physically in the absence of a baby whose care and feeding were
going to have kept me grounded and resting for several weeks. I am
so grateful to all the women around where I live who brought meals
and urged me to rest. I wanted to know whether physically I would

be well – and how I could be, with all my body's systems in disarray.

Nothing at all reconstructed the arguments in favour of low intervention and home birth in the light of a 'bad outcome'. I set about doing the work myself, by talking and talking to friends, plus re-reading the books, *Good Birth, Safe Birth* especially. Are hospital births safer? The statistics for them aren't as good for outcomes as home births. Would a scan have saved my baby? Scans, statistically, do not improve outcomes. Should I have trusted the medical world and done things the conventional way? Babies die in hospital too. It isn't a magical place or a safe haven. Suddenly I knew about every neonatal death in our surrounding area, and every child born with a birth defect – all of them had been born in hospital. Lesley had resurrected a survey of all neonatal deaths from a local maternity hospital for a ten-year period. Look! There were lots of unexplained deaths from anoxia. Could I have done better than make the best-informed decision with love? Could my consultant have done better than exercise his professional judgement in balance with my own wishes? No. He did the best he could – and so did I.

I rehearsed alternative scenarios. Supposing I had gone to hospital and Charlotte had died; I wouldn't have my baby or my home birth. I would have felt robbed and I could imagine the depression I would be feeling now would be quite difficult to shake. Supposing I had gone to hospital and Charlotte had lived, but without any of what they euphemistically call 'quality of life'. Would I then have felt resentment that the hospital had intervened and made a mess of something that should have been perfect and holy – the life and death of a baby?

As I write this, Charlotte has been dead for three months. I still think about her nearly every minute of every day, and I am only just beginning really to cry over what we have lost. I have no idea what I am supposed to be doing right now. I feel pretty much at a loss, though very much supported and loved by people around me. I don't know how I will approach a future pregnancy – whether I could even contemplate another pregnancy. And if I could, where I would try to have the baby. Maybe, by then, things will seem clearer. For now, I treasure Charlotte and all she has brought us, though we miss her every single day.

The Perfect Day

Sarah Mulhall

It all started one day as I was driving to work. Driving along the A27 I noticed a new sign: 'Your baby, your choice – A midwife-led clinic for natural birth.' Eureka! I knew at that moment that my dream of having children would come true – because the last piece of the jigsaw had just fallen into place.

Six months later, Bryan and I were in the local wine bar. I sipped a glass of red wine, and refused it, proclaiming it 'corked'. Bryan tasted it and said it was fine. 'Well then, darling – I think I have something to tell you . . .' That weekend I confirmed my first pregnancy with a positive urine test – I was nine days pregnant! The following day I turned up at the birth centre and met Lynne Coe for the first time. 'Is it OK to have a baby here at Christmas?' I wondered. Whatever Lynne thought about me turning up so early in pregnancy she kept to herself.

I remember being shown around the centre – it felt warm, safe and secure – a bit like a protective womb for pregnant mums. When I was shown the post-natal facilities I just felt a whole wave of tearful emotion spread through me. This is what I'd always dreamt about. Magic happens – allow for the possibility.

I had a wonderful pregnancy – in some ways I wanted to get to the 'other side' safe and sound as quickly as possible, but, more importantly, I wanted to relish the changes that I could feel happening to me. I'd waited a long, long time for this, so I wasn't about to wish it all over. (Freedom from PMT was an unqualified success – I can now understand the reasons for large families.)

Bryan and I had decided to have only the routine blood tests (rubella and haemoglobin), and not to have the AFP blood test or a scan. What we had created we wanted unequivocally.

Apart from the most peculiar taste in my mouth at about thirteen or fourteen weeks, pregnancy was uneventful, but packed with so

The *AFP, double* or *triple* test, performed around 16–20 weeks, looks for certain chemical markers in the blood, the presence of which can indicate a risk of having a baby with a neural tube defect, Down's Syndrome and other chromosomal abnormalities. When it is simply known as the AFP test, the marker it is looking for is raised levels of alphafetoprotein alone. The double test looks for alphafetoprotein and lowered levels of unconjugated oestriol. The triple test looks for raised AFP, low levels of unconjugated oestriol and raised levels of human chorionic gonadotrophin.

In theory, the more markers the test looks for the more accurate its results, but remember this is a screening test, not a diagnostic test. It cannot give you a definitive answer to how healthy your baby is. In fact, the opposite tends to be true. The AFP/double/triple test has been shown to be so unreliable that 90 per cent of those women who show raised levels of AFP and go on to have amniocentesis, will have perfectly healthy babies. This is because there are many things which can raise your AFP levels. One may be that your baby has an open neural tube defect, which is leaking AFP into your blood system, but there are more likely reasons.

Since the level of AFP doubles approximately every four weeks during the second half of pregnancy, you could be further along than you thought. Multiple pregnancies also raise AFP levels. Inaccurate dates and multiple pregnancies account for a quarter of all raised AFP levels. If you have had an early threatened miscarriage, if you smoke, have viral hepatitis or are black, you are likely to have raised AFP levels. The sex of your baby will also influence the outcome of the test: boys produce slightly higher levels of AFP. Being very overweight or insulin dependent can push levels down. If you don't feel confident in your AFP results, you can ask for it to be done again. Because the test is so inaccurate this is usually done as a matter of course in the case of positive results. Chances are that you will get an entirely different result. This is probably the one test mothers most regret having, because of the unnecessary worry it can cause.

many poignant memories that recalling them, even now, is emotional and touches me deeply.

For instance, I was convinced by the third week of pregnancy that I was carrying a boy – I couldn't explain why or how to anybody, but I never deviated from my belief. We had named him by the fourteenth week.

Then there were my parents. Dad is 81, Mum 76, and they had despaired that they would ever see my children. Eighteen months ago Dad had triple bypass surgery and in May 1995 he was having a bit of a setback, requiring hospitalisation once again. Mum was frantic with worry, and neither of them could see where the next bit of good news was coming from . . . until I said, 'I'm pregnant.' I feel that seeing your parents cry with joy is one of the most touching experiences you can ever witness. Dad threw off the setback as if it had never happened (and battled through a debilitating bout of shingles four months later) with the expectancy of a joyous celebration at Christmas. How many proud fathers happily announce, at their son-in-law's and daughter's wedding celebration that the blushing bride is four months pregnant (no wonder she's blushing!)?

Monitoring the baby's heartbeat automatically conjures up the image of an electronic machine of some sort. There are several ways to listen to your baby's heartbeat. The most common is with the hand-held sonic aid. However there is some concern about this instrument, as it uses a particularly powerful form of ultrasound known as Doppler, which has been implicated in neurological damage to the fetus. If this concerns you, you can ask that your baby's heartbeat be monitored in a less invasive way, such as with a Pinard or stethoscope. Both yield the same information as the Doppler and have no possible side effects. If you, or any member of your family, want to hear your baby's heartbeat, you can listen through the stethoscope. These forms of monitoring can also be used effectively in labour.

Then there was the 12-week ante-natal appointment, when Lynne said, 'Let's listen to your baby's heart,' and there it was, twice the speed of mine in the background, and beating within me. I was amazed – how could so much formation occur in such a short period of time?

There was the day when the first flutterings I felt brought home the reality of the creation inside me. I felt my baby kick at 14 weeks – when I awoke early one morning thinking Bryan had his elbow in my stomach, so I pushed it out of the way – and it kicked back. I leapt out of bed shouting, 'The baby's kicking me,' which obviously stunned the baby into complete inactivity for about a fortnight! Bryan couldn't feel the kicks for another four weeks, and he found the intervening period very frustrating, as he felt a bit left out of the experience.

I remember also the relaxing times during the day and night when I would sit quietly, just glorying in being pregnant, and the knowledge that my child was growing safely and securely inside me.

My midwives kept suggesting that I should have a labour plan – and as I got closer to THE DAY, I did finally get it organised. Quite simply they would tell me what I had to do, and I would do it! Having never experienced labour before, and having 100 per cent plus confidence in my midwives, I knew this was the only choice. I (we!) couldn't have been in safer hands.

My baby then decided to throw a spanner in the works by settling into breech presentation, which continued. Badminton and golf, full-time work and a holiday in Spain failed to shift it. At 35 weeks, I thought my baby had turned, the doctor said definitely breech, but my midwives were less sure. Reluctantly I decided to have a scan to be certain and guess who was right?

I worked until December 3rd, and spent the last fortnight frantically painting the newly plastered nursery. Until this point I had been unable to buy anything, for fear of 'tempting fate', and all the wonderful gifts that we had been receiving had been carefully stored out of sight. I talked this over with Lynne who (obviously concerned that the baby was going to be without clothing on the big day) suggested that perhaps I start off with a shawl. I went out and bought a shawl, and then having summoned up the courage to look at baby clothes, bought a multi-coloured long sleeved vest. This done, I got in the car and drove home, sobbing all the way.

My baby was due in late December. On Sunday morning, December 17th, we had just put the finishing touches to the nursery and so went out for breakfast. Knowing that our house had been utter chaos for the last eight weeks, people kept asking us how we were doing. 'Ready for the off at any time,' we said. 'The carpet in the nursery is being laid tomorrow.'

When we got home, I felt really tired and took myself off to bed. Dad rang to speak to me thirty minutes later and it was all I could do to drag myself out of bed to talk to him. As it was the works Christmas do in the evening, and there were Christmas presents to wrap and cards to sign, I didn't return to bed.

Next time, in the final stages of pregnancy, when my body says SLEEP, I promise to sleep . . .

As I was driving to Millbrook Superbowl I said to Bryan, 'These aren't Braxton Hicks, these are the first stages of labour' – but not being ones to miss out on a good evening out we continued to the Superbowl, arriving at 7pm. I have never scored so many consecutive strikes before – but it's hardly surprising since every time I walked towards the bowling lane I'd have a mild contraction and the ball fairly flew out of my hand! I drew the line at playing Crystal Maze or Laser Quest however.

By 11pm contractions were occurring about every fifteen minutes, so Bryan drove us home and I phoned the birth centre at 11.30. Lynne answered and when I said I thought I was in early labour she told me to eat and drink something and try to go to bed. I didn't feel like eating and drinking, and trying to get to sleep was impossible with contractions occurring about every ten minutes. I wandered around the house, trying to get in a comfortable position, but it was to no avail. Then I remembered it was about time to pack my case, which kept me occupied for a while. I told Bryan to get the TENS machine going and then shouted at him because it didn't work. As a general rule, shouting seemed to help, so every time I had a contraction I shouted and got so carried away with feeling free to make a lot of noise that it took the edge off the contractions.

By 5.30am I felt I wasn't coping very well, and Bryan was getting a bit perturbed too, so we packed up the car and I rang Lynne, again feeling desperately guilty about disturbing her. She sounded all bright and cheerful and, having asked a few questions, said I was still in the *very* early stages of labour and to go and have a bath. 'Are you eating and drinking?' 'Yes, yes,' I said ('No, no,' I meant). Anyway, we unpacked the car (which had all the toiletries in) and I ran a bath. I arranged loads of candles in the bathroom and had a big, bubbly bath and sent Bryan off to bed. For the next couple of hours I alternately dozed and groaned. By 8.30am I looked rather wrinkled and was really struggling to cope, so I rang the centre. Kate answered. 'I'm not doing very well,' I wailed in mid-contraction. 'Come on in, then,' she said calmly, as if she dealt with wailing women every morning (but then she does, doesn't she?).

We repacked the car. Bryan went to open the gates and told me to get into the car quickly. I shouted back that he wanted to try doing *anything* quickly whilst having a contraction! We drove there in the early morning rush hour and the journey seemed to take twice as long as usual. I sat in the passenger seat (not very intelligent) and held on to the hand rail, braced my feet into the seat well and screamed every time I had a contraction. The other cars in the traffic light queue at Chalk Hill were intrigued. Bryan just calmly sauntered along, as if he was out on a Sunday picnic, and was really in control, whereas I felt like a gibbering wreck by the time we arrived.

Lynne had come back to meet us (it was really her day off), and I can remember feeling so relieved and so SAFE, to see her at the door. Having negotiated a doorstep contraction, we all went through to her examination room. The examination itself was a bit uncomfortable; where the baby's head was engaging it had slid into my cervix caudally (towards the base of my spine) so Lynne had to move it forward to gauge the amount of dilation. Two centimetres seemed a little disappointing, but I was glad to have it established that I was definitely in labour.

My baby's backbone was on my right-hand side, and Lynne said that until it had moved around to my left-hand side, birth would not proceed.

Having taken us up to our rooms, Lynne established that I hadn't been eating and drinking overnight, and organised breakfast (which I didn't want). She also requested a urine sample. Trying to pee accurately into a small bottle when forty weeks pregnant and in established labour doesn't feature high in my list of easiest things to do. However, I was eventually successful. Having watched me eat breakfast, Lynne went off to test my urine sample, and reappeared soon afterwards with another tea-tray and many small pots of honey. My urine sample had shown a very high number of ketones, which quite simply meant that by not eating and drinking as instructed I had run myself out of available energy. I decided it was time to remember that my birth plan was: 'What Lynne and Corinne say, I do.' Under Lynne's watchful eye I drank a pint of milk and three cups of tea, each with a small pot of honey in. They were quite foul, but the effect on the ketones was immediate: they had completely gone from my next urine sample and I was back on course.

I was, therefore, slightly upset to realise that my contractions were diminishing in strength and frequency. I asked Lynne if I was definitely going to have a baby TODAY, and why had I stopped contracting? Lynne replied that I'd stopped contracting because my body needed a rest and so I could have a sleep – but only after I'd eaten some sandwiches. I said I'd probably be sick if I ate anything else, whereupon Lynne said that vomiting did actually help with

Ketones are the acidic by-products of fat metabolism. When they appear in the blood it is a sign that you are exhausted. You will be using a great deal of energy during labour. The uterus is a muscle and, like all your other muscles, it uses glucose to provide the energy which it needs to do the hard work of labour. If the body is short of glucose, because you have been fasting, it will search for other sources of energy and begin to burn fat. If this goes on for too long, you will become ketonic. You will not be the only one who suffers.

Once ketones appear, you are in danger of compromising placental blood flow, and thus the oxygen supply, to your baby. You are also putting extra strain on other organs like your kidneys which may become damaged due to having to process a greater number of concentrated waste products. Having denied you food and drink in labour, as normal hospital policy, the medical 'solution' to ketosis is to keep you topped up with an intravenous drip of glucose and water. A better alternative is to eat and drink as often as you can during labour.

labour as it helped to engage the baby's head more. A very interesting fact no doubt, but not one that I was able to derive a lot of comfort from as I hate being sick. Lynne re-confirmed that I was really in labour, and that the end result was a matter of time, but how much time was indefinable. This was really frustrating because I just wanted to get on with it. I had waited nearly thirty-five years to have this baby, and I didn't want to wait any longer!

Bryan went off at this juncture to check how the carpet laying was going in the nursery, and I had a couple of hours' rest. Lynne re-examined me at about 4pm and I was four centimetres dilated, so at least I was making progress. I was then instructed to order tea, but when it arrived at about 6pm, the contractions started up with a vengeance and, although I did my level best to eat something, it was difficult. Lynne had to see someone else for an ante-natal check, so Corinne came in just before 7pm. I remember her saying that unless I had a very long labour I should be finished before Christmas Day! Corinne asked how I felt about using the water bath in the birthing room and, although I'd been undecided about it all through pregnancy, it struck me now that it sounded like Heaven on Earth.

Corinne guided me down to the birthing room, pausing only to have a couple of contractions on the way, and once I was there I just couldn't wait to get in the water. It was absolute bliss just to be able to float around and feel free and uninhibited. I was quite surprised still to feel the contractions and I asked Corinne when the pain stopped. Corinne seemed to find this question amusing (though I can't imagine why), and said that she had only ever said that water *helped* with labour.

What was utterly blissful was having my lower back massaged with each contraction. As the baby had decided to 'go the long way around', I found that massage really eased the aching this generated. For me, being able to make a lot of noise was wonderful, and I got so carried away with shouting and screaming that on occasions I quite forgot what I was there for. Corinne and Lynne helped in telling me what type of sounds to make, for instance deeper, and I could really feel the effect of this transmitted through my birth canal.

In the cold light of day it might seem 'out of control' or 'making a fuss' when I talk about all the noise I made, but at the time it felt gloriously primitive and represented freedom of choice – the type of labour I wanted. I believe I'd have been gagged in a hospital situation for disturbing other mums-to-be, but this was my baby and my choice, so scream and shout I did – with utter enjoyment.

After a few hours, Lynne examined me again and said I was now seven centimetres dilated. She and Corinne were compiling my labour notes and I could see that my baby hadn't moved round at all. Corinne then disappeared, ostensibly to get me some food (which I didn't want), but also to ring Kate and ask her to come in tomorrow because they were going to be up all night (it took Lynne and Corinne a long while to realise how acute my hearing is!).

I then went into what, for me, was the most difficult part of my labour because at the peak of my contractions I started to get the overwhelming urge to push. Lynne and Corinne told me not to, but to pant instead when I felt the urge. During the next contraction I felt my waters break, and they were nice and clear, which was good, but oh, did I want to *push*.

I became really quite upset because I couldn't do what Lynne and Corinne were asking me to, and asked Lynne if I could have some gas and air. Lynne said I was doing very well and didn't need any, and could I *pant* and not *push*. I was trying my hardest not to push, and feeling really hopeless because I wasn't succeeding and so felt I was losing control. Corinne tried to distract me by getting me to eat something. Did I want a banana? 'NO! I DON'T WANT A BANANA,' thank you, but I do want to *push*. I asked Lynne for gas and air again, *please*, and she replied that I was doing very well and I didn't need any. I can remember saying that I felt sad because I wanted to push, and I felt that I was letting them down. Lynne said she'd check me again, but I was only seven centimetres last time and that was not long ago and not to expect much, and 'Oh, you're fully dilated, Sarah!' 'Do you mean I can *puuuussshh*?!' Corinne has since told me what I would have had to do to get gas and air out of Lynne – let's just say it doesn't involve using the word please!

Once I was able to push, I felt completely in control again, and when I felt my baby start to move down my birth canal I actually believed for the first time that I was really going to have a baby. I just felt so excited and happy and put a lot of effort, and a lot of noise, into pushing. At this point the phone rang. It was Bryan's mum, ringing to see how I was doing. I was acutely aware of not wanting to have a contraction while she was on the phone, so I started crossing eyes, legs etc. While Lynne and Corinne were having a jolly little conversation about how well I was doing, I was doubled-up trying not to scream. Corinne was far too polite to hang-up in mid-conversation and when she eventually did I let out a howl of relief.

By this stage my baby's head was crowning, and Lynne and Corinne were entranced by the blond hair wafting in the water. I wanted to see this baby that they were talking about and so I summoned up my reserves of strength and gave an *enormous* push, Corinne said to stop whilst Lynne just eased the head out and then . . . my baby was born!

He came up through the water into my arms, and I looked at him. 'He looks just like Bryan,' I said, and I held him . . . and time stood still.

Wave after wave of emotion, elation and excitement flooded through me. The moment was so intense, so wonderful, so perfect. Lynne clamped and cut the cord, and then lifted brand-new baby Jacob out of my arms to check him. I was just gazing at him with wonder.

I got out of the water bath and on to the birthing stool and delivered my placenta immediately. Then I lay back on the futon while Lynne checked me – no stitches required. I really wanted to wash my hair, so the water bath was re-run and I had a wonderful bath and hair wash and felt really refreshed. Jacob meanwhile had been given the all clear and weighed in at 7lb 6½oz. Lynne dressed him in a green vest and his 'hey-diddle-diddle' sleep suit and he just seemed to get more perfect every second.

Once I was dressed, we went back to our room, and Lynne and Corinne got me into bed, and made me eat breakfast. Jacob wasn't rooting for food so Lynne said just to let him be until he asked for food. She then gave him a vitamin K injection, as he'd had a bit of a battering through my birth canal. Corinne said, 'Goodnight, Mum,' and gave me a hug – and I wanted to cry.

Then they both left us alone with our baby. We started December 18th as a couple, and we ended it as Mum, Dad and baby Jacob. Here endeth the perfect day.

Deena and Daisy

Deena Newton-Cox

I set out to write Daisy's story, but I had no idea there was so much to say before her story truly begins. All I know is that by the time she arrived, her father and I truly felt we had reached the limits of our endurance. Having had a previous miscarriage, I was highly attuned to the possibility of a second pregnancy going wrong. I was particularly concerned that the extensive laser treatment and laser cone biopsy to my cervix, treating cervical pre-cancer, be taken into account during my pregnancy.

Despite many alarming symptoms, such as frequent episodes of bleeding, loss of straw-coloured fluid, and the loss of my mucous plug at week fifteen, my concerns were not taken seriously. I was even admitted to casualty, with 'threatened spontaneous abortion', as my notes cheerfully put it. But the consultant refused to examine me, saying I 'had as much chance of being run over by a bus as losing my baby', and 'Laser treatment and laser cone biopsy are of no consequence in pregnancy.' That night, the girl in the bed opposite went through a miscarriage; the nurses couldn't work out why this upset me.

Although it is probably 'right' that the consultant didn't examine her, he seems to be refusing for all the wrong reasons. If the cervix is very unstable, an internal examination can lead to miscarriage, as well as introduce infection into the womb. Unfortunately, he does not explain this to her, preferring sarcasm over providing helpful information. This is unacceptable.

I went home and spent the most miserable Christmas of my life, still bleeding and losing fluid. I pressured my GP into getting me referred to the consultant I'd seen in hospital. One month later, at twenty weeks gestation, I arrived at his clinic, still very symptomatic, only to be told, 'What is your main worry? You're only allowed one.'

I tried to explain the range of my symptoms and my history, but was brushed aside. Eventually, my husband helped me insist on an internal examination. It was THE most horrific experience. As it began, he was admonishing me for making such a fuss and wasting his time. Within very painful seconds (he had to make two attempts to see), he uttered a terrifying statement that still makes me feel dirty, mutilated and hopeless: 'Your cervix is very strange to look at. Not much of it left, and what there is looks like it's been hacked about with a knife. Go straight to hospital. Don't even go home for a nightdress.' With this, he pulled off his gloves and swept out of the room, presumably to arrange admission. I was left half naked and sobbing on the examination table, and was ushered out of the building by the back door, so as 'not to upset the rest of the ante-natal clinic'.

I was admitted to a day bed on a mixed ante- and post-natal ward, where it was assumed I would miscarry. My husband went home alone, in tears. We both feared various versions of the worst, including the idea of losing not only this baby, but any hope of subsequent babies, maybe even my life, through such a mutilated cervix.

The consultant's description made me feel like blackened, ragged, cancerous cave was growing inside me, killing first my baby, then me. After a dreadful night, I met the consultant again, and managed to tell him, through my tears, that his words had been ill chosen, to say the least. He did not apologise.

We negotiated that I would stay in hospital. At this point, he was keen to send me home after one week, because he felt nothing could be done to avert a miscarriage and it was pointless me using up a hospital bed. A scan showed I had a degree of placenta praevia, in addition to my cervical condition. By this time I was hysterical, mostly because I had been trying to make my concerns heard for so long, at such a pitch of isolation and fear. I refused to go home and suffer alone any more.

I was to stay in hospital for the next three months, on total bed rest, with the occasional weekend at home. I spent the whole time alone, tormented by the sounds from the main ward of women being admitted, having babies and then being discharged. No one would acknowledge that this 'unstitchable' cervix problem had ever happened to anyone else. I was made to feel that I was taking up a valuable bed that should have been given to someone else with a

When a cervical smear indicates a pre-cancerous condition many women are offered cone biopsies as a precaution. In a cone biopsy the central core of the cervix is lasered off. It can have implications for future pregnancies since there is sometimes not enough cervix to hold the baby in for the entire pregnancy. Some centres offer a procedure where they put in a cervical 'stitch' shortly after a woman becomes pregnant. A cervical stitch is like a drawstring, which pulls your cervix closed. It is tied in place until you are ready to give birth, increasing the likelihood that you will carry your baby to term or very near.

Unfortunately, this procedure has not been widely evaluated and problems have occurred. If the stitch is put in too early, it may prevent the miscarriage of an abnormal fetus. There have been reports of damage to the cervix and increased bleeding. Those studies which do exist have shown mixed results, with some claiming that it prevents premature birth and miscarriage, and others showing that it makes no difference at all. If you have had a cone biopsy, you should speak to your doctor or midwife and discuss the best way to manage your pregnancy. Contact the Miscarriage Association for information on cervical stitches – see 'Useful Contacts'.

more 'popular' problem, like high blood pressure.

There were a million indignities, like having to fight for weeks on end to gain access to soft sheets – 'only for our post-stitch ladies' – to ease the bed sores and pregnancy rashes, and like having to fight for the right to have my husband in attendance at the highly traumatic weekly transvaginal ultrasound scan.

It is interesting that the doctor refused to perform an internal examination, but did not hesitate to use this form of scanning, which, for this woman, could also have brought about a miscarriage. See 'Birth Basics' for more information on transvaginal ultrasound.

The frequent scans proved what I had been saying all along. My cervix was very short already and as pregnancy progressed, there was simply no more length to draw up, so it started to dilate.

The placenta obligingly moved out of the way and on April 16th, I went into labour, my hind waters having gone two weeks earlier, the forewaters three days earlier. I'd been allowed home at this point. I must briefly mention that the staff on the labour suite did not believe that my waters had gone. Their rather unscientific test consisted of sitting me on a paper towel for the duration of *EastEnders* and deeming that since the towel wasn't soaked, I should go home. No one read my notes. 'What on earth makes you think you're going into early labour?' I was asked several times. I was made to feel that I was wasting everyone's time and only when I insisted on an examination and a lot of liquor was discovered was I re-admitted.

At no time did anyone apologise for misdiagnosis, or acknowledge that my instincts were correct, and had been throughout my pregnancy. I was made to feel like the most difficult patient in the history of the maternity service and I'll admit, at times, the strain of battering my head against the brick wall of the medical profession did make me into a very voluble and anti-social creature.

Because I was deemed to have made a fuss throughout my pregnancy, the staff were agreed on one thing – I was sure to have a dreadful, painful and traumatic labour.

I read nothing about labour, prior to my waters breaking, because I simply couldn't believe that I was going to have a baby, instead of a miscarriage. My local branch of the NCT refused me access to their ante-natal classes, for fear that I would upset the other mothers because of my 'unusual' pregnancy. I was not even permitted to attend at the end of classes to meet other local mums informally.

Armed with one of Sheila Kitzinger's wonderful books, a determination not to drown in fear, Bach Rescue Remedy, aromatherapy oil and my wonderful husband, I entered the delivery suite, still being told I was not in labour.

Labour was wonderful. I was left alone, but never unsupported, by my midwife and got through on gas and air in addition to the aids mentioned above. Rather amusingly, because I'd gone into labour early, which nobody acknowledged would actually happen, and because it was the weekend, my consultant was not available. He'd failed to make any notes regarding my delivery and a locum asked me if my consultant had 'erm, mentioned what we should do with you if you do go into labour?' I told him I thought it might be a good idea to let my body and the baby carry on doing what they were doing anyway, which was preparing for a natural birth.

I made a deal with my midwife, that she would do everything necessary to monitor and ensure the well-being of the baby, *whatever that entailed*, and ensure that the SCBU (Special Care Baby

Unit) was on standby, and my husband would look after me. In this way, knowing that I retained control of myself, but was not being expected to take all the responsibility for this premature birth, I was able to have a really wonderful labour, with no interventions at all.

Daisy was born at 31 or 32 weeks gestation. She weighed 3lb 12oz. I felt her head as she emerged into the world – it was like warm, damp velvet. I will never forget that sensation which seemed to last longer than the actual moment in time that it occupied. She came out breathing. I cried. I laughed. I screamed with joy. She was and is the best thing that has ever happened to me.

Her father cut the cord. She was laid on my chest for a precious second before being whisked off in the incubator to the SCBU. Part two of the nightmare had begun.

I had a bath and returned with my husband to the delivery room. We were brought tea and toast on a tray with a paper lace doily – a touching gesture at odds with the terror I began to feel as the minutes ticked by with no news of Daisy.

We were left alone in a big room with an empty cot, and the scales all ready with a paper towel to weigh a 'normal', term baby, prior to presentation into its mother's arms. My husband ate his toast and drank his tea, tired and relieved. I sat on the bed, watching the clock which loomed larger and larger on the wall.

An hour passed, and still no news. I dispatched my husband to enquire as to whether our baby was still alive, or whether the whole thing had been a dream. The staff were busy elsewhere, delivering babies and dealing with post-natal women needing help. I fitted into neither category. I was temporarily suspended between departments. Daisy was the patient now, the newest resident of the SCBU high-maintenance nursery. Needing no stitches or medical assistance, I had ceased to exist. I eventually managed to attract enough attention to gain access to the SCBU.

I was wheeled in and 'allowed' to look at Daisy, full of wires and tubes, bleeping and whirring away and bearing no relation at all to the lovely, warm, wet little being I had so recently held on my chest. Someone had placed a knitted bonnet on her head – another incongruously polite effort, at odds with the rawness of my fears. It tainted her wonderful newborn nakedness, so natural, so recent, but now so far away as to seem like a dream. It took some time before I felt again as if Daisy was my baby. She was now 'their' baby, dressed by them, poked and handled by them, her tiny feet a pincushion of pricks as they tried unsuccessfully to get a line in to check her blood gases. I was a helpless, distraught observer, getting in the way of vital, brutal procedures. I no longer felt like a mother.

The bonnet indicated the whole tenet of care in the SCBU. It was as if the staff, by calling 'intensive care' 'high maintenance', by dressing small, ill babies in lacy bonnets, could somehow protect us, the frightened parents, from the grim reality of what was happening to us and our babies.

> There is a difference between *intensive care* and *high maintenance*. In intensive care there is one midwife for every four babies, in high maintenance there is one midwife for every two babies.

For me, this had the opposite effect. By denying the reality and gravity of the situation, I felt my own feelings were totally denied and began a process of denying them to myself. This was incredibly painful, and harmful to me, Daisy and my husband, and is only now beginning to be addressed.

I know we were not the only parents on the unit to feel this way. Of course, we were grateful for human touches like cartoon murals and loans of micro garments, but it was definitely required that all parents keep a stiff upper lip, and behave according to some prescribed, medical model of behaviour.

A few quiet tears were acceptable, ranting and raving because the breast pumps weren't working was not. A (male) engineer pronounced the ancient breast pump fine, although it was blowing more than it was sucking. The due date for a manufacturer's service had long since passed, but my request that this be looked into was repeatedly ignored.

There were many other awful incidents from this time, too numerous and distressing to mention, but perhaps they should not be glossed over.

One nurse, manning the ward over a weekend, told us that she'd 'rather be tending amputees than SCBU babies ... at least they need moving about and talk to you. This job is like looking after a vegetable patch.' Naturally I complained.

It was suggested that I move Daisy to another hospital, even further away from my home, in order to remove my 'self-imposed pressure to breast-feed'. I was also told that my expectations of Daisy's care were too high and that I was 'clearly too hard on myself and other people'. This was after I had complained about the nurse mentioned above and also that Daisy had been left for a while covered in sick before I arrived.

We were encouraged to do Daisy's 'cares', but this too, I felt, was illusory. We were not permitted to walk about the ward with Daisy – 'for insurance purposes she must go in the pram' – and on many occasions I was admonished for sitting by her incubator, waiting for her to wake, or for holding her while she slept – 'Mrs Newton-Cox, put that baby *down*!'

I sometimes felt as if I had stumbled into a maternity ward in 1953. If we didn't feel able to do Daisy's cares, or were late, we were treated like naughty children who had failed to clean their gerbil's cage, and who were surely not going to be allowed to keep their pet.

As Daisy's 'release' date drew near, I found the tension between myself and many of the SCBU staff had become so unbearable that I could hardly bear to visit, tricky when trying to initiate breast-feeding. There began a tortuous process of jumping through hoops for various consultants and doctors. Taking a Sunday afternoon off from the endless fights with staff, I rang the SCBU, enquired after Daisy's health, and told them that I would send some expressed milk via my husband, but had essentially had enough and wanted Daisy home as soon as possible. 'Worried for my mental stability', the SCBU contacted a locum GP without informing me. He arrived on my doorstep, believing me to

> Remember, your baby belongs to you and not the hospital. The Department of Health recommends that parents should have unrestricted access to their babies, especially in special care or high maintenance units. If you are in the position of having your visits restricted you should complain to the Supervisor of Midwives.
>
> All available research shows that it is *vitally* important to breast-feed premature babies. Even if they are too little to suck, you can (and should be encouraged to) express your milk and make sure that they get it by spoon, cup or otherwise. Breast-milk contains important antibodies which protect your baby and help aid growth.
>
> Breast-feeding also establishes a vital link between parents and their premature babies, restoring a mother's sense of control and the feeling that she is contributing to her baby's care.
>
> For information on why it's also so important to hold your premature baby see page 180.

be near psychotic, to find me calmly cleaning my windows, preparing for Daisy's homecoming, and enjoying what tiny bit of privacy and space I had left.

The SCBU at our hospital is heavily used, with scant parental facilities. We were told, rather than offered, that we must spend two nights in the 'mother room' (why not a 'parent room'?) before Daisy would be allowed home. This was like some hellish audition, to ascertain whether or not we were ready to be her parents. Despite a promise of privacy, there was no lock on the door and nurses and doctors entered frequently, without knocking, during these, our precious first moments together as a family. Often I was naked and trying to breast-feed. At one point, I had to ask a cleaner, who was using the room as her private restroom, if she could leave so I could perhaps have a rest myself.

Eventually we left, albeit rather under a cloud of having been seen as 'difficult' and very much with the feeling that we were being wilful and foolhardy by insisting that demand feeding could be established at home. 'If it doesn't work out, you can't come back,' we were told. 'She'll have to go to paediatric and God knows what she'll catch there.'

The soft-focus SCBU brochure, like some misleading holiday literature about a half-built hotel purporting to be the Ritz, had left a very bitter taste. The staff, by and large, simply couldn't live up to the claims that parents were to be treated with respect and empowered. We were treated as slightly pathetic, second-class citizens. Everything we did was wrong. Although the brochure warned us against 'looking at, photographing or discussing other babies', nurses consistently talked about other babies and parents between themselves, as if we weren't there and could not hear. We knew we were being discussed in the same, often derogatory vein. Babies were told, 'I don't know where your mummy is, you poor little thing, and she promised she'd be here for you.' Equally, the staff berated parents they saw as attending too frequently, deeming them overprotective and obsessive.

Daisy came home, not a moment too soon, exactly four weeks after she was born, and four weeks earlier than anticipated.

Since then she has gone from strength to strength. She is enjoying three solid meals a day and breast-feeding well. The consultant who told me that 'breast-feeding is an idealistic vanity' has subsequently told me I should 'carry on as long as possible', because Daisy is doing so well. Nine months earlier than expected, she has been fully discharged from hospital follow-ups.

During the long, dark tunnel of that scary pregnancy, a nurse told me that when the baby was born I would find that this period in time would concertina down to nothing. I have not found this to be the case. As Daisy grows daily more robust and healthy, I, almost on a sliding scale travelling in the opposite direction, feel more fragile, distressed and vulnerable. Other people need me to pretend that nothing has happened, but the whole sequence of events, from early miscarriage, through incapacitating pregnancy and SCBU traumas, has occupied a very long and stressful year.

As I hear Daisy breathing softly in her cot beside our bed, I remember when I was told that she needed to be ventilated. I never saw her on the ventilator. The fact that a machine was breathing for her was not really mentioned and is only now sinking in, as I see her laughing, hiccoughing and simply breathing, so very healthy.

I feel her warm, chubby arms wrapped around my shoulders and again sense a chill, recalling the moment that a nurse put a stethoscope against Daisy's thin, naked chest and ran from the room, leaving me to wonder whether I should try to resuscitate her, whether she was just asleep, or whether she was dead. It transpired that she had heard a heart murmur and had run out of the room to get a second opinion, not on the heart murmur, but as to whether or not I should be told about it. I had asked to be told everything relating to Daisy's stay in hospital, clearly an unpopular request. The nurse returned some time later, and explained that the heart murmur was probably not cause for concern. Unsurprisingly, I couldn't equate her dramatic flight from the room, and subsequent bleeping of the paediatric heart specialist, with the words 'no cause for concern'. Once again, I was made to feel that I 'should' be able to feel calmer than I actually felt.

Throughout the last year, I've fought my, my baby's and my husband's corner. Now I'm tired, upset, relieved, happy and sad, all at the same time. The health visitor thinks I should 'put it all behind me, stop breast-feeding and take some valium'. Family and friends who have had easy pregnancies focus, understandably, on the glowing baby in front of them, yet still feel the need to mention the difficulties every time I see them, underlining the fact that there was and will always be something 'different' about Daisy, and my body. Maybe they affirm their own good fortune and physical resilience in

This baby was born premature for a clear and easily understood reason, but many more are born prematurely for reasons we simply don't understand or can't do anything about. The other most usual physiological causes of prematurity are placenta praevia, pre-eclampsia, and growth retardation. There is also a percentage of babies which are born prematurely due to medical incompetence and impatience. Many labours are induced and elective caesareans performed because the doctor was sure the mother was 'overdue', only to find that the baby was in fact pre-term. This is why it is important, whenever possible, not to be pressurised into worrying about your estimated date of delivery. Your baby will, nine times out of ten, come when it is ready to live and thrive outside the womb.

Premature babies are more at risk of dying than others. They are more likely to have difficulty breathing, as well as kidney and liver problems.

There are several organisations which you can turn to for help. Some are more parent-focused than others. Try contacting Parents of Prematures (POPS) or BLISS or Action for Sick Children for SCBU information or complaints about care – see 'Useful Contacts' for details.

this way. In any case, it is tacitly understood that they are the only ones permitted to mention her prematurity, albeit in a conversational 'miracles of modern science' way. My, Daisy's and my husband's experience of tube feeding, jumping when the phone rang in case it was bad news from the SCBU, sobbing myself hoarse at the sight of the empty Moses basket in our bedroom while, ten miles away, Daisy clicked and whirred in a plastic cage . . . all these and many more experiences are consigned to a closed file.

So is there an up side to this story? Of course there is. She is alive, well and eats so much apple purée, I'm convinced she's a fruitarian. She's the miracle of my life, a constant joy. I have to restrain myself from picking her up when I go to bed and kissing her wonderful, soft, living, breathing, milk-smelling skin all over. If I'm not careful, I'd while away my whole life just staring into her huge blue eyes, drowning as her pupils dilate and contract, drawing me deeper and deeper into loving her. As my love widens and deepens, I grow more sentimental: finding myself in tears at tacky TV programmes or even at the checkout in a big DIY store, hearing a song I heard on the radio in the SCBU played over the tannoy. One magical moment in the busy SCBU, I was left alone, holding Daisy, listening to the radio and feeling that I wanted to protect her from all the necessary, but harsh, procedures and realities that constituted her care. The words say it all and though I'd like to be witty and above sentiment, I'd be lying. 'I'll stand by you. Won't let nobody hurt you, I'll stand by you . . .'

The Induction

Theresa Mack

My son was born in the consultant maternity unit of the local district general hospital after a difficult pregnancy. My problem was diagnosed as intrauterine growth retardation due to a poorly functioning placenta and raised blood pressure.

> For information on *growth retardation* see 'Birth Basics'.

The decision was taken to induce my labour at 37 weeks and I was transferred from the ante-natal ward to the labour ward on a Sunday evening. The midwife who showed me to my room did not know why I had been admitted, despite the fact that my notes had been sent down and the induction planned well in advance.

I spent all day Monday having my labour induced by the insertion of prostaglandin pessaries. The baby's heart was never monitored once contractions started, despite assurances that it would be, because staff were busy and the machine was in use elsewhere. Women arriving in labour were told to 'join the queue with everyone else' and were lined up along the corridor. I saw no one all evening until the doctor arrived at 11pm to break my waters.

I had agreed to an epidural on medical advice, since every doctor and midwife with whom I had spoken had recommended it. Their reasons for this included my moderately raised blood pressure, the desire to protect the baby (already suffering from a prolonged lack of oxygen) from drugs such as pethidine, which can depress respiratory function, and to help me to cope with the intense contractions of an induced labour, during which I would be immobilised by monitors and so would find it hard to deal with pain.

It therefore came as a great shock when, after the ARM was done and I was experiencing incredibly intense contractions, no one knew an epidural had been planned and the anaesthetist was busy in theatre.

> An *epidural* can help lower blood pressure and may be useful in this respect for women who are hypertensive, but, like all narcotics, it also 'depresses respiratory function' – slows your breathing down – which means less oxygen gets to your baby.
>
> It is not beyond the bounds of possibility that this woman's blood pressure was raised because she was upset and frightened during her antenatal care and her labour. If a diagnosis of IUGR is correct, it is often kinder to go straight into a caesarean operation, rather than put the mother through the awful ordeal of the painful and intense contractions of an induction, ARM and all the other nightmare interventions which can follow.

Just after midnight (by which time I could not move or speak with the pain, and had received no advice about dealing with it) the anaesthetist arrived to set up the epidural. However, while inserting the needle she accidentally punctured the dura, resulting in leakage of cerebrospinal fluid. Not only was this extremely frightening, but for a moment or so I couldn't see at all and then the room was spinning and I couldn't focus clearly. Severe visual disturbances lasted throughout my labour and for some considerable time afterwards.

A drip was immediately set up and I was made to lie flat in order to try to avoid the severe headache which usually follows a dural tap. I spent the rest of my labour lying flat on my back, tethered to a drip on one side, a blood pressure cuff on the other and, initially, the CTG monitor (until it was turned off because it wasn't working) and later with a fetal electrode in place.

The midwife, who did not introduce herself at any stage, stood over me with a full syringe after the epidural failure and, together with the anaesthetist, badgered me to accept an injection of pethidine. She never gave me any advice on breathing or relaxation or any assurance about my baby's well-being and was impatient to get me wired up and injected so that she could leave the room.

I received no support, no kindness. Her attitude throughout was one of 'first you had to be induced at such a busy time, and now this!' I actually heard myself being described as 'the induction' and later I became 'the dural tap'. I was never seen as an individual. I was worried about the effects of pethidine on the baby and said that I had been advised not to accept it. The midwife became very angry and demanded to know who had told me this. After all the anxiety

> *Pethidine* is an analgesic inasmuch as it provides a general kind of pain relief, but to say it is 'simply' an analgesic is to trivialise its impact. Pethidine is a morphine derivative with a powerful narcotic effect. It does not take the pain away; instead it alters a mother's state of consciousness so that her perception of pain is altered. It can leave you feeling queasy, disoriented and hopeless. Given in high doses, it can slow a mother's breathing down to the point where the amount of oxygen available to the baby decreases. Any midwife or doctor who injects a woman with this or any other drug, contrary to her express wishes, is committing an assault and can be prosecuted.

of a traumatic pregnancy, I will never forget her words. She said, 'Don't bother about the baby. It's you that's feeling the pain, not the baby!' I also stated clearly that I did not want anything that would affect my mind. She declared pethidine to be simply an analgesic and, against my express wishes and without my prior knowledge or consent, gave me an injection containing a tranquilliser. I felt utterly defeated and out of control.

At no time during my labour did I receive a single kind word or information about the progress of my labour. Because of the drugs I was given, I spent my labour in a terrifying, isolated world of pain and confusion, unable to see properly, unable to ask what was happening and unable to communicate the fact that the pethidine had not touched the pain.

The doctor duly arrived, clearly annoyed at having been called. A large episiotomy was made, followed by a forceps delivery. I was not allowed to push during the second stage, in case more spinal fluid leaked out. However, this was never explained so I couldn't understand why the doctor kept shouting at me and telling me not to push. Neither was I told that I would have a forceps delivery.

My son was literally pulled out of me. He failed to breathe or respond to stimulus and had to be resuscitated. I felt that the baby I had carried, had loved, had worried over, was lost. Instead, I was handed a baby that the doctor had seemingly produced. I experienced such a deep sense of loss and grief.

Because of the drugs and the lack of care, the birth had an unreal, nightmarish quality about it. I was unable to speak – underneath it all, my brain was functioning normally, but each time I tried to

A *dural puncture* or *dural* tap is when the protective coating around the spinal cord is accidentally punctured during the siting of the epidural. When this happens, fluid from the spinal column leaks into the dural space. The effect of this, amongst other things, is a reduction in the amount of protective fluid around your brain, causing severe migraine-like headaches, nausea and disorientation. Sometimes these headaches are transient, sometimes they last for years after the birth. The hole can be 'repaired' after birth by putting what is known as a blood patch over it, but the experience of women is that this means a trade off of severe headaches for severe backaches. You should be counselled about this possibility before you have an epidural.

speak, I was aware that it would come out as nonsense. This carried on after the birth when I wanted to enjoy the time with my husband and new baby. I had so much to say, but I couldn't form a coherent sentence.

I can never get that precious time back again.

For two days, I lay flat on my back, attached to a drip, unable to do anything for my baby. When he cried, I had to wait for a nursery nurse to hand him to me to be breast-fed, after which he was put back in his crib with no time for cuddling or getting to know each other.

After I returned home, I experienced great problems relating to my son and accepting him as mine. It took five months before I surfaced sufficiently to write to the hospital to complain about the appalling care I had received. I was supported by AIMS in this and was so relieved to be assured that I was justified in expecting an explanation and an apology.

Following my complaint, I had a three-hour meeting with one of the midwifery managers, during which I managed to see my notes and confirm that I had been given drugs without my consent. Some weeks later, I had a meeting with the midwife concerned who apologised fully and unreservedly for the 'catalogue of disasters' (her phrase) which was my labour.

During that meeting it was revealed that a survey carried out at the unit had shown there to be a shortage of twenty-one midwives. No wonder women were receiving such an appalling and potentially dangerous standard of care! The comment made by the midwife concerned was telling: 'The bottom line is a live baby from a live mother. You got the bottom line that night.'

The epidural, which had been sold to me as the best and safest option for my baby, had led to a domino effect of interventions after its failure. The Director of Midwifery, in response to my complaint, wrote to the Consultant Anaesthetist, asking him to ensure that women are told of the risks of epidurals so that they can make an informed decision when offered one.

I have since asked about the possibility of a GP unit delivery for my next baby, and was told it was impossible because of the forceps delivery. This in spite of the fact that it was necessary purely because of the dural tap. I refused to accept this and it has now been agreed that I can have a GP unit delivery. I wonder how many other women, after an experience like mine, have just accepted the doctor's definition of them as 'high risk' and dutifully returned to the consultant unit for their next birth? As far as I can see, from my own experience, the main 'high risk' factor is entering a hospital when there is a serious staff shortage and accepting, without question, 'expert' advice about the safety of drugs and routine procedures.

Water Baby
Louise Bloodworth

Before I'd even finished my midwifery training – in fact, before I'd even started – I'd made the decision to have a home delivery. I always saw a family with a few children as a large part of my life and so, when I became pregnant during the last year of my midwifery course, I was overjoyed.

Many people, including my colleagues on the course who were already mums, said that they didn't envy me, having a baby now that I had gained such an extensive, albeit intellectual, knowledge of the process during my training. My training, however, had given me the strength of my convictions and made me even more determined to experience my pregnancy, labour and birth in the way I wanted.

In our area we are lucky enough to have The Wessex, a birth centre run by four independent midwives who give total midwifery care throughout pregnancy, labour, birth and the post-natal period to women and their families. Their facilities include a small hotel with a converted barn, all beautifully redecorated and refurbished to make a very comfortable, friendly place for women to receive care and to deliver in a relaxing birth room with a pool, and to stay post-natally with their partners in double-bedded, en-suite bedrooms. The midwives also provide care in hospital or at home, according to the women's wishes.

Although I had the option of using this lovely place to give birth, I had my heart set on having my baby at home and I felt that this was the only right thing for me. I decided that the care I wanted for myself, my husband Mark and our baby could be best provided by the midwives in our home.

Mark had always been aware of how I wanted my pregnancy and delivery to be conducted. To begin with he found it hard to understand my reasons for wanting a home birth. He was not convinced of the safety of birth at home, though he is the first to

The UK has very few *birth centres*. Those which exist are owned and run by groups of independent midwives. The purpose of a birth centre is to provide home away from home facilities which also have access to medical facilities, either at the centre or nearby. Women can be cared for ante-natally either in their homes or at the centre, and the midwives who run it can use all of their clinical skills to support women through pregnancy and birth in a low intervention way. For many women this seems an ideal way to go about birth.

In a more balanced world, birth centres would provide home-like facilities for women who want low intervention care with a named midwife, but whose home is not suitable for a home birth (perhaps they live in crowded conditions, or have the builder in or have partners or parents who oppose the idea of home birth). In reality, they are often chosen by women who have perfectly adequate home facilities, but choose not to use them. It will be interesting to see how birth centres develop in this country and whether the NHS will take the initiative to establish these centres within the healthcare system – to provide genuine *choice* for women who, because of lack of funds or facilities, might not otherwise have it.

admit he was coming from a position of total ignorance. Basically, he felt that everyone else has their babies in hospital, '*so what's the problem?*' When we spoke to my chosen midwife at just six weeks, Mark sat there saying, 'Just tell her, Lynne, tell her she can't have it at home.' It didn't take long, however, for him to realise that he would never be able to change my mind and so, as my pregnancy progressed, he read a couple of books and articles and talked to Lynne. Soon he was as convinced as I was that this was the right way for our baby to be born.

My pregnancy continued with no problems and as time went on I became more excited about the birth and the arrival of our baby. I never doubted my ability to labour and deliver at home and I gained confidence from Lynne, despite statements from others, like my mother-in-law and friends, that I was mad! I knew that Lynne was more than happy to deliver babies at home and I had faith in her skills as a midwife.

As I was going to be at home, I wanted to use water as a form of relaxation and pain relief during labour; I wasn't sure, however, if I actually wanted to deliver in water, even though I knew that Lynne was happy to deliver the baby this way. So we booked a birth pool and collected it, and a TENS machine, two weeks before my due date. We set the pool up in the sitting room, where it stayed until it was needed. We live in a small house, one of many on an essentially 'smarter home' estate, so the pool took over most of the sitting room. Our lodger and our cats were most accommodating of it. Grandparents-to-be, for the most part, kept tactfully quiet, after their initial amazement.

My graduation was on Friday, October 20th, five days before I was due. I spent the morning running around having photographs taken, picking up gowns and mortar boards and meeting up with the others from the course. The actual graduation took place in Winchester Cathedral and, as I waited for my turn to collect my diploma, I kept my fingers crossed that my waters wouldn't break as I climbed on to the stage.

It was while I was in the car, rushing home after the graduation to meet up with Mark, before going to the centre in the evening for an ante-natal check, that I began to feel the odd contraction. I kept it quiet, half thinking it was just my body's way of telling me to slow down after being on my feet all day, but these contractions were definitely different from the Braxton Hicks I'd been feeling for some weeks.

At my ante-natal appointment everything was well. I told Lynne about the odd contraction I was having. In hindsight we both knew I was in early labour, but Mark says, 'No one told me!'

Mark had an evening class at 7 o'clock and, while he was out, I had an overwhelming, and unprecedented, desire to clean the house from top to bottom. I scrubbed the bathroom, disinfected the kitchen and vacuumed every inch of carpet. Mark thought he had walked into the wrong house when he came home, saying that I had done more housework in two hours than I'd done in two years! At 11 o'clock we went to bed. I was still contracting, now about every five minutes, but I was talking through them and you couldn't see that I was in labour. I still wasn't convinced that this was anything more than a false alarm, and even if it was labour, I knew it could be three hours or three days before the baby would come, so I was content to wait and see how things progressed.

I could not get to sleep, of course, and also had really bad indigestion so, at midnight, I ran a bath. Mark popped in every few minutes demanding to know if I was in labour, as if asking for permission to get excited! Although my contractions were still every four or five minutes, and getting stronger, it wasn't until about a quarter to two that I began to think that maybe I would have a baby in the next day or two, and that if this really was early labour, I should be putting the TENS machine on.

At two o'clock, I got out of the bath and, with instructions and diagram in one hand, Mark attempted to stick on the TENS. Looking back, I'm not sure how useful the TENS machine was, though it certainly gave me something else to focus on, aside from the pain. It also made me feel that I was actually doing something for myself. We decided it was still too early to begin to fill the pool, thinking that, as this was my first labour, we probably had quite a few hours before I would use it. But, within half an hour, I felt completely out of control. In my head I was thinking, 'This isn't right. I've been in labour for just a couple of hours and already I'm acting like someone in transition. I can't possibly cope with this for another twelve hours.'

The contractions were coming thick and fast, with just seconds in between. The only thing I wanted to do during the contractions was to stand up, lean forward and scream. For leaning forward, the edge of the pool was ideal to hold on to. Having prepared himself to help me breathe slowly through hours of contractions, Mark felt at a loose end as 'breathing' was the last thing I wanted to do. Screaming, on the other hand, was very helpful! Mark telephoned Lynne at half past two, to my objections as I didn't want to be a nuisance and wake her or call her too early. She reassured Mark that she would come as soon as we needed her and she recommended that I take a couple of paracetamol. As I swallowed the first one I remember thinking, 'What the hell am I doing taking paracetamol? They won't touch the pain' – and so I hid the second one under the sofa when Mark wasn't looking. Mark put on his *Blackadder* videos.

> She is absolutely right. Paracetamol is useless in labour. Some women are offered it so they can feel as if they are 'doing something' about their labour pains, but the effect is unlikely to be anything more than a placebo. Why load yourself and your baby up with useless and unnecessary drugs?

At half past three, having been punched and sworn at, Mark phoned Lynne who, hearing me in the background, said she was on her way. At a quarter past four she arrived and, after a quick examination, told us that I was about six centimetres dilated and that the baby was in a very good position. This was really good news and finally we began to fill the pool, while enjoying a cup of tea. With just a couple of inches of water in the pool, Mark realised that the boiler timer had switched off at ten o'clock and there was not enough hot water. So, with the immersion heater on and every available pot and pan boiling on the cooker, Mark was kept busy pouring water in.

I found that leaning forward over a low footstool was the most comfortable position to cope with the contractions. They were now very strong, giving me just enough time in between them to swear loudly and shout at Mark for not filling the pool quickly enough. The speed of the contractions and the pain I felt in between them really caught me by surprise. I'd always believed that a contraction came and went, leaving time between that one and the next to get one's breath back.

Lynne reassured me that everything was fine and stopped me losing control by being cheerful and calm. She just sat back and let me carry on, listening to the baby every now and then and telling me I was fine and doing really well. I told her that I was not going to do this any more!

I finally got into the pool at about ten minutes to six and immediately the pain that I felt in between contractions went. This was wonderful, as it gave me the little break I needed before the next one.

Lynne's partner arrived at six o'clock and they quietly got organised. I don't recall having much of a transition stage – I just seemed to go from having a normal contraction to having an urge to push. I tried to resist this urge for a few contractions as Lynne said that I wasn't quite ready, but by ten past six I had to push.

The second stage contractions were overwhelming, extremely intense and very scary. I felt frightened and Lynne calmed me down and told me just to do what I needed to do and go with the feelings. Once I'd resigned myself to the fact that I had to do this, whether I liked it or not, I was able to push with the contractions.

I had been unsure whether I wanted to give birth actually in the water, but when it came to it nothing could have got me out. It felt so right. After pushing for just over twenty minutes, Ella was born very slowly and in such a controlled way, under water. She was brought to the surface where she cried immediately.

Our first emotions are almost indescribable. We both just stared

Not all women like the idea of giving birth in the water. Early in pregnancy many plan to labour in water then get out for the delivery. Either that or they are told by their midwives that that is what they *must* do. Yet, once a woman is in the water, it can be very difficult to persuade her to get out – and there is no law or local policy which can make her do so. It's not just that the water is nice and warm and comfortable. In the water pool a woman is protected and autonomous. She is harder to interfere with, harder to monitor, harder to inject with drugs. As the moment of birth approaches, it is particularly important that a woman feels that she and her baby are safe. Water provides that safety zone.

Even if your midwife insists that you get out of the pool for labour, you do not have to. Your birth partner should be prepared to argue this point on your behalf. This is no time for you to be doing battle. The UKCC, the midwives' governing body, is very clear about its policy on birth in the water. It is up to the individual midwife to deliver the baby in any way in which the mother feels most comfortable. Midwives are obliged to keep their skills and training up to date in all aspects of delivery, including under water. It may be best to find out your midwife's attitudes to water birth, and ascertain her level of skill early on, and if you are not satisfied, find another midwife.

down at our perfect, slimy, pink bundle and were shocked by the amount of hair she had. For some reason we were expecting a bald baby and so our first precious moments were spent mesmerised by her hair.

I had chosen to have a natural, physiological third stage and so there was no rush to cut the cord and deliver the placenta. Instead we sat and cuddled the baby in the warm water. Eventually, Mark cut the cord and bundled Ella into a warm towel and went to telephone my mother, so that she could hear her first granddaughter cry when she was just a couple of minutes old.

The placenta was delivered as I stood up to climb out of the pool. We had a cup of tea, dressed the baby and then I fed her while the room was tidied and the pool cleared away.

Being at home in a calm atmosphere, surrounded by people I felt relaxed with, I know was the best way for me to give birth to Ella. Using water was wonderful and I'm sure that being in the pool was the reason I could push so well, and the reason that my second stage was so short and, therefore, the reason that Ella was born so easily and with no stress. I also suspect it's why I needed no stitches.

If using water for labour and for birth is something that anyone is considering, I would thoroughly recommend it as the best way to labour and deliver. The water was wonderful. It was deep enough to relax completely in and the sides were soft enough, yet firm enough, to support me while I pushed. The whole experience was so exhilarating. I can honestly say that I enjoyed it and felt that I could do it all over again that afternoon.

Since the birth of my baby, my career has taken a new direction. Having given birth in such a positive way, I have felt unable to go back to practising midwifery. I find myself wondering how any midwife can teach or care for a woman unless she's had the experience of childbirth herself. Also, I feel very disillusioned about the way I would have to practise if I did go back. As a midwife within the hospital system, it is almost impossible to build up a relationship with a woman. So often your first contact with her is when she is in labour. So, instead, I have turned my energy and attention towards becoming an ante-natal teacher, in order to be a better support to women during pregnancy. I'm very much looking forward to passing on the kind of positive support I received during my own pregnancy.

Asking for the Moon?

Beverley Walker

I was thirty-four when Tim and I decided we'd like a child. Pre-pregnancy, the prospect of giving birth scared me. I just could not imagine that it could do anything other than hurt a lot! I consoled myself with the fact that lots of women go through it, often more than once, and people told me that you soon forget the experience, once you have the baby in your arms. I'd never really talked to my own mother about her three pregnancies (one twin) until pregnant myself and so didn't have the benefit of her positive experiences. Once my pregnancy was confirmed, I did what I tend to do and began to read all about it. Slowly, over the next months, my feelings began to change to the extent that there were even moments when I felt excited about the process of birth itself.

I quickly decided I wanted a Domino delivery – the only option I could see where I'd know the midwife delivering me. Almost as quickly, I discovered it wasn't available because I lived too far from the hospital.

I carried on in the system, happy with the level and standard of ante-natal care I was receiving from my community midwife, GP and consultant obstetrician at the general hospital. I felt slightly uneasy about the prospect of a hospital stay. My main concern was that I did not want to be given routine procedures or interventions unless there was a medical indication. The midwives were lovely – warm, friendly and sensitive – but who was to say which one would be delivering my baby? I knew my 'rights', but I also knew that I didn't want the midwife to be the focus of my attention when I was in labour. It began to feel like a game of chance and it worried me.

As a way out of this dilemma, I made contact with Karen, an independent midwife, with a view to organising our own Domino delivery. At our first meeting we spent a couple of hours talking about labour and birth and about the kinds of things she would and would not expect to do. I discovered a lot about her beliefs and values with regard to women and birth. I felt confident in her and in myself – and found I was beginning to look forward to the actual experience of birth. Lots more reading and talking with others, plus a visit to the post-natal wards in the hospital, influenced my feeling and, ultimately, informed our decision. I was about 36 weeks into pregnancy when I finally decided on a home birth.

At the same time as we decided on birth at home, we received the hospital's refusal of our DIY Domino request. Beyond a point of principle it didn't matter any more (and I didn't want to deal with principles by that stage). I talked to my GP who also felt unable to support my choice. I felt truly outside the system and just a little afraid, but none the less confident about me.

To me home birth meant my labour would be allowed to progress in its own time and way. I didn't feel I had to steel myself up to defend what I wanted; I didn't even feel the need to write a birth plan. I was happy that Karen understood what was important to me and was confident in her skills. I also trusted that she would know if and when a transfer to hospital was appropriate. With all this in mind, Karen took over my ante-natal care and we waited more or less patiently.

At 39 weeks our hopes were dashed when the baby turned into a breech position. I was devastated. It felt as though everything was up in the air again and more choices had to be made – we spent a lot of time talking to Karen over that weekend and she also made us an appointment to see the obstetrician. I read books about caesarean sections and talked to anybody I could think of who might be able to help me make sense of the options. The issue for me now was so

---

Domino stands for DOMicilary IN and Out. On a Domino scheme you are cared for by a community midwife in and out of hospital. She will provide your ante-natal care, either independently or in conjunction with your GP. You will spend the early part of your labour at home and you and your midwife will decide when the time is right to go into hospital for delivery. Once you have given birth, you are free, usually within a few hours, to go home and your midwife will continue to look after you for the statutory ten days post-natally. The Domino scheme provides a way for a woman who wishes to give birth in hospital to receive care from a midwife who is known to her. If you ring the hospital and they send whichever midwife happens to be on duty, this is not Domino care.

far away from home birth – vaginal delivery or caesarean, and if the latter, epidural or general?

I desperately hoped my baby would change its position. Clinging on to what often felt like vain hope, I scoured books for self-help options. I spent the best part of a weekend in strange, uncomfortable positions, trying to stop the baby getting lower into my pelvis so that it would have the opportunity to move back into a cephalic position. At times I'd sink into a state of despondency and despair. Within a couple of days, with some help, it turned back to a cephalic lie. I stopped enjoying pregnancy around this time and even felt a bit alienated from my baby through the experience. I was anxious that it might turn again and did whatever I could to help it remain head down.

We kept our appointment with the obstetrician. Accompanied by both Tim and Karen for support, I promised myself not to commit to any particular course of action that day. I was pretty sure the baby was still cephalic, but I now knew it was unstable and was worried the obstetrician might want to induce the labour there and then, just in case. On examination, the supervisory midwife informed me that the baby was now lying transverse. I could have believed her – that's the frightening thing – but five minutes later the obstetrician confirmed the baby was cephalic and engaged. He advised nothing other than Karen keep a close eye on its position – which she did, daily, until it settled down. What impressed me about that appointment was his response to my choice of a home birth. He was clear that he thought hospital was a more appropriate choice, but he put no pressure on me. I came away from the hospital feeling encouraged.

At 41 weeks I had a show, three days later a membrane sweep. Each morning became a source of disappointment – another day of waiting, wondering whether my baby would ever be born. Karen constantly reassured me that my body was getting itself ready and was doing good work. Resigned to sleeplessness by midweek, we took her advice to find a night-time project, and bought wallpaper to redecorate the dining room. Tim was incredibly supportive and tolerant, sharing sleeplessness when I needed him to.

It was 2am, October 9th, exactly two weeks after my due date. My contractions, following their customary night-time pattern, started once again. As they became more frequent I dared to wonder – again – perhaps this time? I felt quite calm as I sat in my chair in the dark of the dining room. Ready.

By 6am contractions had become a little more consistent. Tim

> *Sweeping the membranes* is one way to stimulate labour. The cervix is covered with a thin membrane which normally stretches apart as the cervix opens. In order to dislodge this membrane your midwife will insert a gloved finger into your vagina, as if she were performing an internal examination, and run it over your cervix. It can be very painful and it can sometimes cause your waters to break.
>
> Since it is to your advantage to keep your waters intact you should weigh up the pros and cons of this procedure carefully (see 'Birth Basics' for information on Artificial Rupture of the Membranes). Like most other forms of induction, it tends to work best on women who are having their second or subsequent baby or whose cervix is very ripe, and about to dilate of its own accord anyway.

tried to be helpful by noting their time and duration. I remember thinking irritably, what an inane thing to be doing . . . I knew they were frequent, getting both longer and stronger, for goodness' sake.

Eight o'clock. Still not sure whether this was real, but we left a message to warn Karen of the possibility that I was in labour. Soon after, I had an unnervingly different and more powerful contraction. There was some blood and I was scared. Another message on Karen's ansaphone. Were things going wrong? Should we go to hospital after all? I sat in my chair, clutching its arms, contracting faster, longer, more powerfully. I clung on to the TENS and my breathing, entering into a battle for control of my body as each contraction built up. No pain, only discomfort as I tried to hang on.

We sat silently together with soothing music playing ever so gently. Our music, Enya. I felt relieved when Karen arrived. Straight away she blended into the atmosphere of calm that had descended by that time, her voice quiet and soft, her touch soothing and reassuring. After the only internal examination I had, she was able to confirm that I *was* in labour and, even better, possibly eight or nine centimetres dilated already. So, the past week of niggling hadn't been for nothing. I suddenly felt pleased with both my body and my baby.

Although aware of the others' presence, I became very much focused inwards on myself and what was happening inside me. Instead of battling with the contractions for control, I tried to welcome them as Sheila Kitzinger suggests. The little that was left of my waters broke. Another visit to the bathroom. I wanted to empty bladder and bowel – but couldn't. Contractions began to overwhelm me with their power and their difference. Tim supported me and together we struggled along the landing in an attempt to get back down the stairs. Confused . . . what is happening to my body now? What was this peculiar feeling in my lower back? Every movement we made seemed to bring on a contraction. I wanted to cry – not because they hurt, just that they were so unremitting. I started to groan involuntarily . . . what a relief, I'd feared I might be too inhibited to let go vocally.

We travelled no further than the end of the landing and top of the stairs – so this was to be the place. We hadn't prepared anywhere, preferring to be spontaneous and go where instinct or circumstances took me. I was vaguely aware of Karen's helper, Alison, arriving. Distant sounding voices around me, soothing touch and gentle massage while I stood hanging on to Tim, arms around his neck, needing him as I've never needed him before. Slowly it was dawning on me that the peculiar feeling was nothing at all to do with my bowels. My God! It was the baby I could feel. So this was what I'd heard described as feeling like a grapefruit. More like a coconut, I thought. And I hadn't expected to feel it there, it should surely be more at the front? Sometimes it would shift, other times it felt stuck. The urge to push was overwhelming when it came. Hard work and slow progress. Hot and sweaty. Thirsty, and desperately, but irrationally, wanting to clean my teeth. I'd not had a chance to wash that morning – it'd all taken me by surprise. My hair needed washing too and here I was, about to give birth on the landing. Such were the preoccupations of this particular labouring woman. I hadn't envisaged it this way. Strangely unreal and yet frighteningly real.

They all kept talking about what colour hair it would have. This seemed wholly irrelevant to me; colour, length, density, curl or total absence – I just wanted it out of my body. Push through the pain, Karen was telling me. Birth was imminent. Then for a moment, somewhere between my legs, I felt pain as I'd never felt it before. I wanted to escape from it, but I couldn't. And then it was gone . . . numb. Karen was telling me not to push. There was an urgency in her voice I'd not heard before. I hung on to Tim, still there. Then it was OK to push . . . out it flopped, warm and wet between my legs.

Kneeling by now, I could only see the little body out of the corner of my eye and feel it against my foot . . . still, lifeless and yellow, like one of Tesco's corn-fed chickens. I daren't move. I'd heard Karen ask for oxygen, and I waited, dazed, to hear that it was breathing . . . and eventually, unaided, it did. A boy. Disbelief. I'd given birth, and here was our baby. This was Jolon.

Looking back I think I went into shock, it all seemed unreal and I felt remote and unemotional. Contrary to the many accounts I'd read of birth, I experienced no orgasmic pleasure and no immediate bonding. There was a funny, slippery little creature that had come out of my body. I was sore, shaky, exhausted and overcome by the sheer physical nature of my experience of childbirth.

It was 12 noon. Photographs taken, first attempts at breast-feeding, placenta delivered, and Mum and Dad informed of the arrival of their first, long awaited grandchild. Stitches were inserted under the influence of gas and air while Alison held our little one, tears (that I can now understand) rolling gently down her cheeks. She, at least, had been touched by the magic of childbirth. Our first bath together was wonderful. We all crowded into our tiny bathroom as I relaxed in the warm water, holding and looking in amazement at this little being with its meconium- and blood-stained body, and funny little face, like 'ET'. And somewhere in all of that, precious, uninterrupted time for the two of us to start to become the three of us.

After initial celebration, I lay on the settee, babe in arms, feeling drained and exhausted, indecently eating my way through a box of Guerlain chocolates in search of some energy. Energy, like the bonding with my baby and the visitors, trickled in over the next few days.

Tim had been with me throughout and was my rock to hang on to. He'd given just what I wanted – very little and yet so much. Karen too. She was exactly what I needed in a midwife. Her presence so quietly reassuring, so skilled and sensitive. She followed what was going on for me, was with me constantly from transition, yet let me get on with it, never interfered, offering only constant encouragement and occasional instruction. How did she know to encourage me at one moment, to gently stroke my skin the next?

Alison came into her own after the birth. Then, she was invaluable – I managed to clean my own teeth but how could I have washed my hair without her? She took the photographs we might have overlooked. And the landing, bedroom and bathroom so tidy, looking innocently as if nothing out of the ordinary had happened that morning. These people together made birth all it was and could have been at home. Not only did I feel in control, but empowered too. I'd come a long way from my starting point.

It has taken another experience of pregnancy, labour and birth to appreciate just how wonderful our first midwife was. By this time, I had co-founded a home birth support group and had become an advocate of choice for women. I wanted women to be both informed and encouraged to make choices that reflected what mattered to them as individuals, rather than simply do what everybody else does or what they've been told they should do. On that basis, home or hospital didn't really matter.

I was hoping for a home birth again and this time had gone the route of the community midwife and GP. I had one or two niggles about the choice – would my known community midwife attend the birth whenever it happened? Would she be free enough of the 'system', and its prescriptions, to be able to exercise her own judgement, over the length of labour for instance, or the length of pregnancy? I knew both women from my first pregnancy, knew the midwife regarded home birth as a viable option, even if the doctor was more reluctant. I liked both and, overall, felt confident enough about birth and about being at home to feel able to work with these concerns without involving an independent midwife.

As time went by I became frustrated. Neither my midwife nor GP seemed relaxed about the pregnancy or birth – their approach to ante-natal care seemed to focus on problems and the need to test or scan or intervene 'just in case'. For example, by 37 weeks the baby wasn't engaged (nothing unusual from what I'd read), but they seemed surprised and suggested a low lying placenta or some other

---

A baby is said to be *engaged* when its head sinks down into your pelvis. First babies tend to engage somewhere around 37 weeks and you may feel as if you are walking around with a coconut swinging between your legs. Some babies, however, do not engage until labour. The babies of black women do not engage until labour because of the slightly different tilt of their pelvises. Breech babies tend not to engage because their bottoms don't fit so neatly into the pelvic inlet. Second and subsequent babies tend not to engage until the last minute either, so there is no need to panic.

Engaging is a normal, healthy sign, but if this is your first baby, and it has not engaged by the time labour starts, there is no need to worry. Some babies simply don't and nobody understands why, but it is unlikely to affect the course of your labour, nor is it likely to indicate any problems such as your pelvis being 'too small'.

blockage might be the cause. A late scan was advised. Their anxiety was infectious, so I did as I was told, even though it didn't sit comfortably either as a diagnosis or a course of action. The scan showed no blockage, just a big baby, lying transverse and with lots of room. They talked about admission to hospital just in case labour started, and about medical intervention to stimulate labour. Disaster scenarios were presented as if they were likely to happen. From then on ante-natal visits became a source of tension to fuel my anxiety as we wondered what action they would suggest this time.

At the same time, it was slowly dawning that, unless we were very lucky, my known community midwife may not be the one attending the birth. Her dog had itself given birth some weeks earlier and she was limiting her availability. Continuity of carer was important to me. Having talked about it with her weeks earlier, I'd felt confident about her commitment to being there for me. While I could understand she had a personal life and commitments there too, I nevertheless felt hurt and rejected. Who in the eleven strong community team would deliver our baby now?

I started on a downward spiral where my belief in myself and my body was being worn away. What I needed were some words of encouragement and reassurance to boost my flagging morale. Perhaps, too, an exploration of options based on more balanced information. I very much wanted things to happen in their own time again, and for my body to have the opportunity to prepare itself without unnecessary intervention. I certainly didn't want a prolonged stay, waiting in hospital, either for myself or for our vulnerable two-year-old. I was still only 37 weeks. I just wanted time, and to know that whoever was going to help deliver our baby felt confident about, and committed to, birth at home.

I desperately needed another viewpoint, some information, something positive to stop me simply handing over my pregnant body to the labour ward. I found what I needed outside the system in the form of three other midwives (two independent, one NHS, but all experienced practitioners). From Jane, the information and balance she offered during our lengthy chats were invaluable in boosting my flagging morale; from another Jane, whose flexibility and willingness to step in and provide care at home or in hospital, should I need

For more information on midwifes see 'Birth Basics'.

it at the last minute, I received the back-up and on-call support I needed; and Mary, a one-time nomadic midwife, helped me to set everything in the context of my first pregnancy and put me back in touch with the magic of childbirth. What a wonderful woman she sounded and how I'd love her to be helping deliver this baby. All offered support and encouragement and common sense views. They, too, seemed to think it was OK to let things be for a while.

My sense of balance restored, I spent a large part of the last stages of pregnancy crawling around the house – great fun for our two-year-old! – or lying bottom up, shoulders down whenever I sensed the baby trying to move into a breech or transverse position. When its head was down, I'd go walking to encourage it to drop into my pelvis. I'd agreed to call a midwife when I had any indication that labour might be starting, so its position could be checked. For me this was a much happier solution than an extended stay in hospital and suggested induction. I was doing all I could and was happy with that.

I'd tried not to attach too much importance to a due date, being unable to remember the date of my last period, and anyway, I'd gone to 42 weeks the first time around. By Friday the 10th, 41 weeks into pregnancy, I was feeling just a little bit disheartened, as well as extremely big and uncomfortable. However, that evening, I had a show, very slight, but straight away I began to feel excited that, at last, things were on the move.

We rang the on-call midwife, hoping she might be someone familiar. She wasn't, but Yvonne arrived and I liked her immediately. She kicked her shoes off and laughed as she told us that she'd been in the bath when she'd got the call. She was relaxed and light, as if this was the most natural thing in the world. Which, of course, it was.

Yvonne's presence was refreshing; with her I felt confident. She left us with a sense of quiet excitement, confidence and calm – also the knowledge that the baby was low enough in my pelvis to make a change of position very unlikely and the home birth a good option. We hoped our baby would be born while she was still on duty. We had until 8am the next morning.

Contractions started later that night, not strong, but enough to warrant TENS. I lay with my bulk, my contractions, my husband and, later, my son. Jolon never said a word, just snuggled. The only sound was the click of the TENS. I longed for the morning so that we could reasonably ask Mum and Dad to make their journey and help with the coming day.

Yvonne rang as 8am approached. We took her good wishes, but were disappointed to be handed on to another unknown member of the team.

The next on-call midwife rang later that morning to see how we were, but explained that she was very busy and, as long as everything was OK, wouldn't be round to see us until later in the afternoon. I would like to have met her; I started to feel a bit alone and unimportant.

Contractions came and went throughout that Saturday, sometimes fairly powerful and frequent, but then they'd stop before building up again. Similar pattern to last time, when it had gone on for a week. I was restless and not very sociable as each contraction worked its way through my body. I carried on with things in what had become my customary slow and cumbersome way, not knowing whether I was in labour or not. It surprised me. My second experience of this and I still needed somebody to tell me whether I was in labour – and there was nobody to do that for me. I did have two or three more shows, much more significant than the first. They suggested progress of a kind and helped to keep me going.

We didn't see, or speak to, the on-call midwife after her initial call. By evening I felt very much alone and unsupported. Anxiety returned too, as I wondered what the midwife would be like. When should we call her? How would it go? Why hadn't I gone the independent midwife route that had served me so well last time?

I felt alone and a bit panicky. I had no way of contacting my community midwife, nor any of the team directly. Even at this late stage, I was torn between trusting that the system would take care of me and asking Jane to come and be with me after all. I decided to ring the hospital to see what information they could give. To my amazement, they tried to reassure me by saying that I wasn't in established labour yet!

More agonising. I felt in need of more support than was available. Anyway, still harbouring the possibility of the independent route, we rang Jane . . . who wasn't there. We left a message, asking her to call back. That was that. Again, I'd done what I could. We cleared the supper dishes away and began to think about bed.

By 11pm I felt dreadful. No contractions now, but all sorts of upheaval inside me. My fantasy was that this baby was trying to move back up and out of my pelvis. I couldn't believe it. I knelt against the side of the bed feeling all these confusing, uncomfortable movements and sensations. I felt desperate. I wanted to cry. I was frightened and, for the first time ever, I could see the advantages of electing for a caesarean section and avoiding all of this! I carried on doing what I'd been doing . . . breathing deeply and looking for comfort. I heard Tim say he thought I was managing well and keeping calm, bless him. Not what I felt. This confusion lasted for an hour before the sensations eased and, almost as quickly as it had left, the calm returned.

The benefit of hindsight leaves me thinking that I was going through transition during that hour and experiencing the irrational thoughts and emotions common to it. If I'd recognised it as such, I might have felt better about it. As it was, the only 'medical' information available to me had told me I wasn't even in labour!

With TENS back on, I lay in bed, drifting in and out of sleep. I vaguely heard Jane's return message – call if we needed her, she was home. In that hazy state, I slowly started to listen to the contractions rather than trying to ignore them. They were getting stronger and quite frequent. One o'clock . . . time to call someone. In the short time it took Tim to call the hospital, I'd started to feel the urge to push. Returning our call, the on-call midwife promised to be with us as soon as she could – about thirty minutes. Another midwife would be coming too – we mistook her identity and took comfort from thinking it was our midwife after all. In spite of everything, I looked forward to her presence.

Soon there was no mistaking the urge and very quickly it became very powerful. I could feel that familiar feeling I'd dreaded – the coconut/grapefruit in my lower back. The difference this time was that it didn't feel stuck. I didn't need to work or push to get it out. No need for gravity this time, quite the opposite. I realised I was going to have to do something to keep it in!

I wanted to shift my position to make the baby's journey uphill, but the mechanics of such a movement, given my bulk and the contractions, were not easy to contemplate. Then I remembered the breathing; breathe light and quick, pant to overcome the urge. It worked for a while, but it was such a fine balance at times not to let go of my control and let the contractions take over.

One especially strong contraction and I was alarmed to feel something shift. Down came the membranes. Scary. They rested between my legs somehow tied up with the knickers I'd still got on. It felt warm, taut, but strong and still intact. I hoped it was my membranes because I couldn't think what else it might be! I wondered whether I could hang on long enough for the midwife to reach us. Unspoken, there was the fear that we were facing a DIY delivery.

The midwife, Kathy, dashed up the stairs at 1.45am. I was beyond caring, but she sounded OK and she knew about birth. That was what mattered now. I lay with my back to her, unable to move. Helped throughout by Tim, I could hear her struggling to put on apron and gloves, to get instruments and saline solution. I wondered how to tell her I didn't want it on my perineum! Every now and again she told me I was doing well.

Meanwhile the urge to push continued unrelentingly. I could feel the pressure on my perineum increasing with each contraction. The baby was coming and I couldn't stop it anymore. I needed to tell them. I wanted to know if she could deliver me with perineum intact. Kathy was telling me I'd need to change my position. I could see no way of making the 90-degree shift she wanted. As soon as I moved an inch I knew that everything would go and I was desperately trying to hang on to those waters, at least until she'd managed to get her gloves on. I could hold on no longer. She gave up on the gown and changing my position, and was ready.

A quick nick to the membrane and out came water, baby and all, much to the astonishment of my mum who'd just poked her head around the door. The time was 1.52am, only seven minutes since the midwife had dashed up our stairs. Seven minutes had never lasted so long.

They asked if I wanted to hold my baby, my daughter. I turned to see her looking at me with her beautiful big dark eyes. This was Leisha, 'the dark before midnight'.

I was overwhelmed, elated and full of emotion. Against all the odds, a girl. Not without its problems, but so straightforward when it came to the birth itself. She was big too – 9lb 12oz – and I felt so proud of us both and wanted to shout to the world. So happy that I had a healthy baby and no stitches to boot!

Jenny, the second midwife (who'd arrived just after the baby), helped me to the bath, clutching two incontinence pads between my legs. I remember seeing my dad and walking towards him like that, wearing my big washed out birthing shirt. What a sight it must have been. Both of us probably just a bit embarrassed, but both of us probably not really caring too much.

Not the long, sociable bath that I'd enjoyed with Jolon, I left my baby behind this time. It was functional. Clean me up and give others the chance to clear the bedroom and weigh/measure Leisha. I chatted excitedly with Jenny about birth and home births. Here was a midwife, hospital based, who understood some of the things that were important to me about wanting the birth to be at home. I hoped one day she would be able to work in the community.

Returning from the bath, I still felt high as a kite, thrilled that all had gone well and that we had a baby girl. We nursed and cuddled her, introduced her to her brother and grandparents. Within an hour or so she had taken her first feed and the midwives had gone.

Tim and I spent the next while ogling our baby; slowly relaxing, feeling physically exhausted, but enjoying the calm that was gently descending on the house. By 6am everyone was back in their own (or their grandparents') bed.

Looking back, I am grateful to those three women outside the system who provided such nourishment at a time when I needed it most. I only got to the point where the birth was able to happen in the way it did because of the information and support they gave. What they gave stopped me from feeling like a passive recipient of medical care. They restored me so that I felt, once again, empowered and able to give birth to my child.

In a sense, I feel very lucky. The birth was smooth and without difficulty. Kathy was able to offer just enough verbal encouragement during those seven minutes for me to feel reassured by her presence. However, there was no touch or physical contact and I didn't feel the empathy that I'd noticed so powerfully the first time. Our first conversation didn't happen until after the baby was born. I knew she had no idea what was important for me about giving birth. The 'system' meant we were unknown to each other. Asking for anything else, it seems, is like asking for the moon.

Sometimes Things Go Wrong
Michelle Morris

The drama started almost straightaway. When I found out I was pregnant with Audrey I had all the usual check-ups. The ultrasound scan showed that my placenta was a bit low, but I was told it was nothing to worry about. I decided to have the AFP blood test and it showed high levels of alphafetoprotein in my bloodstream and I was given a 1 in 20 chance of having a Down's Syndrome baby. This was very distressing news and I went on to have an amniocentesis to confirm the results of the AFP test. The two-week wait for the results was awful. All during that time I kept asking myself, 'What am I going to do if this is a Down's baby?' It was a very stressful and traumatic time, but the tests came back negative so my pregnancy went ahead and I felt relatively reassured.

Then, when I was about 25 weeks pregnant, we decided to go back to New Zealand to visit the family. I checked with the hospital that it was OK for me to fly and they said everything was fine, so off we went. However, I had only been in New Zealand for a week when I started to bleed. I woke up one morning with this show of blood and was rushed to hospital where a scan revealed placenta praevia.

Clearly, I should never have been allowed to fly in this condition in the first place. Even worse was the fact that now I was being told that, not only would I not be allowed to go back to London, but I would also not be allowed out of hospital for the rest of my pregnancy. The news was devastating. I had planned to have Audrey at home in London and quite literally overnight, all my hopes and aspirations for a natural childbirth had gone. If she had been born right there and then, her chances of survival would have been very slim. So, I was given two courses of steroids (to help her breathe) in case she did arrive very prematurely.

I was put on to the pre-natal ward at the National Women's

Respiratory problems are uncommon in babies born after 34 weeks. It can be difficult to predict who is at risk of going into labour this prematurely. Because of this, a doctor may suggest a prophylactic course of steroids in order to reduce the likelihood of breathing and other related problems for your baby. As a short-term measure steroids may well avert breathing problems in preterm babies, but this is not a course of medication to be gone into lightly. Steroids are very powerful drugs and there is overwhelming evidence of the damage they can do. For the mother, the risks are osteoporosis, hypertension, delayed wound healing and masking signs of infection (both these are important if you are having a caesarean), damage to your eyes and muscle wastage. Your baby could be born with hypo-adrenalism and may seem 'flat', and could suffer longer-term problems such as eczema and asthma. Steroids can be life savers, but you should always be given the facts about potential problems.

Hospital in Auckland where I spent the next three months, bleeding intermittently. As my pregnancy progressed, I bled more and more. Obviously, the bigger I got the more the placenta was being stretched, and all we could do was hang in there. There were a few close calls where I started bleeding in the middle of the night and, of course, every time I had a bleed the surgeon would come and I would get an IV put in, just in case I needed surgery. The extreme stress of this situation was compounded by the fact that my partner had to fly back to London to work and wasn't due back until November, when Audrey was due. So, I spent much of my time just lying there, hoping that she'd stay put and that I wouldn't have a major bleed. I went through bottles of Rescue Remedy which helped with the stress and anxiety I was feeling.

They say that there's a positive side to everything. Maybe that's true. The good side of this experience was the care that I received in Auckland. The midwives on the ward were exceptionally kind and loving people. I really think it was due to them that Audrey and I did as well as we did, because they really were on the case. They let me have all the information I needed. I had access, on a daily basis, to my records. I could consult with doctors about the possibilities, about what could happen, all the way along. When it got close to the time that I was due for a caesarean, we discussed other possibilities, such as being induced or whatever – though ultimately it was out of the question because the placenta was so low.

When the time came to deliver Audrey, I had to have a general anaesthetic and they ended up cutting through the placenta to get to her. I lost quite a lot of blood and it was quite a hair-raising operation, but they were very quick and everything turned out well.

For me, the most memorable things about my experience of being in hospital for that length of time were the friendships I made with the other women who came and went, and the amount of complications in pregnancies that I saw. I used to go down to the intensive

---

Placenta praevia is a condition where the placenta is sited over the cervix. It occurs in around 1 in every 200 pregnancies, and often the condition is accompanied by a baby which is lying in an unusual position. Early in pregnancy many placentas appear, on the ultrasound screen, to be lying low enough to constitute a risk of this condition. However, in the majority of cases, as the uterus grows the placenta moves out of the way. If you have placenta praevia, your baby will need to be delivered by caesarean. Doctors will usually advise bed rest, although there is no evidence that this will improve the outcome for your baby. You will also be advised to have an elective caesarean before term, usually around 37 or 38 weeks. This may be a reasonable course of action, given the risks of maternal haemorrhage and umbilical cord accidents, although there is some evidence to show that, compared with a group of women whose placenta praevia was diagnosed early in pregnancy, those babies for whom the condition was not diagnosed until labour fared just as well. The majority of women with placenta praevia, however, will begin to bleed at some point during pregnancy. If placenta praevia has not been diagnosed before then by ultrasound, this is one of the most common indications of its existence.

It is very important that you do not let anyone give you a vaginal examination if placenta praevia is suspected, as this may cause you to haemorrhage further. In fact, the most dangerous haemorrhages can be those provoked by vaginal examinations. Ultrasound examinations will provide all the information needed, though you should avoid the more invasive transvaginal ultrasound which may cause further haemorrhaging. If the placenta is lying over the cervix and is anterior (to the front of your abdomen), as in this story, the surgeon will have to cut through the placenta to get to the baby. It can be a difficult operation, so the exact site of the placenta should, as far as possible, be ascertained before surgery.

care unit for babies to visit with a woman who was in the bed next to me. She had a little baby at 28 weeks and he was touch and go for a while. I got to see the kind of things that can go wrong in pregnancy and felt very strongly that women are not really adequately prepared to deal with some of these. We're told about how 'normal' pregnancies go, and yet some of them don't go normally. For me it's been a profound experience, to realise that sometimes birth is not much like the fairy tale that most of us want to believe.

The day-to-day, week-to-week care on the ward was amazing. For example, there were relaxation classes once a week where we could all go, lie on the floor, meditate and completely relax our bodies. This was really helpful. Most of the nurses and the mid-wives were very well informed about alternative medicine and had a lot of helpful advice to give about things like homeopathy, herbal-ism and acupuncture. There was an acupuncturist who came round and treated a lot of the women who were suffering from very severe morning sickness. By all accounts, it was very effective for relieving the nausea.

We also had a counsellor who came round to check that we were OK emotionally and coping with the situation – which 9 times out of 10 we weren't! That feeling of not coping and being very frightened is so common, and fairly acute, in the early days when you first go into hospital, but our counsellor was brilliant and she was there for me right through the whole ordeal.

I was also able to choose the midwife who I wanted to come into theatre with me, and I had another midwife who was there to take photos so that I could see the birth for myself afterwards. Basically, they were just a very together group of women. They were very interested in, and saw the value of, loving and supportive care and they took the time to provide this in every way possible.

It was also hospital policy to encourage something called 'kanga-roo care'. When a baby is extremely premature, it's usually put in an isolation tank. In many hospitals that's where it stays. With kanga-roo care, as soon as the baby's strong enough, the mother is encouraged to hold her baby. Even if it's so young that it still can't suckle at the breast, the mother is still encouraged to have that skin to skin contact with her baby. What they've found is that this really improves the baby's chances of survival.

Also, as soon as the babies are able, mothers are encouraged to

Kangaroo care was developed in response to the needs of mothers and babies in Third World countries, where expensive high tech care is out of the question. With the kangaroo method, once the baby is stabilised, it is placed in a sling in skin to skin contact with the mother's breast – next to warmth and food, while the mother goes about her usual routine.

Babies cared for in this way have more regular heartbeats and fewer breathing problems. They are likely to thrive and leave hospital earlier. They have nearly four times less serious illness than babies cared for in incubators. Mothers who carry their babies around this way will also produce more breast-milk, and at six months old babies who have been carried around like this cry significantly less.

It is such a successful way to ensure the health of pre-term babies that it is hard to see why hospitals all over the world have not adopted it (and critics of the maternity services say the reason is simply that there is no profit to be made from it).

put them to the breast and, in fact, breast milk was the *only* milk that was encouraged in intensive care and for special care babies. All the mothers, even if they had been discharged and their babies had remained in hospital, would come every day, and express their milk. I felt this was such a positive step and obviously so good for the mothers, as well as the babies. It also meant that on the special care and intensive care wards, the atmosphere was very loving and special and very touching – much the same as it was on the ante-natal ward.

I was allowed to make phone calls to my partner in England from the sister's room. Also, because I was there for so long, at one point, I found myself in a room by myself, so they moved me to another ward so that I could be with other mothers. Like all the mothers, I could choose more or less who I wanted to be with and the midwives were careful to arrange the wards in a way which they felt would be most supportive for all the women, so we could help each other and give each other support. Things like that made a big difference to the way I felt about having to be in hospital for such a long time. There was even a woman who came round and taught us how to knit, so we occasionally passed the time knitting toys for babies.

Even though I was discharged before Christmas, I went back for a Christmas party that they put on for all the women and their babies who had been there during that year. I remember there were photos of mothers and babies everywhere and there was a poster up on the wall, which I will never forget, which said, 'Tell your baby you love it – every day.' This seemed to sum up the attitude that prevailed throughout the ward.

I got over the caesarean very quickly. I remember being on my back for a couple of weeks and then I was fine. After three months, we came back to England. Looking back I can see how my feelings about the birth were constantly changing. Disappointment became disillusionment became acceptance, and then I was very grateful that I had been in such a caring environment.

Before I had Audrey, I had strong feelings about the way modern medicine is practised, and I still have some of those feelings now. I feel a lot of doctors just hand out drugs and not much else. That's why, whenever possible, I choose to go with alternative therapies and medicines. It was these feelings which were the force behind my desire for a natural childbirth, but the fact remains that, in this particular situation, if it hadn't been for modern medicine I would have died and Audrey would have died. So, I was humbled by that experience and thankful for the way it made me appreciate just what a good thing modern medicine can be.

As far as birth choices are concerned, I didn't really have many options. I was in a situation where I was completely compromised by the fact that if I walked upstairs too hard or ran around too much I would bleed. My only choices were centred around finding ways to cope with the fact that I had to sit still, carry the pregnancy as far as I could and get the baby out in the safest way possible.

It affected me very deeply and for about a year afterwards, I would have – in fact I still occasionally do have – a dream of being back in the hospital with the baby, going around the wards, seeing all the women, and hoping that my baby's not going to die. In fact, for the first year after Audrey was born, I was afraid for her life. I think, partly, it was due to being a first time mother, but I also think that it's to do with the fact that I was in hospital for almost three months and for a while everything was simply touch and go.

I'd also like to say something about how I think all this affected Audrey, because I think the high level of stress I was feeling, her being in that kind of unstable situation and the way in which she was born did affect her quite profoundly. Caesarean babies have a different introduction to life. They don't have the preparation of coming through the birth canal out into the world, which is the natural way for a child to be born. One minute they're floating around in a warm, comfortable womb, the next minute – and it really is the next minute – they're out in the world. Just looking at the photos of the birth confirms, to me, that it's a very traumatic way for a baby to be born.

After she was born, I noticed that she had very, very tight shoulders, in fact they were quite 'clicky'. Nobody could give me any answer as to why that was. When I came back to London, I took her to an osteopathic centre that specialises in working with children. They had a look at her and said she had a lot of blocked energy through being traumatised at birth. So she had a year of osteopathy to release all this blocked energy and also to press and release her skull.

As a baby comes down through the birth canal, its skull is compressed and then, quite suddenly, released as it comes out. Caesarean babies don't have that important experience. Audrey's head was still waiting for that to happen, so we did it with cranial osteopathy and it really helped her. At the end of that year, she had a nice relaxed body and all the clickiness and the tension had gone. That was Audrey's physical experience. I may never know how it affected her in other ways, though I'm convinced that a difficult birth does have an effect on the baby as well as the mother.

My birth experience was a positive one because I was providential enough to be in New Zealand, even though I shouldn't have flown. It could have been a lot worse if, for instance, I had started bleeding on the plane or been stuck in LA with no health insurance. I doubt, also, whether I would have had the same level of care and support if I had simply stayed in England. As it is, Fate played a hand and I was lucky to end up in a really loving environment. I have since met a lot of women who weren't that lucky. Some women lose their babies, and some pregnancies don't go 'normally', and a lot of the care these women receive is very, very poor. I think this should be made clearer ante-natally so that women can be prepared and perhaps give some thought as to what they would do if they were in a situation like mine.

She is right to say that mothers do need to be prepared. Unfortunately, the prevailing wisdom is that we shouldn't tell women about the down side of birth or the unpopular possibilities such as abnormalities, pregnancy and labour complications, because it will frighten them. If a woman is grown up enough to have a baby, she is grown up enough to contemplate the options without turning into a gibbering wreck. Besides, telling women about all the possibilities doesn't alter the facts – the vast majority of pregnancies – some 98 per cent – go without a hitch. This is precisely why those women with complicated pregnancies, which don't go 'normally', feel so cut adrift and why so many practitioners are so inept at dealing with problems of this nature.

A Long Time Coming

Jenny Goodman

I have been catapulted into a new universe. I can barely remember life before the birth of my baby. When I see evidence of it – a book I once read, a dress I once wore – I believe in it only as a dream, a fiction somehow vaguely connected to me. Another life, another world. I have done what I promised a childless friend I would not do – turned into a different person. Instantly, choicelessly, irreversibly. The busy comings and goings of the world feel far away, a façade I was once involved in. The only reality is here, with this brand new precious little person and the bond between us. Ecstasy, exhaustion, smiles and tears. The rest is commentary.

My son Yossi was a long time coming. We tried seven years for a baby, and when I finally conceived we chose to have no scans and no amniocentesis, although I was thirty-nine. So we knew nothing about the baby who was coming to live with us, only that we would love and accept him/her whatever. I was radiantly happy during pregnancy, despite being very sick in the first twenty weeks and tired and enormous towards the end. I went to every class and workshop at the Active Birth Centre; I was fully informed and very well prepared – except that one cannot prepare for a cataclysm.

For the last three weeks of my pregnancy, a big blue birthing pool occupied most of our living room, and I manoeuvred with difficulty around the furniture that was crammed into the dining room. We were looking forward to a natural birth in our own home, with soft candlelight, music, massage, beautiful smells and loving support. And indeed, we got all those things. There was no intervention, no men in white coats came and robbed me of the experience. The birth plan was followed to the letter. But the labour lasted 91 hours. No, that's not a misprint. Ninety-one hours. Four days and nights. Without sleep. By the end, I was so desperate that I would have given anything for someone to come and rob me of the experience.

My due date came and went with no sign of the baby arriving. Ten days passed. We started doing what people do to get labour going: long walks, hot curries, making love. All thoroughly enjoyable, but still no baby. At 10 o'clock on Saturday night my partner, Stuart, gave me a massage using clary sage oil.

At midnight the contractions started coming, in text book fashion, every twenty minutes. I was able to breathe through them quite easily, but found it impossible to sleep in between them as the midwife had suggested. This was because I found that the position I needed to be in during a contraction was standing upright, leaning against the wall. I felt very connected to the baby. He ('it' then!) kept moving about, fluttering like a little bird, and I felt he was scared. I kept stroking my belly and talking to him, saying, 'It's OK, baby, it's fine, it's meant to happen like this.' The baby calmed down every time I did this. I thought, 'I know what is going to happen, but does the baby?'

The contractions continued every twenty minutes for twenty-four hours. By Sunday night/Monday morning they were every fifteen minutes and by Monday evening every ten minutes. I was facing the prospect of a third sleepless night, and the midwives were still calling it 'pre-labour'. I still needed to be vertical to breathe through the pains, but was too exhausted to remain upright between them. Heaving myself up off the bed as a contraction began became more and more difficult, especially as the pains began quite suddenly, with no warning and not much build up.

Our bed was a big mattress on the floor, in anticipation of sharing the bed with the baby. So we decided to spend Monday night resting on the sofas downstairs, as we thought it might be easier for me to stand up during contractions. I simply couldn't endure the pain unless I got vertical. The repeated effort of struggling to my feet, even with help from Stuart and my sister Lynda, pulled something out of place in my back. I felt it go, and the discomfort between contractions became almost as severe as the pain during them. It was now Tuesday morning, I was raw and ragged and it all began to take on the contours of a nightmare. The midwife said my cervix was probably only one or two centimetres dilated. It was still 'pre-labour'.

For some time I had been longing to get into the pool, but I'd had repeated warnings that getting in too early (that is, at less than five centimetres dilation) would lessen the pain-relieving qualities of the

It can be unbelievably disheartening to be told, after hours of painful contractions, that you aren't more than a centimetre or two dilated and you are still in 'pre-labour' or that you are not in 'true labour'. From a medical point of view, labour is something which progresses and is measured by the consistent dilation of the cervix. This is one of the many places where medicine and the experience of women diverge. Interestingly, midwifes who have experienced long and slow 'pre-labour' tend not to use the term, which they now recognise as rather callous.

water in transition, when they would be most needed. I was now desperate to get in the water, but the midwife suggested going for a walk instead to 'get things going'. It is hard to convey how impossible and appalling that suggestion sounded, partly because of exhaustion, and partly because the level of pain, which was increasing all the time, seemed quite incompatible with being in the street or the park. And the expression 'get things going' really grated.

I burst into tears and phoned my friend Jackie. I was sobbing incoherently down the phone. I didn't ask Jackie for anything but she just said, 'Right, I'm coming over. I'll take you for the walk.' But when she arrived I was in the pool; I simply couldn't stay out of the water any longer. The relief was tremendous – not from the pain of the contractions, which instantly went from every ten minutes to every three or four minutes, and became much longer and stronger – but from the severe discomfort between them. Within a minute of getting into the pool I had a second 'show', much bigger than the one I had during the first night of labour. We phoned the midwife, who relented about the proposed walk, but evidently still thought the birth was a long way off.

I spent the next twenty-four hours in the pool. I was eating only yoghurt and honey and taking sips of water. I vomited five times, fortunately not into the water. I was so exhausted that I kept momentarily falling asleep between contractions, and slipping under the water. I would wake with a start, and come up spluttering and frightened, just in time for the next contraction. To prevent this, Lynda and the midwife, who had now joined us, tried to help me find a position in which I wouldn't slip under the water when I fell asleep. This involved leaning back on the pool side and putting my arms along the sides of the pool to support myself. As I put my left arm over the side, I felt a searing pain down the left side of my back. It was an intensification of the damage I had done in repeatedly getting off the sofa to deal with the contractions on land. I was now in agony, and it was agony that continued between contractions.

I was seven to eight centimetres by the midwife's estimate; she didn't do a vaginal examination until some hours later. It took every ounce of will power to breathe through the contractions, and at the end of each I felt wrecked and drained. The brief gaps between contractions now brought no relief. It had become unbearable. I was saying things like, 'Put a bullet through my brain' and 'I just want to die.' Hearing myself say this, I asked the midwife if I was in transition. The answer, yet again, was 'Not quite yet.' I was surrounded by three caring people, but I felt profoundly alone in my extreme, unshareable pain. 'Oh please, please put me out of this misery,' I pleaded. 'Well, do you want to go to hospital and have an epidural?' responded the midwife. It was a challenge, not an offer. She is a radical midwife, who shared my horror of obstetric meddling. 'You know I don't,' I gasped, and gathered breath for the next excruciating wave of pain.

In the early hours of Wednesday morning my osteopath came to the rescue. His diagnosis was that my eleventh rib on the left was out of place and dipping down into my pelvis. That was why the pain in my back was worst at the end of a contraction and persisted throughout the brief intervals during which I would otherwise have been able to rest, meditate and recuperate a little. While I was thrashing around in the water, still somehow managing to breathe through increasingly severe, long and frequent contractions, he spent an hour or so gently and calmly re-aligning me. There was no instant relief, because the accompanying muscle spasm persisted for several more hours, but I do believe he saved me from a possible hospital admission, epidural and caesarean.

Why did I not want an epidural? It was partly that, even through the pain, I remembered the dangers it would pose to the baby and myself, and the whole cascade of interventions that would be likely to result. The baby's heart rate remained, thank God, fine throughout the labour, and I wanted to keep it that way. It was equally because I knew that the pain relief an epidural would bring was hours away; I would have had to get out of the pool, which seemed physically impossible, get dry, get dressed, pack a bag, travel to the hospital (a good half hour away), check in, deal with obstetricians and, quite possibly, wait for the anaesthetist. And then, I remembered many women's accounts of the slow, painful, hit-and-miss procedure of inserting the anaesthetic. Indeed, I had seen how crude the technique could be, in my own days as a medical student. I also remembered one friend's experience that after she had requested an epidural, and had the prospect of total pain relief, she lost her capacity to breathe through the contractions. So, I just kept breathing, breathing through hell.

> See 'Birth Basics' for information on pain.

Afterwards, I wondered: if I had called for an epidural and meant it, but my birth plan said 'no epidural', which of my wishes should the midwife have followed? What if the calmly thought-out, clearly stated intention of the birth plan conflicts with the desperate pleas of the labouring woman in extremis? They are both her truth, but which is the greater truth? I do not know.

I remained in the pool until I was ten centimetres dilated. It was the most appalling pain – deep, internal, terrible. I did not scream. This was not from inhibition. I am a person with very few restraints on emotional expression normally, and I scream and shout freely if I need to. But this pain was so shocking, so total, so awful, that I knew if I screamed I would get lost, I would drown in the pain and lose what coping mechanisms I had. I would plead for an epidural and mean it. And I also knew that screaming would make the pain worse. It was not a pain that could be catharted, only breathed through and survived.

Several things helped me through the pain: Stuart's and Lynda's hands on my back and eye contact with them during the contractions, and breathing in jasmine and frankincense oil on a tissue in between contractions. This seemingly small thing made a significant difference: the beautiful and heady smell boosted my strength to handle the next contraction. The midwife's notes at this point say, 'Jenny coping brilliantly', and I guess this is how it looked from the outside. I don't really understand what it means to 'cope'. I breathed and I survived – what other option did I have?

Eventually, with great difficulty, I was helped out of the pool. It was 11am Wednesday morning, I had been in the pool about twenty-four hours and my hands and feet looked as if they belonged to a creature from another planet. I had been unable to pee in the

> This is one case where a shot of pethidine might actually have helped. Pethidine can act as a muscle relaxant and encourage dilation early in labour – used before you are five or six centimetres dilated it is likely to work its way out of your, and your baby's system without any unwanted side effects. See 'Birth Basics' for information on the length of labour.

pool, and with assistance from Lynda and the midwife I struggled upstairs to the loo, where a combination of running taps, drinking cold water and having my sacrum tickled finally produced the desired result.

'Walk about,' said the midwife, 'you've got to walk about to bring this baby down.' It was like being asked to fly to the moon. 'I can't. I can't . . . *I'm exhausted.*' But I did, partly because I wanted to get the baby born this side of next week and partly because I found that there was no position in which I could comfortably rest. Sitting, standing, squatting, lying, kneeling, on all fours – I tried them all to rest between contractions, but as soon as I stopped the back pain was all over my body, so I just had to keep moving.

I walked around the house and the garden, again and again, sweating and stark naked, oblivious of the neighbours, leaning against Stuart with every contraction. The contractions were changing, they felt 'downwards and outwards' rather than 'upwards and inwards', and were less frequent and more bearable than in transition. I was so exhausted after four nights without sleep that I kept literally falling asleep on my feet. I would half collapse and jerk upright suddenly. I just kept walking, using every last ounce of strength and every atom of willpower to keep going.

After several hours, the contractions changed again. The midwife did a vaginal examination and broke the waters and the pains became more intense. I was now leaning over a bean bag and finally breathing in the gas and air for which I had been pleading for hours. It was quite useless. I remember yelling, 'This is a bloody placebo, give me the real thing.' Nevertheless, I grabbed the gas and air like a lifeline, held on to it and sucked furiously. The cylinder was small and half empty and when it ran out I was angry, even though it hadn't really helped. The second midwife, who had now arrived, said, 'You don't need it any more.'

And then I was standing, half squatting, in the middle of the living room, holding on alternately to the edge of the pool and to

Gas and air, also known as Entenox, is a mixture of nitrous oxide (laughing gas) and oxygen. To use it, a mother places a rubber mask over her face (or sometimes a small tube in her mouth) and inhales deeply. The apparatus is fitted with a valve which opens when you inhale and closes when you exhale. Gas and air will not take the pain away, but, in combination with the deep breaths you will need to take to inhale the mixture, can help take the edge off. If used in moderation, it appears to have little effect on the baby.

Some women find that gas and air makes them nauseous, disoriented and disconnected from the experience of birth. Others find that it has no effect at all. The best time to use gas and air is probably towards the end of the first stage, when you are experiencing the intense contractions of the transition phase. If used during the second stage of labour, this form of pain relief will interfere with the bearing down efforts needed to get the baby out, and thus delay the birth.

Stuart's and Lynda's arms. They were one on either side of me and their arms took several days to recover. An extraordinary surge of power and energy flooded through me. Having been literally collapsing from exhaustion, I was suddenly filled with a strength that was not quite human. I could feel the baby's head coming down. Although the pain was severe, it didn't have the terrible relentless quality of the last contractions of the first stage. These were pains to scream out – deep, massive yells from the depths of my being. I think they could hear me at the other end of the street.

It was a magnificent, incredible process, but it was also wild, ruthless and brutal. I felt torn apart, ravaged, raped by the cosmos. I felt that Nature was using me, using my body to bring forth new life, and that I as a human being, a person, was irrelevant. Nature didn't care that my body was occupied by an individual consciousness. The force that was ripping through me was utterly impersonal, nothing to do with me. I was merely the vehicle.

There was a picture of the Goddess Giving Birth on the wall. She looks as peaceful as the Buddha, as does the baby emerging from her vagina. I was screaming at the picture: 'It's a lie, it's a goddamned, *fucking lie!*' I was screaming at my former self, at my naïveté, my romantic hope that the birth would be some kind of spiritual experience. It was not, and the soft light of beeswax candles and the exquisite strains of the 'Panis Angelicus' filling the room could not make it so.

The midwives were telling me to push, but I had no urge to, and remembered many women's stories of the damage done by pushing before their body told them to. I was just opening and letting go, and it now felt right and productive, despite the dreadful pain. I was pouring with sweat, gasping for cold compresses and sips of water between contractions. All the muscles in my arms and legs were pulled, but I didn't notice till the next day. At last, the midwives glimpsed the baby's head, high up in my vagina. I saw it too, with the aid of a mirror and torch – a tiny, coin-sized patch of dark hair like mine! This is what made the second stage bearable: seeing the baby's head coming down with each contraction, sliding back up again between them, descending oh so slowly, so slowly, so slowly. Getting bigger, here comes another overwhelming wave, breathe, let go, let it come. It was going to be over two hours, from that first glimpse of Yossi's head, to the moment when he was finally born.

The pushing, when it came, was enormous and absolutely involuntary. It was not me pushing; the pushing happened to me, through me. It was totally instinctual. Whereas the pain of the first stage had to be endured, and required willpower and training to breathe through, the second stage seemed something my body was more naturally equipped to deal with; the breathing and the sounds I was making actually served to release the pain, rather than just enabling me to survive it.

They say it is like shitting a pumpkin. It did feel as if the baby's head was in my rectum – then there was a definite moment when I felt it clearly in my vagina. There was the burning, stinging sensation I had heard described – it did help to have been warned about that – and a stretching, tearing, opening of my body beyond anything I would have believed possible. My son was born.

I saw his beautiful little face in the mirror, perfectly composed, eyes tight shut, a soul suspended between two worlds . . . waiting. I did not tear as his head emerged, because I had smothered my perineum in jojoba oil just before he came out, and because I had resisted the finally overwhelming urge to add voluntary pushing to the pushing my womb was doing. However, he had his hands crossed over his chest, so both his shoulders came out at once, and at that point I sustained a second-degree tear, which healed without stitching.

The cord was round his neck, arm and shoulder and, even after some very deft unravelling by the midwife, it was still unusually short, so that I couldn't lift him to the breast. Once it had stopped pulsating, it was cut. Stuart held him first, as I sat down, with the midwives worrying about blood on the carpet, and me not caring. He was very slippery to lift, being covered in oil as well as blood and meconium. We sat together and held our baby. At last.

Yossi cried loudly at being thrust out of paradise. Suddenly here was gravity, air, and loving, but clumsy, hands holding him – it was nothing like the beautiful underwater births we had seen on video, where the baby swims peacefully up through water with calm, wide-open eyes, and gazes around. This was more like a birth on a TV soap opera, the baby entering screaming and bloody into this vale of tears. All that was needed to complete the scene was some idiot saying, 'Healthy pair of lungs!'

Yossi was born at 7 o'clock on Wednesday evening. Seconds later, just as a sense of wonder began to dawn, there was a moment of high drama. 'Prepare yourselves for a surprise,' said one of the midwives, 'we think there might be another one in there.' I was too exhausted even to respond to the prospect of twins. If we had two babies, so be it. They started feeling the top of my womb – which was still huge, indeed as if I was still pregnant – and listening for a fetal heartbeat. They thought they heard one, and began preparations to receive another baby, but it was a false alarm. The bulge was caused by a huge blood clot and a high (fundal) placenta.

This sounds dramatic, though it seldom is. Blood can build up behind the placenta, before it separates from the uterine wall, particularly if the mother is not urged to change position soon after the baby is born. To help avoid this, and possible severe blood loss, you should find a position where your knees are lower than your hips and you should remain upright.

When I finally held my baby in my arms, I felt relieved and incredulous, but not ecstatic. I was too numb and shattered to bond instantly, but I also knew this was OK, and that I would grow to love the baby over the next few days. Indeed, he slept on my tummy all that night, and by the morning I was already falling in love with him.

Somehow I had known, when I got out of the pool on Wednesday morning, that I wouldn't be getting back in to give birth. Yossi was born on land and in the event it didn't matter at all. About twenty minutes after the birth I got into the pool with the baby. Shortly afterwards, Stuart also got into the water and cuddled the baby. I decided to stand up and push the placenta out. As I stood up, I fainted and crashed back into the water, apparently narrowly missing Stuart and the baby. I am told that I was then hauled out of the pool by the midwives; all I remember is that one minute I was standing in the pool and the next I was on the living room floor, with the two midwives scrabbling over me, and I was saying, 'Why are you waking me up?' I had lost a lot of blood, and I was hot, dehydrated, starving and exhausted.

Most of the rest of the evening consisted of the midwives medically attending to me, while Stuart held the baby; he was busy bonding while I was being catheterised! The midwives prescribed five days' bed rest, which I certainly needed. I think Stuart and Lynda could have used five days' bed rest too, as they had stayed heroically awake with me throughout my marathon ordeal. We phoned the new grandparents, and we tied blue balloons to the front door to let the neighbours know our good news. Then, at last, we slept, and in the morning began the lives that were changed forever.

I struggle to come to terms with the most overwhelming experience of my life. The shock of the birth still reverberates through me, and as I wrestle with it, struggling to integrate it into my soul and my world view, I am left with many questions. All the 'bad' birth stories I had heard involved hospitals and high-tech interventions, women feeling that choice and power were taken from them by men (and sometimes women) in white coats. They felt violated. No human being violated me or took away my power or choice, but I felt violated by Nature herself. The power belonged to the forces of Nature, not to me, and I had no choice about what was happening in my body.

I had been a devotee of the Active Birth movement, and indeed I still believe it does vital work in promoting healthy alternatives to conventional obstetric practice. Technically speaking, Yossi's entry into the world was very much an 'active birth', but my subjective experience was not that 'I gave birth to the baby', it was that I allowed the birthing to happen through me. I facilitated and co-operated with Nature, that was all. I could choose candles, incense and music, but I did not choose the agony or the sense of annihilation.

I had lived my life by the highly simplistic equation 'natural

equals good'. It was not that I didn't expect pain, and no one in the
Active/Natural Birth movement denies that birth is painful. Nevertheless, I think that the movement encourages a subtle romanticising
of the birth process, which I very willingly embraced. For some
women, the birth process may indeed be a beautiful experience. For
me it was, to quote a friend's words, 'savage and merciless'.
According to the midwife's notes, I cried out at one point, 'Why
should women have to go through this agony?' There is no answer.
Here is a uniquely female, uniquely awful experience, and I can't
blame the patriarchy for it. I can, however, now see how all the
religious ordeals and initiation rites men have invented are but a
pale imitation of this original earth-shattering event. Certainly it is
transformative; I will never be the same person again.

For two or three weeks after the birth, I had flashbacks and
nightmares, reliving parts of the labour. I had one dream in which
the bed was buckling underneath me, and there was terrible noise
and chaos in my body. In another, a huge machine came down from
the ceiling and picked me up. I would wake up screaming, and
shaking uncontrollably. Every time I drifted into sleep, I had a

Post-traumatic stress disorder (PTSD) is very common among
soldiers, particularly after a war, or men and women in the
emergency services such as firemen and police. But it can affect
anyone who has had a traumatic experience, and when it occurs
after birth it is sometimes called post-natal stress disorder
(PNSD). There is still debate about whether it really is a separate
'disorder' or whether it is an acute form of depression and
anxiety, with all the attendant symptoms such as difficulty
sleeping, irritability and mood swings, shaking, sweating, loss of
appetite and nightmares. In addition to these symptoms, suffer-
ers will also experience flashbacks to the traumatic event,
indeed it will seem to take over their lives, sometimes long after
it has passed.

Those with severe PTSD will need intensive counselling to
work through it. Others, like this mother, simply need to talk and
talk and talk about it with a sympathetic person close to them. It
is worrying that something so essentially 'normal' as birth can
produce such a terrible response, but it can, particularly if the
woman experiences birth as a loss of her 'self', in both its
everyday and more profound sense. It can also occur in labour,
if the woman has had a traumatic childhood experience in
relation to her body, such as being sexually abused.

terrifying falling sensation, like I was falling back into hell. For several weeks there was a tremulousness in my hands and, when I tried to sing to the baby, I noticed that there was a shaking in my voice. I knew these were all symptoms of Post-Traumatic Stress Disorder (PTSD), and I debriefed endlessly at poor Stuart, in the middle of the night, between feeding the baby. I couldn't help it, and I knew it was healing me.

I had always loved water and been a keen swimmer. I'd had fantasies of spending some time each day after the birth in the pool with the baby. In fact, I became quite water-phobic for some time, and when I was physically able to go downstairs again, a week after the birth, I had to steel myself to enter the living room where the birth had taken place, even though the pool was no longer there. But there was something I needed to do in that room. I went up to the poster of the Buddha-like Goddess, tranquilly giving birth to her Buddha-like baby, took it off the wall and tore it up. It was an act of anger, but I think it marked the beginnings of acceptance. My birth was how it was: on land not in water, bloody and brutal not peaceful and spiritual. I would recover.

Lucy

Annette Collins

Lucy Marie entered the world at 3.30am on Thursday, March 16th with my knickers on her head. This was a first for both doctor and midwife!

I was offered a home birth early on in this, my third pregnancy, but since I live a good twenty minutes from the hospital, I decided to keep my options open by booking for a GP unit delivery as well.

As my pregnancy progressed and I read more and more about home births and the risks involved, I became increasingly confident that my bedroom was the best place for my baby to be born. Statistics were even telling me that, given my circumstances and past history of two 'normal' deliveries, we would be safer at home than in hospital.

We started going to NCT ante-natal classes, which proved very useful and supportive, even for a third-time mum. Peter, my doctor, gave me a refresher course in the use of self-hypnosis as a means of pain relief, something I had found so useful in my second labour. Moira, my midwife, started calling in at home for coffee and a chat, as well as to do my ante-natal checks. We looked forward to her Sunday visits, real family occasions with Stuart and the children gathering round to hear the baby's heartbeat.

A friend in the village is a qualified aromatherapist and masseuse. She came round a couple of times, once tramping through thick snow, to teach Stuart some basic techniques, using some wonderful smelling blends of essential oils which she had concocted. In no time at all, Stuart was not just rubbing my back as he had in previous labours, but administering a proper massage in just the right way and in just the right places. The difference was enormous and proved to be such a help when the time came.

As the weeks went by, Lucy decided she preferred the breech position, and by 36 weeks the home birth was beginning to look doubtful. I was facing the choice of allowing Peter to try to turn the baby, or a hospital delivery where I would be encouraged to have an epidural, probably forceps, or even a caesarean. Peter said that, if it came down to it, he would be prepared to deliver a breech at home. It's funny how, when the menu changes, you really want the dish that's no longer available. That's how I felt about the home birth, and when Lucy suddenly turned at the end of 37 weeks, a hospital delivery was no longer a consideration for me.

I went into labour on Sunday and again on Monday, had a rest on Tuesday and started again over Tuesday night, only to stop once more on Wednesday morning. My house was hoovered so many times and the dogs had more walks over those few days than they normally get in a month.

Moira was phoning or calling in several times a day. Stuart didn't know whether or not to go to work. My parents rushed up from Oxford. And still we waited.

At 6pm on Wednesday, the contractions started again every ten minutes. Would they keep going this time? Towards 8 o'clock I had my wonderful jasmine bath, reputed to gently stimulate and strengthen uterine contractions. I felt quite humble when I remembered being told that as many jasmine petals as would fill the whole bath had been used to make those few drops of oil. No wonder it's so dear.

Just after 8.30, Moira arrived, followed shortly by Peter. I intended to give birth in a semi-squatting or kneeling position, leaning against the side of the bed and in front of the wardrobe mirror. I wanted to see this time! We prepared the bedroom with a plastic sheet on the floor covered with a cotton one, and a large floor cushion, protected under its cover by a small rubber sheet. I was concerned about the bed moving, so Stuart took the wheels off, but that made it too low, and it was only when the bed was upended a second time that Stuart discovered they were not designed to be removed and wouldn't go back on!

At this point a salesman arrived at the door to give us a quote for installing an alarm in our home. Stuart had been trying to phone him to cancel the appointment, but had been unable to get through. Having promised to buy three, he eventually got rid of him and I was able to go downstairs to the comfort of my own lounge, my own soft music and lights, surrounded by the people and things that I love most in the world. Peter left to get some sleep, Moira having

This is a very unusual scenario. While GPs provide the majority of ante-natal care in this country, less than 1 per cent of GPs actually attend births. Even in GP units, births are attended by midwives (which is why GP units are also known as Midwifery Units). If your ante-natal care is being provided by your GP, bear in mind that very few GPs have any experience of birth at all, and this obviously can affect their views about the kind of care which is appropriate for women.

promised him a progress report around midnight. Mum and Dad were there and we all chatted and joked in a totally relaxed atmosphere, with me kneeling up and leaning over the settee every time a contraction came. Stuart began using the jasmine massage oil on my back. It made such a difference to the degree of discomfort I felt with each contraction, and it was very soothing in between because I was experiencing a lot of low back pain all the time. It was so nice to be at home: I could do what I liked, when I liked and how I liked. There was no decision to make about when to go into hospital and no contractions to deal with in the back of a car.

Contractions came in short bursts with a rest of about fifteen to twenty minutes between. It was nice to have a breather, but towards the end of each quiet spell I knew I would have to pay for it with six or seven strong contractions in quick succession. It also meant that it was quite a long drawn out affair, compared to my previous labours, which became rather wearing towards the end. I felt very dispirited at one stage, when we went back to the bedroom and I was found to be only four centimetres dilated.

Back downstairs we went for more music and massage and the 'team' sat around eating pizza and chocolate cake. I didn't have any – just the smell made me feel quite green.

Dad went to bed, Peter was given an update and I began to get really sleepy between contractions. The hours went by quickly really, with everyone taking bets on what time the baby would come. I had thought 1.30am (some hope!), Moira said 4am and Mum said 3am. At no time did I feel anxious about the safety of myself or the baby. Moira oozed a calm confidence and regularly took my blood pressure and played the baby's heartbeat over the sonicaid before, during and after contractions. It barely changed at all.

We eventually went back upstairs. Still my waters had not broken (hence the knickers and sanitary towel), unlike my previous labours when that had been the first sign. I went to the loo and had to cope with three contractions in quick succession, with no time to get into my kneeling forward position. At this point, clinging to Stuart's neck, I reached the 'I don't want to play this game any more' stage, but I recognised the signs of snapping at those around me and knew it couldn't be for much longer.

I returned to my bedside position, and Moira took control of my back pain by exerting a steady pressure there. I needed to see Stuart now, and we started counting through the contractions together. Mum was working hard, rubbing and massaging my thighs through each contraction. The contractions were getting very strong now. Stella, my four-year-old, woke up at this point and stood in the doorway, taking it all in. Fortunately, having just finished a contraction, I just smiled and told her the baby was coming and that, if she went back to bed, when she woke up the baby would be here. For once in her little life she did just what she was told without saying a word.

I decided to try some gas and air and crawled on to the bed, just for two minutes. At first the relief the Entenox gave me was terrific. I wondered why I had waited so long before having it and started to sing about it being nice having babies, but then I had too much and everything became frightening and unreal. Moira began getting concerned about my bed, as it had no protecting covering on it at all, and was asking if I still intended to get on the floor. Head swimming with Entenox, I couldn't be bothered to reply, but I did manage to swear at poor Moira, who asked me to move over so that she could put a small rubber sheet under my bottom. Finally, they lifted me like a baby and slipped something under me, before calling Peter back for the final phase.

Although painful and unpleasant towards the end, everything was made so much easier for me because I was in my bedroom being helped by people I felt so close to. I did not give birth to Lucy on my own. It was a real team effort with everyone concentrating hard on their tasks to get me through each contraction. The hypnosis was helpful, especially when Peter put his hand on my shoulder and talked as we had done in practice sessions.

I felt a very slight pushing urge just at the end of a contraction and thought, 'Right, this is it! If it happens again I'll get down on to the floor.' It didn't. Instead, I had seven or eight more strong contractions and then, suddenly, my body heaved all on its own and my waters broke. 'Oh! The bed,' groaned Moira (she had promised no mess), and then, as Peter was putting on his gloves, Lucy's head was born. One more heave and out came her little body. I did not push once – my body did it all on its own.

She was handed straight to me and needed no sucking out at all. I was not given syntometrine, and we left the cord intact until the placenta had detached from the uterus.

Such joy and elation! We, the team, had done it! 'Welcome to the world, darling little Lucy.' In the dimmed bedroom lighting, love and happiness shone on everyone's faces. Stella woke once again and was so excited to greet her new baby sister. She quickly unwrapped the toy rabbit she had carefully chosen, gave it to Lucy and rushed along the landing to wake her grandfather. 'Poppa! Poppa! Wake up! The baby's come!'

Poppa came rushing along in his dressing gown. Some champagne arrived and William, my 22-month-old son, woke up, determined not to miss out on anything. Such a close, happy little family gathered round to adore the latest addition. And then, another bonus of home birth: once bathed and changed (and the mattress turned over), there was none of that lonely little girl lost and abandoned feeling that I had experienced in hospital when Stuart left. Instead, I snuggled down under the covers, with him cuddling up alongside me, and listened to Lucy's soft breathing in the carrycot, placed so I could easily watch her from my pillow. Sheer and utter bliss.

As things have turned out, there is, sadly, a much more poignant reason why it was right for my Lucy to be born at home. When Moira returned at 10 o'clock and handed her to me in daylight, we could see straight away that she had Down's Syndrome. Peter came back very soon afterwards, followed by a consultant paediatrician from the hospital.

The grief and confused emotions were only made bearable by the fact that we were at home, surrounded by family and friends. For not one second did Lucy or Stuart leave my side. I shall be forever grateful to Moira and Peter for not telling us immediately after Lucy was born. Words cannot describe the blissfully happy little family scene we had all experienced in the early hours of that morning, and no matter what, no one can take that away from us.

Some people said I was brave to have my baby born at home.

Down's Syndrome is the most common chromosomal abnormality. It occurs in about 1 in every 700 births. The risk of Down's does increase with the mother's age, but this is not the only factor and 75 per cent of Down's Syndrome babies are born to women who are under the age of thirty-five and not thought to be at risk of having a Down's baby. It is most likely to be caused by abnormal egg formation, but can also be caused by abnormal sperm formation. A baby with Down's has an extra No. 21 chromosome, which is why the disorder is also called Trisomy 21.

Deciding about Down's is never easy. There is no way, through ante-natal testing, to tell the extent to which your child will be affected by Down's. In some it is barely noticeable, in others more so. Children with Down's will have mild to severe learning difficulties and restricted growth. However, they are also loving and sensitive and more and more Down's Syndrome children are making good education progress with sympathetic and consistent stimulation from teachers and parents.

Others said I was foolhardy, and some (I think most people, deep down) were envious. Bravery certainly did not come into it. We went into all the facts thoroughly beforehand and were fully aware of all the things that could 'go wrong' and what action would be taken if any of them did. Above all, we had absolute faith in Moira and Peter, having got to know them well before the birth.

There won't be a next time for me, but if there were, I would have no doubts at all about where I would like my baby to be born. After all, what could be more natural than a home birth?

Perseverance Pays Off
Debbie Chippington Derrick

I confidently booked to have my first baby, Phillippa, at home. However, during an ante-natal visit with my GP, who was very supportive of home birth, my midwife happened to come in to speak to him about something else. When she heard I was intending to have my baby at home, she commented that she didn't like first time mothers having babies at home because they didn't know whether they would cope with the pain. She suggested I book into the GP unit instead.

Since I was unaware that I could have asked for another midwife who would have been more supportive, later that day I visited the GP unit and booked for a 6-hour discharge, under the misnomer of 'Domino'. There was to be no continuity of care, but frankly I felt I would rather have someone else with me during labour.

At 42 weeks I was referred back to the consultant who wanted to see me again on Monday to discuss induction, but on the preceding Saturday night I went into labour. I laboured well at home and late Sunday morning we went into the GP unit. My contractions slowed down drastically, and an internal showed me to be three or four centimetres dilated. Progress was slow after pethidine and the

GP units are the same as midwifery units. They are staffed by midwives and traditionally mothers book into them when they want low intervention care in the community, albeit with the back-up of medical facilities if necessary. GP units are the closest thing to a birth centre available on the NHS, but many of them are being closed down as part of cost cutting exercises. Unfortunately, more and more GP units are adopting the high intervention policies of hospitals. So, if you are looking for low intervention care, in a unit like this, it is best to book with one which is not attached to a hospital.

artificial rupture of my membranes. This, and being 43 weeks pregnant at midnight, meant we were transferred to the main maternity unit in the same building. Syntocinon drip, fetal scalp monitor, and epidural all followed, accompanied by failure to progress and fetal distress. A caesarean became the only option.

We were kept informed of what was happening and the anaesthetist was brilliant. Phillippa was checked over within my sight and then handed to us and tucked up beside me for the transfer from theatre to the labour ward and, later that morning, to the post-natal ward. I had no pelvimetry done, since my GP explained they were of questionable value. He encouraged me to believe that next time things would be fine and, since I didn't seem to be traumatised by this caesarean, I was very optimistic about future births. I intended to have our next baby in hospital as I believed, at the time, this was a prerequisite to having the third one at home. If only I had known the truth.

We moved house a week before our next baby was due and I encountered a very different opinion of postmature pregnancies; the consultant's policy was to induce at ten days over. I was unaware that I could have asked for a second opinion or changed consultant. Over the next eight days I had five lots of prostaglandin pessaries and even negotiated going home twice during the fiasco. Eventually, I was taken to the labour ward where an attempt was made to break my waters with an undilated and posterior cervix. It was unbelievably painful and they managed to convince my husband, Tim, to go and get himself lunch while they did it.

A syntocinon drip was also tried, but with no effect, and later that day I was manoeuvred to theatre for another caesarean. I still don't know quite how this came about, but I suspect some of the procedures were carried out simply to prove to me that a caesarean was necessary.

> The neck of the womb, or cervix, protrudes into the vagina; you can feel it through self-examination as a hard lump at the back of your vagina. It can point or curve any number of ways. A posterior cervix is one which is pointing towards your back. The mechanics of trying to stick an amniohook into it, dilated or otherwise, don't bear thinking about. Why were this woman's waters broken? Why was her husband dispatched to get something to eat while she went through this alone? This is very bad practice.

For information on caesareans see 'Birth Basics'.

Haddon was born angry and, at eight years old, frequently still is. He didn't want to be born yet and he was separated from us, once we had seen him briefly, until I was taken to the post-natal ward. His mother's emotional state can't have helped. I was distraught at the idea that any other babies of mine would have to be born by caesarean. By the time I was pregnant for the third time, I knew I had the right to choose a vaginal delivery and a home booking, and had informed the Supervisor of Midwives that this was what I intended to do. Six midwives agreed to be involved with my care and I was asked to see a consultant at a nearby military hospital. He and his registrar were happily taking on VBACs after two sections, and leaving mothers to go to 44 weeks, providing everything, including the levels of amniotic fluid, which were measured every few days by scanning, was well.

I knew there had been plenty of amniotic fluid in both my previous pregnancies, but this one was to prove different (could it have been the raspberry leaf tea I was drinking?). I was over 43 weeks and the amniotic fluid was declining when I started to go into labour. It faded away in the morning, only to start again the next night. I then went to my hospital appointment the following morning and the scan showed negligible amniotic fluid. Because of the concern this caused, I agreed that I would go in for induction the next day, if nothing significant had happened. This I did, after another night of contractions which faded in the morning.

My mother, daughter and I sat and cried that night, but I felt I had no option. I tried in vain to find further information on the risk of low amniotic fluid. The support of the midwives was disappearing and I didn't have the inner self-reliance to carry on. After one lot of prostin gel, a few hours of mild contractions and a fair amount of walking around, I was delighted to be told I was one centimetre dilated and fully effaced. However, sixteen hours of much more intense contractions, most at three minute intervals, brought no further progress.

On standing up in the morning, things became very hard to cope with and the midwife, whom I had never met before, suggested I may be in transition and asked to examine me again. I refused as I had no confidence in this midwife or in my body's ability to make that sort of progress so rapidly. I demanded an epidural first. It was a while before I got the epidural, and in the interim I was coping again, despite being on the bed attached to a monitor. Yet I still had the epidural. The internal showed I was six centimetres dilated, the cervix was loose and floppy, and not applied to the baby's head as it had previously been. I felt I must have gone backwards and afterwards spent many sleepless nights regretting not having listened to that midwife.

Several things can make your labour go 'backwards'. If you are very tired or stressed out, or if your uterus is over-stimulated by oxytocic drugs, the tissue in your cervix can start to swell and thus 'close up'. Also, since epidurals make your pelvic floor muscles limp and unable to rotate the baby properly, your baby's head may not be pressing as forcibly as it might against the cervix. Without this pressure, it will not continue to dilate.

There were signs of fetal distress, so my waters were broken and a scalp electrode fitted – several times. The waters were a thick meconium sludge and the midwife called the registrar immediately. He was very calm and said that with minimal amniotic fluid that was to be expected. After several hours, which included taking fetal blood samples half-hourly and giving me a syntocinon drip, there was no further progress and, although Toby's blood pH levels were now within normal limits, I couldn't put him or myself through any more and we asked for a caesarean.

Tim, my mother and I all cried, too numbed to comfort each other. Despite agreement that Toby would not be separated from us, he was taken to the office of special care to have his stomach washed out, since he had swallowed meconium. My mother accompanied him, which helped us all to cope with this brief, but unnecessary, separation. I spent a very disturbed night on the ante-natal ward (they were unable to take me to the post-natal ward as repairs being carried out prevented getting a bed into the lift), listening to two other women in the early stages of labour. Toby was unsettled and I was coping with my arm in a splint, having complained that the drip was pulling sideways in my arm. I discharged myself, against medical advice, the following day, just over twenty-four hours after the operation. It was such a relief to be home and I am so pleased that I made that decision. I knew the day that Toby was born that I was going to have an independent midwife next time around.

This time, I organised my care before I was pregnant. It was wonderful to be in control, I had no scans, no visits to hospital or doctors and no tests, other than a few blood tests. I felt it was important for me not to treat this pregnancy as a medical event. I was able to spend hours talking about my pregnancy, previous births and my hopes and concerns for this birth. The children got to know the midwives and I felt at ease and not under pressure. I had some acupuncture and homeopathy to try and prevent the pregnancy going very overdue. However, I was almost 43 weeks when, at 6am on a Sunday morning, I awoke with contractions. At eight we called my parents and asked them to come, and bleeped the midwife, Val, who rang us and arranged to ring back in a couple of hours. We filled the pool and I switched on the TENS machine. The kids and Tim were getting on with various things around me, but I was very focused on what I was doing. When Val rang again at about 10.30am, she listened to me during a contraction, and said I could get into the pool if I wanted, which I did.

Val arrived at about midday, just before my parents. She wanted me out of the pool to do an internal, which I knew I was going to find difficult, but I started to make pushing noises at the end of each contraction, so she decided she would examine me in the pool. I was only four centimetres, but she said my cervix was very thin. My waters went during this examination and there appeared to be meconium. Photographs taken later show there can't have been, as the purely blood stained liquor can be seen. We suspect there was a large quantity of stained mucus from around the cervix, as I'd had a very small bleed several weeks earlier. Val explained that it could be some time yet, but I was so focused on coping that I wasn't really thinking in terms of time, although I did start to panic some time around then. I was able to tell my mother I was panicking and vocalising this was enough to allow me to regain my focus.

About forty-five minutes later I felt Max's head move back up suddenly, after a contraction. The second stage was less than an hour, despite the contractions slowing down towards the end. I feel that I may have been distracted by the phone call from the Supervisor of Midwives during this time. Once his head was out, I was asked to stand and he came out easily with the next contraction. He was slow to breathe, but he still had the cord pulsating, and Val gently encouraged him to breathe and gave him oxygen. Phillippa, who had been with us throughout, rushed upstairs to tell her younger brothers and my father.

Maxwell's breathing gradually improved and he began to open his eyes and move a little. Things improved markedly after his first feed, at just over half an hour old. Tim called an ambulance at Val's request, as her cylinder of oxygen was running low and she wanted another one in reserve. I thought I would have found the presence of two ambulance men hard to cope with, but this was not the case and they seemed intrigued by the whole situation and the way Max was being dealt with in my arms. Also, the front door was wide open, as Phillippa went to let the neighbours know that everything was OK. Again, I would have thought this would have bothered me, but it was really nice to have the sunlight streaming in.

Val felt it would be a good idea for the paediatrician to check Maxwell over, and asked if I would go in the ambulance that was already sitting outside. I was helped out of the pool and really taken aback at the amount of clutter around the room. The placenta came out easily with a push (a totally physiological third stage). Maxwell was fed and the pair of us dressed to make the short journey. I was delighted to be able to walk and went to sort out my contact lenses myself. At hospital, Maxwell was undressed and checked over three times in succession by a nurse, registrar and paediatrician before we returned home. We refused a glucose test. His temperature was still a little

> In healthy, full-term babies hypoglycaemia is rare, so if your baby seems well there is no need to subject it to a blood *glucose test*. Even so, some hospitals have a policy of performing routine glucose tests on all babies under a certain weight regardless of any other clinical indications. The test results are measured against 'standard' charts, many of which are completely out of date, and the result is that many babies are being given unnecessary supplements of formula. This is a devastating policy for mothers who wish to breast-feed since bottles can interfere with the successful establishment of breast-feeding. Babies' blood glucose levels tend to drop in the first hour after birth anyway, when the infant is using all its energy to adjust to life outside the womb. Breast-feeding is the most effective way to 'right' the situation. Keep your baby next to you and feed as often as your baby needs or wants to.

low as the pool wasn't as warm as it could have been, and he was in it after he was born for nearly half an hour.

He fed about half hourly for the first twenty-four hours. I suspect he was slightly hypoglycaemic and that he righted the situation perfectly well himself. He was over his birth weight in four days. He is now seven months, crawling well and still solely breast-fed, except for a small piece of carpet! One day I wondered aloud why Maxwell's birth was so easy when the others had been so difficult. Before I had finished the question, I knew I already had the answer.

Still Hoping For A Miracle

Ailsa Washington

Ben was born after four days of strong contractions; I was weary from lack of sleep and my resistance was low. I needed guidance on relaxation and all the midwife would say was, 'You're coping really well,' when, really, I felt I wasn't coping at all. I had hoped to give birth to him at home, but when the other midwife offered to let me go to hospital so I could get some sleep, I agreed. I was only two centimetres dilated, I felt I was getting nowhere, and there was always the promise that I could go home again in the morning if all was well . . .

On arrival at hospital, I was given pethidine, but then I had an almighty contraction which just went on and on. My husband timed it at seven minutes and the pain was incredible. The midwife examined me, said I was three centimetres and suggested the birthing pool, which really helped. Five hours later, however, I was still only three centimetres. I was feeling very frustrated and getting very angry as I was having all this pain with no gain. I was coerced into having a epidural and I have to admit that, after seventy-eight hours without sleep, it was a relief to relax.

The doctor came to see me the next morning and she said she would like to put a catheter into my uterus which could measure contractions; this would be part of her research. I point blank refused, at which point she said she didn't think I was really contracting anyway. When I heard this I became really angry. What did she know? It was me who had been experiencing this pain since Monday – and it was now Friday. I have since seen on the monitor readout that there were three peaks in five minutes. She went away, angry, and tried to get the consultant to come and force me to change my mind. Apparently he pointed out to her that I could not be made to comply.

In the end I was so desperate that I requested a caesarean. I wish that someone had then explained to me the emotional consequences of a caesarean. Half-way through the operation the epidural wore off. I

Occasionally, women in labour and newborn babies are recruited into research projects for a new procedure, or a new drug. You have an absolute right to refuse to be involved and no pressure should be brought to bear on you to take part. If you feel coerced, you can report the practitioner to the medical ethics committee. Before getting involved in any research project there are certain questions you should ask:

• Has the project been approved by the relevant ethics committee?
• What are all the likely side effects of any drugs being used?
• What effects can the research have on the baby?
• Will there be a long-term follow-up of yourself and/or your baby?
• Will you be told the results of the research?

If you are not satisfied with the answers, you can refuse. Even if you have already accepted, you can change your mind at any time. Groups like AIMS and Consumers for Ethics in Research (CERES) can be helpful in advising you of your rights – see 'Useful Contacts' for details.

could feel them stitching me up. I was shouting at them to stop, but all they did in the end was give me enough pethidine to put me to sleep. After the operation, I really felt I had failed, but the one thing that kept me going was the prospect of breast-feeding my baby. When he was born, we discovered he had a slight cleft palate, but, when he seemed interested, I put him to the breast. He was such a natural and he had a very strong suck. It was such a wonderful feeling, knowing I was nourishing my son. For the rest of the day he fed perfectly, every three or four hours. I felt so proud of myself. Maybe I couldn't deliver him normally, but at least I was feeding him.

That evening, after I had just finished feeding Ben, he seemed fidgety. I offered him my breast again but he refused, so I presumed he had wind. My instinct was that a cuddle would settle him, but when the midwife on duty for the night came to see why he was crying she insisted he was still hungry, and said, 'Let's try him again.' I told her I had just offered him my breast and he had refused, but she dismissed this. I thought that she knew best, so I let her help me. That was my biggest mistake.

For over an hour, she held Ben tightly by the head, forcing him on to my breast. He was screaming by this stage and obviously very distressed. I felt totally helpless. Whatever I said to her, she just ignored me and carried on. It felt as though she was raping me, the way she was pulling at my breast. Thankfully another midwife came to my rescue, took Ben away from her and gave him a bath and a massage to try and calm him down. After his bath, she suggested I try feeding him again, but as soon as I got him into position he just screamed, so she gave him a bottle and he fell asleep.

Right from the start, I felt the first midwife had an attitude problem. I am a nurse myself, and I worked in gynaecology for a long time, so I know about post-operative recovery. The first encounter we had was when she gave me a morphine injection. She stabbed me hard and purged the syringe very fast. I nearly hit the roof. Morphine is an irritant and it burns when it goes into the muscle. For that reason you do it slowly and steadily. The morning after Ben's delivery she came at 5am to do my observations. She told me I should be getting out of bed and sitting in the chair, as I had to get moving. I explained to her that I knew about the importance of early mobilisation and I would be quite willing to get out of bed, at a more reasonable time, and once I was pain free.

Next morning, I tried Ben on the breast again, but he screamed and his arms were pushing me away. I have never felt so rejected in my life. Throughout the day, I kept trying but got the same response. That evening, I gave him a bottle since this awful midwife was back on duty and I didn't want a repeat of the previous night. I was so on edge. Every time Ben murmured I picked him up. The next day, my milk came in and consequently I cried the whole day. In the evening I was so distressed I bleeped my community midwife who came and discharged me from the hospital. As soon as I got home I felt more relaxed. I hired a breast pump, but still tried him at the breast. He just kept pushing me away. For two and a half weeks I tried desperately to feed him, but when he was weighed he had lost 1½ pounds, and the health visitors were starting to take more than a casual interest. I could not cope with any more pressure, so I realised my battle must end.

From then on I put him on the bottle and he seemed a lot happier and put on weight.

I was so full of anger that I wrote to complain and I was informed that the midwife had been suspended, pending an investigation. It was a long time before I heard any more. I became very depressed because of this event. I felt that it had put a barrier between Ben and me. Every time I tried to cuddle him, he would push me away. I felt so rejected and I felt as though he was blaming me. My husband also noticed that Ben and I never cuddled properly and it's only because he persevered with us and supported us that we now have a normal mother and son relationship. Today, he is a very cuddly little boy, but I had to go through lengthy counselling to work through everything that happened. I had so many feelings of anger and hatred towards that midwife and I felt for a long time that justice had not been done.

When I finally became pregnant with my second baby, after two years of trying and eventually resorting to infertility treatment, the first thing I did was contact my community midwives. I knew they would support me in whatever I wanted and I was determined that I did not want a repeat of the last time. I asked the midwives about the prospect of a home birth and they said yes, providing that if they felt it was time to go into hospital, I would consent to go. As I knew them well, and had no desire to put my baby's life at risk, I agreed.

My pregnancy went well, except when they began to suspect gestational diabetes and sent me for two starving blood sugar tests, not very pleasant when you are pregnant. Both tests were negative, but when I went to the doctor he suggested that perhaps he should do another one, just to be sure. I now suspect that this was a ploy to get me to have a hospital birth. I refused, saying that surely if I was going to be diabetic, it would have shown up by now. The doctor's reply was, 'Yes, you're probably right.'

I went into labour amidst a house of chaos: we were decorating our bedroom, ready for the baby coming. I was two and a half weeks early. My waters broke at 4am – which was totally unexpected. I decided to have a good breakfast and started taking my homeopathic remedies. For the rest of the day I felt nothing except period type pains. I had lots of family around me and I felt quite relaxed. At about 9pm, I started to get stronger pains. I called the midwives and, naturally, the midwife on call that night was the only one who had doubts about me having a home birth. She tried to talk me into going to the hospital, but I refused. It was so unfortunate that this particular midwife was on call, because from that moment on I started to feel uptight.

She did come to see me, but we just rubbed each other up the wrong way. She kept telling my husband I had backache pain when I was feeling all the pain at the front. So I said to her that I didn't have backache pain. In spite of this, I heard her whisper to my husband, 'I know she says she hasn't got backache pain, but I know she has.' I suddenly felt furious, and I yelled at her. She responded to my fury with sarcasm, 'OK, Ailsa, you can have whatever pain you want.' There were other incidents. The cylinder of Entenox wasn't working properly, but she told me it was my fault for not breathing it in properly. We were getting through a canister every fifteen minutes. To make things worse, when a replacement arrived that was broken as well.

I felt out of control and under a lot of pressure to go into hospital as it was nearly twenty-four hours since my waters had broken. I finally went to the hospital at 8.30am and was greeted by my favourite midwife. When I saw her I just burst into tears and kept repeating, 'Why is my body failing me?' She tried to reassure me and make me feel better. She said, 'Look, Ailsa, you got pregnant and that is incredible.' But because I had to take Clomid to help me get pregnant, this only made me feel worse – chalk up another failure for my body. Apart from that, she was brilliant. She calmed me down and prepared me for the fact that I was probably going to have another caesarean.

I had an epidural so I could rest, but I sat as upright as possible so the baby would come down. However, the longer the labour went on, the further back up the baby went, so it was decided that it would be best if I had a caesarean. They topped up my epidural and I started to throw up. I continued being sick all the way through. Once again the epidural wore off half way through, and this time the operation took longer, as they couldn't stop the bleeding. Luke came out sucking desperately on his finger, so as soon as I was recovered enough from the operation I fed him. He took to it in exactly the same way as Ben had, but this time I was ready for any interference from anybody.

I think everybody on the ward knew of my past experience and, while the managers and midwives kept coming up and seeing if everything was to my satisfaction, nobody tried to tell me what to do. Two days after the operation I went home – before the operation I made them agree to letting me go home when I felt ready.

When I was at home I felt really weary. I was very anaemic, but I was enjoying every second of breast-feeding; it was the most fantastic feeling in the world. I still feel the same way eight months later and even though I'm hoping for a miracle – another baby and a natural birth – I never take what I have now for granted.

Is Anyone Out There Listening?

Pat Thomas

I've spent my whole life listening to other people. First as a dutiful daughter and attentive student. Later as a researcher, journalist and psychotherapist. Later still, as the wife of a man whose communication skills left something to be desired, and the mother of an articulate and intellectually precocious toddler. Listening is a skill. You can get it down to a fine art if you practise. You can learn to listen to words as well as beyond words. You can even 'listen' to bodies and facial expressions. Listening. It's not the simple, passive activity of the powerless which it is made out to be.

What's all this got to do with having babies? More than I might have realised five years ago. I've told my story before – in the fluid, chatty atmosphere of groups of women and in the stark, irretrievable black and white of print. The birth of my son and the events surrounding it are burnt into my brain. They have made me who I am and yet, as I grow and change, these events, or rather the way I perceive them, shifts. Events and emotions which seemed so prominent in my early experience of motherhood move in and out of focus. Same events, different perspective.

So how do I tell it this time? What feels important? It dawned on me early one morning when my son had awakened me for the second time to adjust his covers. Hot with adrenaline, brittly awake and wondering why I ever wanted a child in the first place, my mind began to spin. Among the most important aspects of pregnancy for me had been negotiating the gap between listening and speaking up, and weathering the soul destroying impact of not being heard.

As a good listener, pregnancy was the single most startling experience of my life. It was when I first discovered I had something to say. I read all the books (another way of listening) by Sheila Kitzinger and Janet Balaskas and was grateful for their encouragement to 'speak up'. The first person I spoke to was my partner.

'*I'm pregnant.*'

Actually, I said it through tears. At the time I didn't understand why I was crying, but I do now. The implication of those two little words, the effect it would have on my life, was simply enormous. Jay's response was silence, then ambivalence bordering on disinterest. It lasted for months. He told none of his friends, nor did he tell his family. I told the people I knew and loved and met their individual responses, ranging from 'How wonderful' to, curiously, 'Are you going to keep it?', as best I could. I'd heard of mothers not acknowledging their pregnancies until some ante-natal test or other confirmed the baby was 'perfect', but even after he saw proof of his perfect creation on the ultrasound screen, Jay remained silent, and seemed resentful and defended against the mention of babies or baby books. When I was nearly five months gone, I practically had to threaten to leave him before he would telephone his family to tell them the news.

'*I'd like to give birth at home.*'

There was the now familiar silence from my partner. My GP responded though: 'Sorry, we don't do those. Here's a list of hospitals in the area for you to consider.' Did she hear me? I walked away, clutching the list, utterly dejected. I hadn't just requested a home birth, I'd told this woman something about myself. Seven words this time, but again the message was enormous. Seven words which also said: I care about my health and my baby's health; I will not simply be directed into the system (I'm not even sure if I trust the 'system'); I want to give birth in familiar surroundings with few interventions; I am an individual. Didn't this deserve some respect?

The community midwife (whose brief is, after all, to support women in their choices) didn't hear me either. She dropped in on me one day and said she didn't like doing home births (not encouraging news), especially with first time mothers. 'It's a matter of obstetrics, dear. You see?' What on earth did that mean? Was the word 'obstetrics' meant to frighten me? Actually it did, but not for the reasons she probably hoped. Obstetrics is a medical speciality – the care of women with complicated pregnancies. I didn't fall into that category, and it certainly was scary to imagine what kind of care I might receive at the hands of a man (probably) whose job it is to treat unhealthy women. I was healthy. My baby was healthy. Too bad the midwife wasn't. Today, I can chuckle at her parting shot.

She apologised for coming to my home alone and said, astonishingly, 'I usually bring another midwife with me. That way, if there is a dispute over what's been said, I have someone to back me up. Pregnant women don't always *listen* very well.'

Actually, I think pregnant women listen too well, and usually to the wrong people. In order of importance I recommend pregnant women should listen to the following people: 1) themselves and 2) their babies. Everything else is just noise. Tales told by idiots. Sound and fury signifying nothing, or, if you prefer, as one modern author calls it, 'Birthcrap'.

Somewhere around three months I stopped listening and began learning how to speak. It was a painful process for a lifelong listener. '*I want a home birth*' took up a lot of my time (though the process was helped along by transferring to a helpful GP for the duration of my pregnancy).

My mother's response was silence, uncharacteristic for her, but

---

Some women who request home births are automatically transferred to other GPs' practices for the duration of their ante-natal care. Some other GPs are more irrational about it and there has been a great deal of concern expressed by groups like AIMS, the NCT and the Association of Community Health Councils about the number of women who are being struck off for wanting a home birth. Of course, if your GP strikes you off simply because of this, you are probably better off without him or her, but it can be quite a blow to your confidence. At all other times your GP is not obliged to give you any reason for, or warning of, his intent to strike you off, but once you have registered with him for your ante-natal care, you cannot be struck off without your consent or without the GP first applying to the Family Health Services Association (FHSA) for permission (and he will need a good reason).

Likewise, if your GP is not on the obstetrics list (indicating that he or she has had some training in obstetrics) you may wish to transfer to one who is – GPs who are not on the obstetrics list should not be providing ante-natal care – though even here levels of skill and care can vary enormously. If you wish to transfer out of your GP's surgery, you do not have to wait for a referral (or to be struck off). You have the right to do this at any time, and you do not have to provide any reason for doing so. You can get a list of GPs in your area from your local library or FHSA.

she quickly reverted to type: 'Are you doing this because you can't afford proper care?' She's an American, so her bottom line is always money. That the American medical system regards midwifery and home birth as some kind of second-rate compromise is both sad and shocking.

Then there was the classic parental question – 'Are you going to get married?' I told her that focusing on parenthood seemed a daunting enough job for the moment. I just wanted to put my energy into that, and not into plans for a wedding. She began to make the plans for me (or herself?) anyway – without my knowledge or consent. At thirty-two years of age, this was a 'favour' I could do without.

'When will you be getting married?'

'*I don't want to get married.*'

'Summer weddings are always nice.'

'*I don't want to get married.*'

'But I've made plans.'

'*I DO NOT WANT TO GET MARRIED!*'

I tried to shrug it off, but the truth is, my unexpected pregnancy, along with learning to speak up for myself, caused a rift between myself and my mother which has never really healed. She has never acknowledged her status as grandmother (a role too frightening for her to contemplate) and never seen her grandson and we are all the poorer for it. As for getting married, well, let's just say I should have listened to myself a bit more carefully.

Out went the happy fantasy of sharing this time with my mother. We had less in common than at any other time in our lives. She hated pregnancy and birth and resented the demands of motherhood. I found it, and still do, exhilarating, challenging and surprisingly fulfilling. She feels more secure when things remain stationary. I try to stay open to the cyclical turning of Life's wheel, even when it's taking me in a direction I'm unsure of. Happily, there were enough 'mother substitutes' in the world of pregnancy, childbirth and mothering to sustain me. They appeared in the obvious forms of Kitzinger and Balaskas, as well as in the women at AIMS (The Association for Improvements in the Maternity Services) and, curiously, even in some of the men I met: Michel Odent, Yehudi Gordon and Norman Stannard. OK. So maybe I was privileged. More importantly, years of journalistic training had taught me how to seek out the information and support I needed – but, like listening, it's a skill anybody can acquire.

My healthy baby and I ambled along happily enough through all this. Whatever was going on outside me, inside I was content and enjoying myself. I confess I loved being pregnant. The night I first felt Alexander move, I was co-facilitating a women's dream group and I was so knocked-out that I had to withdraw quietly from the proceedings. I enjoyed eating what I liked, when I liked. As women we're taught, from an early age, to deny and control our bodies, but I found the inevitability of pregnancy very reassuring. Life was growing inside me and there was nothing I could do to stop it. This was a creative act that would reach its own conclusion without any conscious act of will on my part.

There were also breaks in our increasingly stormy relationship. I can recall lazy afternoons when Jay would read *Just So Stories* to my ever-increasing bump. I genuinely enjoyed our trip up to the Cerne Abbas Giant (an ancient fertility symbol carved into a hillside – you can see his penis for miles!) when I was eight months pregnant. Jay was in his element and laughed as he regaled passers by. 'It works!' he shouted to their curious smiles. In these brief moments, I enjoyed a much needed taste of 'happy families'.

Hardened feminists should cover their eyes at this point because, social connotations aside, I also loved being barefoot. In fact, being barefoot and pregnant was quite an important part of my process. Both feet firmly on the ground. Finding my feet. After years of wearing high heels, they were quite a revelation. Moving slowly. Finally coming to terms with the fact that my natural rhythm, physically, mentally and emotionally, is quite slow was also a difficult, but valuable experience.

As it turned out, I needed both feet firmly on the ground, because at 32 weeks my baby turned into the breech position. Although the community midwives said there was nothing to worry about, they quietly set about sabotaging my plans for birth at home and transferred me, without my knowledge, to consultant care. I only found out about it when I showed up at the clinic for a 34-week check-up and was greeted with 'What are you doing here! You're not supposed to be here!' Anyone would think I was carrying an infectious disease rather than a baby.

As the breech persisted, I had a harder time making people hear me.

'*I want a trial of labour.*'

'Of course you can have a trial of labour – in hospital.'

'*No. At home.*'

One day, some of the midwives at the local clinic hustled me into a side room. To me they were suddenly like menacing witches. 'You'll never be allowed to have a home birth now,' cautioned one. 'You're lucky to have been allowed a home birth at all,' and then adding insult to injury – '*at your age*,' snided another. 'I'm afraid you'll have to do what the doctor says,' remarked the third. I left the 'meeting' in tears. A few years later, I was surprised to see this occasion recorded in my case notes as 'Patricia has been reassured . . .' *Reassured?* Were they serious or just plain stupid? My call to the hospital a few days later to check the policy on breech deliveries was recorded in a similarly snotty and grudging manner: '[Midwives] apparently told her (*so client says*) that she has to have an elective caesarean section.' I recommend every mother get hold of her case notes and read them. They can be rollicking good fiction. Sadly, they also show how inept most healthcare practitioners are at listening.

At 37 weeks my consultant said, 'Frankly, if you don't consent to have an elective caesarean next week, I will withdraw my care. Then where will you be?' '*Better off,*' I thought, but said nothing and once again left in tears. Let's be clear. I didn't want his care in the first place. It was foisted on me by midwives so unskilled in almost every department that it was a toss-up as to who would provide the most inappropriate care, them or the obstetrician. Also, how truly 'elective' would an elective caesarean be, given the amount of emotional blackmail involved. True to his word, the consultant withdrew his care.

'*I want a trial of labour. At home.*'

I said it so many times, occasionally very loudly, that eventually someone heard. First, it was my partner, whose involvement thus far in my plans for a home birth had been to speak to a woman he knew, who had a friend, whose sister's cousin's wife had a home birth and her baby needed to be transferred to hospital care (or something equally convoluted). It was never revealed why, but he used this as irrefutable proof that our baby would be born dead or damaged. (Years later, when we divorced, he would still be claiming that I tried to kill Alexander by wanting to have him at home.) However, one day, unexpectedly, touched by my increasing distress, he

The Access to Health Records Act of 1990 says that, from November 1991, everyone has the right to copies of their case notes. The Data Protection Act gives consumers the right to all computerised information about them. These two things are valid for users of the maternity services, since medical records are kept both in longhand and on computer. Your right to your records applies to any records your GP holds, as well as those held by the hospital. Many hospitals and clinics operate a scheme where mothers carry their own case notes. If you are on a scheme like this, you have a right to take copies of your notes, and it is advisable to do so. If you are carrying a 'smart card' – a computerised card, the size of a credit card, which stores all your maternity records on it – you still have the right to all the information it holds.

During the course of your pregnancy, and for forty days after the last recorded entry, you can obtain copies of your case notes for the price of photocopying and postage. After that, you can be asked to pay a statutory fee of £10. Many hospitals try to jack the price up, showing a total disregard for the law. You may find it difficult to get them to comply with the Act. In cases like this, you can try to get your local CHC to intervene on your behalf.

You do not have to give a reason for wanting your case notes, passing them on to you does not depend on the consultant's approval, and you should not be asked to 'prove' your identity through a commissioner of oaths. Any reasonable form of proof of identity should be acceptable.

Why is it important to get your case notes? you might wonder. First of all, you would be surprised at how other people interpret your remarks and the course of your pregnancy. Even women who have the most straightforward births can learn a lot about this period of their lives from reading their case notes, and it can be particularly useful if you are contemplating having another baby. If you have had a traumatic birth experience, it is very important that you get hold of your case notes before you make a complaint (and before you tell anyone you are going to make a complaint). There have been studies to show that case notes of less than straightforward births have a strange habit of 'getting lost' – making legitimate complaints very hard to pursue.

phoned the NCT for advice, and they gave him the number of an independent midwifery practice with experience of breech deliveries at home. It was the kindest thing he ever did for me and I'll always be grateful. Having engaged these two powerful women, I found that things began to fall into place.

They read my birth plan – the first ones to do so as far as I knew. They talked to my GP, the hospital and my partner on my behalf. By 38 weeks, I felt a great weight had been lifted from my shoulders. They listened to me as I recounted the difficulties I'd had being heard, and carried the burden for me. They were there on the other end of the phone when, ten days before Alexander's birth, my father died and I wasn't sure what to do. Should I go ahead and grieve his loss now, or file it away and get on with the equally demanding business of birth? Which of these legitimate impulses do I follow?

In fact, my father's death crystallised certain things for me. Pregnancy, and now the impending birth of my son, had hurled me into the unknown in many ways. First there was this speaking-up stuff. Then there was the matter of learning to set boundaries and prioritise. All of a sudden, it wasn't so simple and I didn't have much of a role model to refer to. My own mother always believed that as long as she was happy and fulfilled – 'doing her own thing' it was called when I was growing up – I would also be happy, but the feminism of the day played a cruel trick on us both. Neglecting the needs and experiences of mothers – 90 per cent of women, after all – has left a yawning chasm in our psyches. If this is what women are built to do, and we deny the process, where does that leave us? My mother's philosophy also failed to acknowledge that a mother needs to be happy in the same room – or at least the same metaphorical space – or it doesn't work. Mum was happy doing her own thing, but she was never at home.

For myself, I noticed very early on how many things I had to negotiate now, just to make a single choice, and how often my needs seemed to conflict with my baby's. By this time it was clear Alexander had 'chosen', by whatever unfathomable, primal process, to be a breech baby. Maybe he misheard all those Beach Boys records I listened to as a girl in California (no, no, darling boy, they were singing about *beach* babies, not *breech* babies). Whatever it was, his choice was in direct conflict with my need to have a straightforward, non-interventionist birth at home. How do we resolve this one? 'Our children don't always do what we want them to,' said the very wise doctor who, three times, tried and failed to turn him. Amen. And maybe it was a gift to learn this so early. I noticed this conflict elsewhere, too. For instance, ante-natally: some of the procedures (CVS, amniocentesis and possibly ultrasound) which are used to detect abnormality, and thus reassure mothers (and, I suspect, doctors) that their babies are perfect, can end up damaging babies. Another example: the more effective the pharmacological method of pain relief, the greater the risk of harmful side effects for the baby. Some mothers can successfully shut their minds to the conflicts, but we listeners aren't built that way.

Labour was another surprise. I knew it was near because I'd had Braxton Hicks-like contractions and a niggling lower backache for a week. I'd lost my interest in sex and spicy food – both potent labour inducers – a couple of weeks before, but one day, impatient to move things along, I found myself masturbating on and off all day. It must have done the trick. That night, unable to sleep (again) I lay in bed trying to figure out whether I should go to the loo (again) or whether I could hold on and stay horizontal (my then favourite position) for just a little longer. I decided to wait. Ooops! Suddenly there was a pop and a dramatic gush of water.

'*Jay, wake up! I need a towel.*'

He didn't hear me the first couple of times and I don't think he quite comprehended what was happening. He stumbled to the bathroom, muttering about being in the middle of a dream ('*Eternally,*' I thought to myself) and returned with the towel.

This was it. My contractions established themselves soon afterwards and were enough to take my breath away by the 12-hour mark. The TENS machine broke down. '*Never mind. It was useless anyway.*' To my partner this was irrelevant. We'd paid for the damn thing, after all. So, at ten o'clock at night, he engaged himself in one of those pointless, heroic struggles to get the company which supplied it to send us another one in a taxi (they did, as well). '*It doesn't matter,*' I said. But my midwife, who had guessed the score, winked at me. 'It'll keep him busy.' '*Hallelujah,*' I thought.

Later, I wanted a bath. I needed to be in the water and feel some heat on my back. I called for my partner to help.

'*Could you squeeze the water over the small of my back?*'

He began to rub the sponge on my back. It felt excruciating, like broken glass on my sensitive skin.

'*No. Just hold it above my back and squeeze the water out.*'

He continued to rub. 'Like that?'

'*No. Don't touch me.*'

'What do you mean?' I can't describe how much I *did not* want to be having this conversation, so typical of our communication difficulties, with him at that moment.

'*Dip the sponge in the water, then hold it above my back and dribble the water on me.*'

'How far above your back?'

'*Christ almighty, Jay! Just a few inches.*'

'How many is a few? Three, six, ten?' Clearly, by this point, all loving empathy had gone bye-bye.

'*Forget it.*'

That was pretty much the end of our contact during the rest of my labour. He slumped off to watch TV and I stepped out of the bath and wrapped up. Still needing to at least hear running water, I turned on the taps and flushed the toilet repeatedly. It honestly helped.

Twenty-four hours and nothing. At last check, I was hardly two centimetres dilated, yet my contractions were intense, often double-peaked and without much of a break in between. '*Are you sure this isn't "true" labour?*' I built myself a small, womb-like tent of towels and dressing gowns. I was on all fours underneath it, warm and moaning through each contraction. I talked to my baby. He was fine. I was fine too, but I couldn't shake the feeling that things weren't going very well.

'*Something's not right.*'

I said this to my midwife. She listened and agreed. By myself, without any pressure, I decided to go to hospital (so much for us crazy mothers persisting in our crazy ideas to the detriment of our babies). I was totally worn out and my midwife suggested I consider an epidural so I could get some sleep. If things were progressing better after that, I could carry on in hospital or come home again. She left to talk to my partner.

'*I want to go to hospital.*'

Wouldn't you know it. After seven months of opposition, my man spent the next half hour trying to convince me to stay put just a little bit longer. What can I say? It's a power thing. Men, doctors, really anybody to whom society assigns the role of being powerful and in charge, seem to find it hard to step out of that role. The dances they do to remain in charge are both comical and scary. They don't even mind contradicting themselves if they can, in the final analysis, claim to have 'won' or influenced the outcome.

'*I WANT TO GO TO HOSPITAL. NOW.*'

The ambulance ride was agonising. '*Can I sit upright?*' 'Sorry, it's against safety rules.' Until you've experienced labour pains in an upright position and labour pains when you're flat on your back, you wouldn't believe the difference. My advice to any woman is be smart – stay upright.

The acute staff at the hospital were marvellous. The registrar was so sympathetic (I believe genuinely so) to the enormous psychological and emotional shift that had to take place in me before I could come to hospital. The anaesthetist was kind, calm, skilled and efficient. Everyone avoided the c-word for an hour or so. Eventually, it was the registrar who said it: 'I really think you are going to need a caesarean.'

It's hard to describe what followed. I completely lost control. I wasn't able to move my legs, but I flailed my arms and head about, like a trapped, terrified, wounded animal, and howled, '*No! No!*' I can't remember ever sobbing so deeply. My partner, shocked by this unrestrained display of raw emotions, moved away. My midwife grabbed my arms and spoke deliberately and firmly to me. I looked her straight in the eye and slowly began to calm down. We both knew it was necessary – after twenty-eight hours of labour I was only three centimetres dilated, and I had a large (9lb 6oz, as it turned out) breech baby – but putting it in words was like plunging a dagger into my heart.

At 6.05am, nearly thirty hours after my waters had broken, and with his father beside me, Alexander Jordan was pulled from me. I still don't consider it a birth. He opened one eye and grunted, as if to say, 'What's all the fuss?' (he's always been a cool kid). He was the spitting image of his father. The moment I saw him, I knew he had been born the way he needed to be born; he was a big baby with a large head and, even delivering him this way, the registrar had a job getting him out. An hour later we were still in a recovery room. My move to the post-natal ward had been delayed because of a bomb threat outside the hospital. I was grateful for the privacy, especially since Alexander was busy teaching me how to breast-feed – the first of many profound lessons he has given me.

I made a deal with my midwife that the moment I could walk to the toilet she would take the extremely uncomfortable catheter out. I was up and walking within eight hours. Some of the staff were so amazed that they refused to believe I'd had an epidural. When I said, '*I'm hungry*,' they refused me food on the grounds that, to be mobile so quickly, I must have had a general anaesthetic. I wondered to myself, '*Do women really tell lies about which anaesthetic they've had in order to get hospital food?*' Since my midwife and my partner had gone home, I had to make a real fuss before someone took the time to examine my records and cold scrambled eggs and toast duly appeared. I left hospital the next day.

As far as Alexander's birth was concerned, I knew I had done the 'right' thing, and yet, it was a couple of years before I started to feel 'right' about it. I can certainly identify with the American comedian Roseanne, who, in reply to a question about why she was having yet another baby, said that she was going to keep on doing it 'until I get it *right*'. That's how I feel. One day I want another shot at it.

Why am I telling this story this way? For many reasons. Firstly, I feel obliged to put myself on the line in the same way as I have asked other mothers to do for this book. I often wonder about the women who write books about how wonderful childbirth is. Do they really have perfect husbands? Angelic mothers? Obliging children? Orgasmic births? We'll never know because there is a line which 'experts' of any kind are reluctant to cross. Personally I doubt it. It's easy to write about how birth should be, it's harder to write about how birth is.

Secondly, there is a lot of talk these days about choice, but making choices in childbirth is not like choosing between brands of cola or soap powder. Mothers make their choices based on many different, and often very personal, aspects of their lives. I was astonished at how much opposition I received to what was a very important, and in the end quite reasonable, choice. Except for my mother and husband, I will never know for sure what kind of lives these opposers had, what their education and training was and how it affected the way they treated women like myself. What I do know is that none of them stopped to consider what kind of life I had, why it was so important to feel supported, or what effect their opposition would have on my pregnancy, labour and the rest of my life. Motherhood is tough enough without having to start it as an emotional wreck. I'll remember the opposers forever and it won't be with kind hearts and coronets.

Women never forget their birth experiences. Not ever. Not even for a moment. I'm a listener, but in the process I also learned to speak up. Some women who don't, fare a lot worse and carry the burden of their birth experiences, in relative silence, with pain, bewilderment and shame. I know. They have come to my home and cried and cried and cried, and, just when they think they are all cried out, they cry some more. Birth should be an empowering process. In order for women to be empowered they must be listened to and trusted. Their expertise about their own needs, and the tightropes which they walk to accommodate so many different people and situations, must be respected. It's interesting that women are encouraged to listen to and trust their practitioners, come what may. Practitioners, on the other hand, are taught not to listen to or trust the women in their care (whether we like to acknowledge it or not, studies shows that this is a specific problem between medical practitioners and female patients – male patients, at least, get a hearing).

One day, in a more rational world, it will be the other way around. Scepticism, and the profound ability which pregnant women have to disrupt the status quo, will be admirable qualities. Ante-natal education will nurture these qualities and take every opportunity to remind women of their rights: to find out for themselves and make decisions based on the evidence; to change practitioners at any time; to seek a second opinion; to follow the dictates of their lives and their own individual pregnancies; to change their minds without fear of reprisal or derision; to complain if necessary. On the other hand, practitioners will be taught to listen to and trust women, their bodies and their babies and otherwise back-off until they're needed. Until then, I hope more women will begin to tell their birth stories and not worry too much if they ruffle the surface of our happy, and somewhat one-dimensional, perception of pregnancy and birth. There will always be someone willing to listen.

Birth Basics

The stories in this book give rise to some questions about basic and routine procedures in modern maternity care. The information in this section is not meant to be exhaustive. Instead it relates to some of the specific issues raised throughout this book.

Artificial Rupture of the Membranes (ARM)

There is *never* any indication for breaking a woman's waters, otherwise known as artificial rupture of the membranes. Research shows that it will only speed up your labour by two hours at the most. In spite of this, nearly 40 per cent of all maternity units do it routinely. To perform an ARM, an instrument which looks like a crochet hook will be pushed into the cervix to puncture the amniotic sac and release the water which surrounds the baby. Our doctors and midwives do it because they've always done it and there has been little or no formal evaluation of whether it really is helpful, though it can have serious side effects for you and your baby. ARM is often presented as a kind of benign trade off. A midwife or doctor might tell you that if you let them do this, you can avoid other forms of induction.

Certainly with ARM the resulting contractions will not be as intense or painful, but it is worth considering keeping your membranes intact and waiting for them to rupture spontaneously. As long as your membranes are intact your baby is protected. When your membranes are ruptured, there is the possibility that the umbilical cord will drop down between the baby's head and your pelvic bone and get crushed during contractions. This is called cord prolapse. By keeping your membranes intact, you are first and foremost protecting your baby from this possibility and the brain damage which results from it.

When your membranes are ruptured you are at greater risk from infection and so is your baby. The membranes provide a sterile environment for your baby. Once they are broken a kind of unspoken countdown begins and labour must be kept moving along at a pace. If your labour slows down, you will be put on an oxytocin drip. In hospital the likelihood of getting an infection is also greatly increased due to routine vaginal examinations.

According to an NCT survey, the length of labour is less important to women than the support they receive during it, the amount of control they feel they have over the proceedings, and that they maintain their ability to cope with contractions through their own efforts. Once you have ARM you become a 'patient' and many of these things will be lost to you.

Assisting Labour – Episiotomy, Ventouse, Forceps

There are several ways of assisting labour. The single most common procedure is *episiotomy* – a cut made in the perineum, between the opening of the vagina and the anus. There is no doubt that episiotomy is grossly overused. In some hospitals episiotomy rates can be as high as 90 per cent, and throughout the country the average rate is 70 per cent, the majority of these being performed on first time mothers. Do more than two-thirds of women really need this kind of radical intervention to get their babies out?

Usually it is not the cut but the stitching which causes problems later on. Often students are given women to sew up, so that they can 'get some practice in'. The results can be badly stitched, painful perineums which never really feel right again and make everything, from sitting down to having sex, painful. You can insist that a qualified midwife, and not a student, stitches you up. Episiotomy can be avoided by not accepting an induction or acceleration of labour, by allowing your epidural to wear off before the 'pushing' stage begins, and then by not entering into vigorous pushing in order to get your baby out.

Ventouse or vacuum extraction is a method by which a small suction cup, made either of rubber or metal, is attached to the baby's head and used either to rotate the baby into a more favourable position for birth or to pull the baby out. Interestingly, women who have epidurals often need some help, either rotating the baby or getting the baby out. It's not just that they can't feel to push, but the epidural can leave the pelvic floor muscles limp and ineffective, unable to perform their task of rotating the baby for birth. There is a higher rate of malpositioned babies with epidurals.

Ventouse can be a very useful tool in an emergency and does not seem to cause the terrible damage which forceps do. If you have ventouse you are also less likely to need an episiotomy, though it is sometimes performed on a 'just in case' basis since ventouse has a very high failure rate – between 10 and 20 per cent. If the ventouse fails, your practitioner may go on to try forceps. If these fail, the next step is a caesarean.

Forceps are spoon-shaped metal blades which are inserted into the vagina until they grip the sides of the baby's head. Once they are in place, your practitioner will pull the baby out. Forceps are associated with all kinds of problems, including damage to the baby's head as well as to the mother's internal organs. You will need an episiotomy if your practitioner uses forceps. The failure rate with forceps is around 10 per cent. When a forceps delivery fails, you will be given a caesarean and may find you have to deal with profound feelings of failure as well as a higher degree of physical trauma.

You can avoid all this by staying upright and working with your contractions and gravity instead of against them. Methods of fetal extraction like these should be reserved for women and babies who are genuinely in need.

Birth Plans

Birth plans are now so much a part of the fabric of pregnancy and birth that we seldom, if ever, question why they have become necessary in the first place. Unfortunately, the birth plan arose from the negative experiences of women who had interventions without being consulted. They are the almost inevitable result of the communication breakdown between women and their carers. In the past, women have said that they have asked for specific kinds of care and a wider range of choices, but were never given these things; practitioners said they didn't provide choice because women never asked for it. Birth plans are a way of articulating, in an 'official', black and white way, the kind of care you would wish to receive – and your wishes should be respected at all times.

Some doctors and midwives resent birth plans. They feel they are an affront to their professional status and dislike being dictated to by a 'patient'. But pregnant women aren't really 'patients'. Because they are not sick, pregnant women have needs which are very different from other people who are being cared for within the hospital system. Many of these centre around the need for birth to be more of a partnership.

One problem with birth plans is that it can be very easy for everyone to start believing that they are written in stone and this, in turn, will make it harder for you to remain flexible. Since flexibility is one of the keys to a more satisfying birth experience, it may be more useful to think in terms of a 'birth guideline'. You can alter your birth guideline at any time if, for instance, your baby turns into a less than favourable position and you need to think about alternative methods of delivery. Equally, you may wish to stray from your planned course of 'no pain relief' because your labour is longer or more intense than you anticipated. You should be able to do all of these things without feeling guilty, or as if you have 'failed'.

Caesareans

The caesarean rate in Britain is 15 per cent and rising, and yet research has shown that more than half of these operations are totally unnecessary. All the available data suggests that the rise in caesarean rates has not contributed to the fall in baby deaths and that any rate above 7 per cent ceases to improve or make any difference in the overall outcome of labour.

Caesareans are routinely performed for breech babies, and twins. The other most common reasons for performing a caesarean are 'failure to progress' and 'fetal distress'. It cannot be stressed enough that 'failure to progress' is a subjective opinion and not a medical diagnosis. Because so many hospitals apply time limits to labour, more and more women are being told that they are not progressing when, in fact, their labours are progressing at the level which is right for them. First time mothers are the ones most likely to be told that they are not progressing quickly enough (and indeed first time mothers are the ones on the receiving end of most of the routine interventions used in labour). Some labours – particularly first labours – are simply long.

There is no evidence to show that long labours lead to fetal distress. In fact, there is evidence to show that a period of labour is beneficial for babies, since the stress hormones released during labour help dry out the baby's lungs and prepare it for life outside the womb.

It is important to remember that a caesarean is not a 'section' but an 'operation' and mothers who have caesareans experience all the usual side effects of major abdominal surgery. These include increased susceptibility to depression, pain, increased use of drugs post-natally – including antibiotics, analgesics, anti-depressants and tranquillisers (all of which can enter the baby's system via the mother's breast-milk) – and increased risk of infection. Because it is a major surgery there is a much increased risk of dying from the procedure – up to six times greater than those delivering vaginally. Women who have caesareans also appear to have greater difficulty resuming their sex lives.

In addition, caesareans have implications for future fertility and pregnancies. Women who have caesareans are less likely to go on to have another child. This may be in part because of the secondary infertility which can be the result of caesareans. Since many hospitals believe 'once a caesarean, always a caesarean' you may have a battle on your hands to have a vaginal delivery next time around (see **Vaginal Birth After Caesarean**).

Unless absolutely necessary, a caesarean is an aggressive 'solution' to labour difficulties.

Consultant Obstetricians

Consultants are supposed to be specialists in abnormal pregnancies. So why do they so often end up looking after healthy women with healthy babies? Even the most recent government reports on the maternity services recognise this. *Changing Childbirth*, the government's mandate for making the maternity services more 'mother centred', has recommended that consultants should restrict their activity to those women who have complications which could result in health problems for their babies, or which may complicate labour – and yet consultants seem to be involved in every step of the birth process.

Because they learn about birth from the perspective of all the things that can go wrong, they are in the habit of looking for problems. Often they find them where none exist, and the remedies they apply can cause more complications than they solve. The consultant obstetrician will set the policy for his particular team at the hospital. So, if he believes that birth is inherently a dangerous process, or that it is 'only safe in retrospect' (something so many consultants say), this will be the point of view from which your ante-natal care will be structured. Some women may feel more secure under the care of a consultant, but it has to be said that the majority of women could never see a consultant, and it would make not a jot of difference to the outcome of their pregnancies. The irony, of course, is that women seldom see the consultant they are booked under. Usually they see a medical student called a senior house officer (SHO) or the registrar.

Epidurals

When it comes to obliterating any hint of pain, the epidural is the one form of pain relief that does live up to its promise. As with all drugs, however, there is a price to pay.

The drug used in epidurals is a cocaine derivative, so of course it will have side effects for you and your baby. To expect anything else would be naïve. Many women will be told that the epidural is completely safe and does not cross the placenta. Yet even the manufacturers of Bupivacaine, one of the most widely used products in epidural anaesthesia, are compelled to warn on the label that the anaesthetic 'rapidly crosses the placenta' and, in addition, can result in (among other things) long-term paralysis, lowered blood pressure, urinary and fecal incontinence, headache, backache, slowing of labour and increased incidence of forceps delivery.

Babies born to mothers who have epidurals may have more difficulty sucking and tend to be less alert and more 'fussy' in the weeks after birth. This is likely to be because their bodies are under enormous strain, trying to rid themselves of a powerful narcotic. Their muscles will be more limp, their bodies generally have less tone and occasionally they may be born with a slight blue tint, due to being starved of oxygen.

For women, the most well-known, and well-documented side effects of the epidural are headaches, resulting from dural tap, and backaches. Evidence about dural taps is quite clear. Evidence for backache as a result of an epidural is less so. What we do know is that 15 per cent of women will develop backache after giving birth, regardless of what kind of pain relief they have, but it has been estimated that around 60 per cent of women who have an epidural will still be suffering from backache eight years, or more, after the procedure.

The name epidural describes several different kinds of spinal anaesthesia. A *spinal block* is a single injection of local anaesthetic, given between two vertebrae in the lower spine. It is quicker to perform than an epidural, but the effect does not last as long. Some hospitals still use this routinely instead of an epidural. Others reserve it for situations where there is a need of an anaesthetic but there is no time to site an epidural, or where a general anaesthetic is inadvisable. Another single injection method is the *pudendal block*, where the anaesthetic is injected inside the vagina to numb the area prior to delivery. The *epidural* which most women know is injected in-between the vertebrae in the lower back and, depending on where it is sited, can provide total loss of feeling anywhere from the breasts downwards. A *mobile epidural* or *walking epidural* numbs the abdomen but leaves the mother's legs free to move, which sounds ideal. However, the opiate used in mobile epidurals is different from that in other epidurals and has not been subjected to much rigorous testing. Also, women have fallen using the mobile epidural, since it is sometimes hard to know when one's feet are firmly on the ground.

To site an epidural, your skin will be disinfected and a local anaesthetic given to numb your lower back. A thin tube called a cannula will be inserted and the anaesthetic will be fed through this throughout some or all of your labour. A catheter will also be inserted into your urethra to drain off urine.

In about 8 per cent of cases the drug does not take effect – nobody knows why. Once you have an epidural you must have the whole range of other interventions, including electronic fetal monitoring (EFM), to monitor the baby's heartbeat which can be affected by the drug, and to gauge the strength and consistency of your contractions. This will be the only way to judge how your labour is progressing.

Epidurals will make you feel hot because you will be retaining more heat by breathing and sweating less. Because of this, it will also raise your baby's temperature. A third of all babies whose mothers have epidurals will have skin temperatures over 38°C (100.4°F); 10 per cent will have temperatures above 39°C (102.2°F). Because research is so thin on the ground about epidurals, it is difficult to say what lasting damage this can do, but these high temperatures have been shown to compromise the health of animals in similar experiments.

Because you will be lying down after the epidural is sited, you are at greater risk of depriving your baby of oxygen. To reduce the

risk of this, try to make sure you lie on your side and that you get
help to change position from time to time.

Fetal Distress

Fetal distress does exist, but can be difficult to diagnose. The usual
criteria are if the fetal heart rate rises above 160 beats per minute (or
falls below 100–120 beats per minute); if there is an irregular
heartbeat; or there is a passage of fresh meconium. The problem
with relying on any one of these things is that the baby's heartbeat
does vary during the course of labour. It may slow down during
contractions because the action of the uterus contracting can temporarily restrict blood flow through the umbilical cord. The placenta
compensates for this by storing up blood as a contraction
approaches, and having it ready for the baby when the contraction
passes. Fetal distress can also be caused by lack of oxygen brought
on by many of the drugs used in labour.

Doctors have tried to detect fetal distress more accurately by
continuously monitoring women. Their main concern is the possibility of cerebral palsy in infants who have been compromised in
the womb, but research shows that the only outcome of continuous
fetal monitoring is higher rates of unnecessary forceps, ventouse
and caesarean deliveries. Although electronic fetal monitoring
(EFM) can detect certain problems which are associated with
neonatal seizures, the type of seizures which it can detect are not
those associated with long-term health problems in children. What
this means is that the argument that EFM is 'better' or 'safer' for
babies has no basis.

Research into mothers' attitudes to fetal monitoring shows a
certain ambivalence. Some mothers feel reassured because they feel
the monitor confirms that their baby is alive. Others feel it raises
anxiety levels in unpredictable ways. EFM belts reduce mobility
and can be uncomfortable. Some mothers feel as if the monitor
interferes with their care, since their doctors and midwives tend to
look at the monitor and not the mother. Because the belts can
become easily detached, the trace is often inaccurate, and sometimes the mother's heartbeat (which is slower) can be mistaken for
the baby's – causing practitioners to erroneously diagnose fetal
distress. Women who are intermittently monitored with a Pinard,
stethoscope or even a hand-held Doppler tend to feel more positive
about the experience, while the over-riding feeling of those who

receive continuous monitoring is that they feel 'too restricted'. You have the right to refuse continuous monitoring and, if you do not want any unnecessary exposure to ultrasound caused by the hand-held Doppler, you can request that the baby's heartbeat be monitored intermittently by Pinard or stethoscope during labour.

Conservative management of 'fetal distress' is a better way of dealing with things than threatening instrumental delivery or caesarean operation. To increase blood flow to your baby shift position. Often just getting yourself upright or turning over on your side can relieve the problem. If your labour is being accelerated with oxytocin, get your practitioner to stop the drug, since the powerful contractions which induction and acceleration cause can compromise your baby's health. Even giving a short burst of oxygen to the mother can help improve things. Epidurals dilate maternal blood vessels and cause the mother's blood pressure to drop. This can mean the baby gets less oxygen and this should be taken into account when a mother chooses this form of pain relief. If you do have an epidural, you will have to be 'pre-loaded' with intravenous fluids to prevent this.

Growth Retardation

Intrauterine growth retardation (IUGR) is a serious condition when it genuinely occurs. Because of this, there is a tendency for practitioners to over-diagnose it and take inappropriate measures to try and prevent it. Remember that size and growth are not the same thing. Your baby's size at any point during your pregnancy may fall above or below the average sizes printed in medical text books. This does not usually indicate a problem since babies vary enormously in size, especially after the first three months of pregnancy.

Nobody really knows what causes IUGR. Its root is usually in other problems, such as pre-eclampsia, which affect the efficiency with which the placenta provides oxygen and nutrients for the baby. Certain aspects of some mothers' lifestyles will also increase the risk of IUGR, such as if she has an inadequate diet, if she smokes or drinks heavily or is under a great deal of stress. (Often these things are present in combination – for instance, smoking can be a way of coping with stress.) The risk is not just that your baby might be smaller than average – it is that growth retarded babies are more likely to be born premature and are therefore at a greater risk of dying within the first six weeks after birth.

When your baby fails to put on weight, or its weight drops dramatically, this can be a sign of growth retardation. Many practitioners rely on ultrasound measurements alone to diagnose IUGR. However, because this is such a serious condition, with implications for when and how your baby is delivered, you should insist on a whole range of tests to diagnose it. These should include:

- Asking you what you think. Does your baby appear to have stopped growing? Have you stopped putting on weight? In most cases, the mother is the best judge of what is happening with her body and her baby. Your views should be taken into account.
- Abdominal palpation and measurement of the fundal height (the distance between the pubic bone and the top of the uterus) and a measurement of abdominal girth at the level of your belly button. Since the size of your uterus is directly related to the size of your baby, your practitioner should make these measurements as a matter of course.
- Asking you to keep a kick chart, in other words to count fetal movements throughout the day. This test, however, can only give you a guide to what is happening with your baby. It will not predict growth retardation but will give an indication of reduced movement which may be, but isn't always, associated with growth retardation.
- An ultrasound scan. This may be helpful, but should never be relied upon to produce a definitive diagnosis. For measuring a baby's size early in pregnancy it is a fairly accurate tool, but, as already stated, babies grow in their own individual ways after the first three months, and research shows that ultrasound can only provide a 'best guess' answer.

There are other chemical tests which can be performed to measure levels of oestriol and human placental lactogen and other biochemical markers in the mother's blood. Some practitioners advocate contraction stress testing, where mild contractions are stimulated in the mother to see how the baby's system reacts to labour-like conditions. Few of these tests reveal any useful information, nor do they solve the original dilemma of what to do if a baby is genuinely growth retarded.

Medicine has very little to offer mothers whose babies are growth retarded, bar inducing their labours or performing caesareans. The problem is that there is nothing to prove that substituting a special care baby unit for a womb is all that effective. In the end, whatever you choose to do, whether it is to induce, deliver by caesarean, or simply wait and trust that your body will do what it can to support your baby, you need to be comfortable with the decision. A 'wait and see' mother should not be pressured into a caesarean, and a mother who has weighed up all the risks and wants a caesarean should not be pressured into an agonising wait.

Home Birth

Any woman can have a home birth, regardless of whether this is her first child or not, and regardless of any perceived risk factor. The safety of home birth ceased to be an issue as much as twenty years ago, when it was shown that women who give birth at home produce fewer low birth weight babies and that rates of perinatal death (stillbirth or death of a baby up to six weeks after birth) are half the national average. What's more, half of those babies who do die at home would have died regardless of where they were born, due to congenital abnormalities.

The issue then is why, if as many as 16 per cent of women would like a home birth, do only 1.8 per cent achieve one? Many surveys have been done to ascertain what happens when a woman requests a home birth. The Association of Community Health Councils has discovered that some women get struck off their GPs' lists when they request a home birth – a powerful persuader for a vulnerable pregnant woman to do what her GP tells her. Both AIMS and the NCT have files and files of cases where women are told the most amazing things by their GPs and midwives including: 'We don't do those here', 'It's illegal', 'You can't have a home birth with a first baby', 'It's not possible because the midwife will be on holiday when you are due', and even 'It'll ruin your carpet'!

The first mistake that most women make is 'requesting' a home birth from their GP. Although GPs provide the bulk of ante-natal care in this country, they are rarely involved in the delivery of babies and know very little about the process of birth. Many GPs resent referring a woman on to midwifery care because they see it as an insult to their professional abilities and also because they don't get paid if they do. The internal politics of the maternity services, however, should not be your concern.

If you want a home birth, contact the Supervisor of Midwives at your local hospital directly (you do not need to consult with your GP or get his permission) and tell her this is what you want. The onus is then upon her to make sure that you get the care that *you* want.

Induction/Acceleration
Surveys show that most women aren't as concerned about how long labour lasts as much as they are about how much support they have during labour. Medical practitioners, however, have a kind of morbid fascination with the subject. So much so that they have developed tables and charts to illustrate how long the 'ideal' labour should last. These are called 'partograms' and sometimes 'cervico-grams'. All hospitals which practise 'active management' – that is to say, just-in-case interventions – use these tables, and all women who enter into these institutions are expected to conform. Hardly any women ever do because every body and every labour is different.

Many hospitals put a time limit of twenty-four hours for the first stage of labour for first time mothers and twelve hours for second time mothers, and a further time limit of one hour for the delivery of the baby for first time mothers and half an hour for second time mothers. If the mother's labour does not conform to this timetable, some action will be taken to induce or accelerate and eventually deliver the baby by mechanical or surgical means.

There are many different ways in which hospitals seek to move labour along. Often labour is induced or accelerated by first artificially rupturing a woman's membranes (ARM).

In addition, two types of drugs are used to induce or accelerate labour.

Prostaglandin pessaries (or sometimes gel, though this seems to have more dangerous side-effects) are usually inserted into the vagina at regular intervals of between 6 and 12 hours. Their effect can be to 'ripen', or soften the cervix within 24 to 48 hours. This in turn stimulates labour. They tend to work best on a woman whose cervix is already fairly ripe (which makes you wonder why they're being used in the first place) and because of this they have a failure rate of around 60 per cent. They can work very quickly indeed and should never be given to women in established labour as they will over-stimulate the uterus, resulting in powerful but uncoordinated contractions and, eventually, a complete inability to push the baby out. If you have had a previous caesarean, you should not use these pessaries because they soften the uterus as well as the cervix and increase the risk of scar rupture. When prostaglandin pessaries fail, the next route is usually syntocinon.

Syntocinon is usually given via an intravenous drip or infusion. Attached to a drip, you will find it much harder to remain mobile, and the sometimes overwhelming contractions produced by this drug will make moving around a less attractive prospect anyway. If you are finding the contractions too hard to cope with, ask your practitioner to adjust the speed of the drip.

The powerful contractions produced by these drugs are not good for your baby. During a contraction your baby is temporarily starved of oxygen. When the contraction is finished, oxygen is once again released to the baby. Drug-induced contractions are more intense, more frequent and have fewer periods of rest in between, leaving your baby without oxygen for longer periods of time. Fetal distress is much more likely to be diagnosed in women who have had their labours induced or accelerated.

Both forms of induction interfere with your body's ability to produce natural pain killers called endorphins. In a normal labour, the intensity of your contractions will build up gradually, allowing your body time to meet the increased demands for endorphins. With an induction or acceleration, powerful contractions can come almost immediately. This is usually when someone suggests pain relief – and it is usually accepted.

Labour – How Long Should It Last?
How long should labour last? Nobody knows. Labour is a totally individual thing and *no one* can say how long an optimal labour should be. The reason often given for truncating the length of labour (with forceps, ventouse or caesarean) or trying to speed it up (with syntocinon or prostaglandin) is that it is better for the baby not to go through a long labour. There is absolutely *no evidence* for this. A healthy baby is as capable of enduring labour as its healthy mother. Not only that, but labour is essential to prepare a baby's lungs and other internal organs for life outside the womb. Labour is also a period of transition for women, and as such its importance should not be trivialised.

Long labours are hard on everyone. Mothers are exhausted and sometimes deeply disappointed by them; midwives and doctors simply find them tedious. Some, inexplicably, even see labour as some kind of barrier to birth. If you don't want your labour to be curtailed or speeded up, you have the right to refuse any, or all, of your practitioner's suggestions, and that refusal should be respected.

On the other hand, if you are finding labour just too difficult to cope with, but you are unsure of what your alternatives are, there are certain self-help measures which may help revive you enough to carry on or make a clear decision whether or not to intervene:

• Clear the room of unnecessary people. You have a right to your privacy and lots of people talking around you can make it difficult to focus on more important matters.
• Lie on your side for a while. Although lying down is generally not recommended, lying on your side is unlikely to restrict blood flow to your baby and many women find it a very comfortable way to get a little rest. Your midwife can continue to monitor your baby in this position.
• Go for a walk or change the atmosphere in some way. Put on some music, burn some essential oils, change the lighting.
• Eat or drink something light or try some glucose tablets. Your body may be crying out for a little extra energy.
• Are you afraid of something or angry about something? Can you articulate it? Sometimes just being able to speak the unspeakable helps to clear the air and can move your labour along. Don't underestimate the way your body and your baby can co-operate with your innermost feelings and fears.
• Once you've ruled out any mechanical problems with labour (that is, the baby in a difficult position), remind yourself that it's meant to be this way.

As long as your baby is fine, you can take whatever time you need to come to your own conclusions. If none of these things work, and you feel that you just can't go on, you have the right to choose whatever help you think is necessary, without feeling as if you have 'failed'. For a variety of reasons, some women genuinely do need help. It should be given to you without your having to argue about it and without the content of your birth plan being used against you as a form of punishment.

Midwives
There are many different kinds of midwife. If you want to have midwifery care, it is important to understand something about their

backgrounds and the kinds of jobs they do.

Some midwives come from nursing backgrounds. They are used to viewing the people under their care as 'sick' and are trained to take corrective and preventative action. They may have taken up midwifery as a means of advancing themselves professionally, and not because they were particularly interested in mothers or babies. They may not even have children of their own.

Other midwives come from 'lay' backgrounds; in other words, they have made a definite choice to train as midwives, perhaps as a second career after having children of their own, or as a natural progression from being ante-natal teachers. All midwives are fully trained, autonomous professionals and they are the *only* practitioners whose training revolves around the care of mothers and their babies. Unfortunately, the places in which midwives work can have an enormous influence on the kind of care women receive, and the degree to which it can be called 'mother-centred'.

Hospital midwives generally work only within the hospital. Much of their job may be taken up with routine administration, filling in forms, ushering women into cubicles, assisting the consultant during examinations. It can be very difficult to practise midwifery fully under these circumstances because hospitals, like all large institutions, demand a certain amount of conformity. Also, in a hospital, the consultant, his beliefs, even his personality, dictate the policy and those who work under him must follow that policy. Some midwives are happy with this kind of work; they do not want, and would even resent, greater freedom to practise independently from the consultant. If they come from a nursing background, they may have been trained to believe that the consultant knows best. Others in this situation do what they can to make sure women get the best care possible within the system, and there are some excellent hospital midwives, such as those who are members of the Association of Radical Midwives.

Community midwives practise out of small clinics located inside the community. They are the midwives who will attend your home birth and may attend your labour on a Domino scheme. More and more community midwives are working in small groups or teams to provide mothers with greater continuity of care ante-natally and in labour. Quality of care and levels of skill can vary enormously among the community midwives, as it can in hospitals. While some midwives believe that practising in the community provides them with an excellent opportunity to use their full range of skills, others see it as an extension of the hospital system and act out a philosophy which says: 'If the woman won't come to the hospital, we'll bring the hospital to the woman.'

Independent midwives practise outside the NHS system. Women usually book with an independent midwife because their needs are not being met within the NHS. For a woman who wants a home birth or a water birth, there is the reassurance which comes with knowing that independent midwives often do little else. However, independent midwives can also attend your delivery in hospital and, indeed, some mothers book an independent midwife just so they can be absolutely assured of having the same midwife who cared for them ante-natally with them during labour. Because independent midwives do not have to answer to the consultant, they tend to be more skilled in many aspects of ante-natal care and birth. They may have more experience in delivering breech babies or twins, and mothers who are usually denied choice within the system, such as those with physical or mental handicaps, may also benefit from their care.

Whatever kind of midwife you are choosing, shop around. You do not have to accept one who is allocated to you, nor do you have to stay with a midwife whom you initially chose, but now have doubts about.

Miscarriage

Miscarriage is still a bit of a medical mystery. Because the vast majority of miscarriages are not examined in detail, it is not always clear what goes wrong. The usual line is that it happens when the fetus is profoundly damaged, but this is rather too simplistic. There are different categories of miscarriage. The phrase *primary miscarriage* is used when a woman has never had a live birth; *secondary miscarriage* is used for women who have had at least one successful live birth; and *recurrent miscarriage* describes women who have had three or more miscarriages in a row.

Chromosomal abnormalities are more likely to be the cause of primary, or one-off miscarriages, while immunological factors seem to be connected with recurrent miscarriages. It is only possible to identify causative factors in about half of all miscarriages, which leaves a large proportion unexplained. Several theories have been put forward. Because women need a certain amount of body fat on them to conceive and carry a baby to term, women who are very underweight may be more prone to miscarriage. The socially unacceptable solution of 'put on ten or fifteen pounds and try again' is hardly ever suggested, even though it is likely to have fewer debilitating side effects than hormonal therapy.

There has also been some research to show a link between parents who were of a very low birthweight themselves and recurrent miscarriage. Other factors which may influence miscarriage include the mother's and father's age, lifestyle (for instance whether you smoke, drink or take drugs), stress, fibroids and other organic or anatomical anomalies. Certain routine obstetric procedures can increase the chance of a miscarriage, particularly in women with a history of miscarriage. These include amniocentesis, chorionic villus sampling (CVS) and repeated ultrasound scans – the very procedures which are likely to be encouraged for a woman who has had a previous miscarriage.

You can contact groups like the Miscarriage Association, SATFA, and the National Association for the Childless for support and advice about miscarriage. You can also find information from Foresight and the Maternity Alliance about pre-conceptual care.

Overdue

Most babies come when they are ready to come. It is almost impossible to tell with any certainty how many babies are genuinely 'overdue' because the routine for so long has been to induce mothers if they go more than ten days past their 'due date'. Other terms used are: 'post dates' – meaning that you have gone two weeks past your due date, and 'post mature' – meaning that your baby's health is compromised due to the extended length of pregnancy. There are some risks involved with going past 42 weeks. The placenta can start to fail and the baby will not be getting the oxygen and nutrients it needs to thrive. Although you may come under enormous pressure to induce labour, you should try to rely on your instincts about your baby and your body. Chances are high that it isn't your baby which is late, but your doctor's calculated estimated delivery date (EDD) which is wrong.

Fewer than 10 per cent of babies actually arrive on the day they are supposed to. An estimated delivery date is just that – *an estimate*. Ultrasound dating is not significantly more accurate than a mother's own dates and should only be relied upon if you are very unsure of when you conceived or when your last period was. Otherwise, you are better off relying on your own dates, rather than your doctor's or midwife's. It makes much more sense for women and practitioners to work around a range of dates, rather than to focus on one, and then feel frustrated, or worse take inappropriate action, when the baby doesn't make an appearance.

Pain

Labour is painful. Childbirth hurts. Those are the inescapable facts. How painful it is, however, depends on a number of different factors, including each individual's threshold of pain, what drugs, if any, have been used to induce or accelerate labour, whether or not you are upright, whether or not you have adequate emotional support and what kind of stress you feel you are under – for instance, if you are giving birth against the clock. There is also evidence to show that women's expectations of pain may influence how much pain they feel, or perhaps more accurately how well they cope with the pain they feel. A woman who expects her labour pains to be unbearable often finds that they are. This may be, in part, because she is quicker to accept labour interventions, which she thinks will stop the pain; don't forget, your body can speak volumes about your emotional and mental state.

In some cultures, pain is seen as an important part of the process, marking the transition into another phase of womanhood and offering a unique opportunity for self-discovery. In the civilised world, we openly scoff at this idea, and yet surveys show that the women least likely to report a sense of satisfaction after birth are those who have had the pain of labour and birth completely eradicated by an epidural.

In ante-natal classes across the nation, women will hear the idea that pain is purposeful. Usually, this is taken to mean that it has a purpose of pushing the baby out, but it also has a more subtle physiological purpose. The different types and levels of pain a woman feels provide useful information about her labour. Denied this, or disconnected from it, a woman ends up having endless, often very painful, internal examinations to see 'how far along' she is, increasing her discomfort and limiting her mobility. If her waters have broken, it exposes her to possible infection; if they have not, it increases the risk that they will get broken accidentally and unnecessarily. Relying on others to tell her how far along she is only further disconnects her from the process, and a vicious circle is begun.

There is no doubt that pain, next to tearing or episiotomy, is the thing women fear most about labour. There is a common misconception that women who want a 'natural' childbirth do not want to use pain relief. But *all women use pain relief in labour*. This can take the form of being upright and mobile, yoga, Alexander Technique, meditation, music, massage, baths and showers, water pools, homeopathic or herbal remedies or various breathing techniques. It can span the realm of birth paraphernalia from the TENS machine and the birth stool to rather more risky (for mother and baby) methods such as pethidine and epidurals.

Which method a woman chooses depends as much on her individual personality and her attitude to life, birth and motherhood as it does on where and how she is giving birth. A woman at home with lots of emotional support may not feel the need of any drugs to relieve the pain. A woman in hospital with an unknown midwife, whose labour is being medically directed, may be experiencing such intense pain that drugs to relieve it aren't so much a choice as a necessity. Some women simply don't want to feel anything, and actively choose to have an epidural from the word go.

Labour is not a test and you won't have failed if you need to ask for help handling the pain. For the woman who wants to use pharmacological pain relief, there is seldom any argument, especially in a hospital. However, for a woman who feels committed to a labour without it, and has made this commitment clear to her midwife, asking for it, and sometimes getting it, can be very difficult.

Staying Upright

Most of the pictures you see of women giving birth show them lying down on a bed. This is, in fact, one of the worst positions to give birth in (after standing on your head!). The importance of staying upright during labour cannot be stressed enough. The idea of giving birth with the aid of gravity isn't just some trippy, new-age fad, but based on sound principles. During a contraction the uterus tilts forward. If you are lying on your back, your uterus will have to exert more energy to achieve the same effect, leaving you exhausted and making your progress very painful and slow. When you are upright, the weight of the baby is pushing against your cervix, helping it to dilate. The more the baby pushes against the cervix, the more oxytocin is released into your system to help your labour along. Being upright also means you are not sitting on your tailbone – which, in women, is hinged to give your baby more room to pass through. This is why being 'upright' while sitting in a birth chair doesn't always produce the same effect. Because of all this, a mother labouring in an upright position will find her contractions are easier to stay on top of, and will feel less tired at the end of it all.

Lying on your back isn't simply more tiring and more painful, it is also very unhealthy for your baby. When you lie down, the weight of your uterus compresses the main blood vessels leading, via the placenta, to the baby. This starves your baby of oxygen and can lead to fetal distress.

Early on, mobility is also important to help establish labour. One reason why it is a good idea not to go into hospital too early is that you will, in most cases, be obliged to lie down (to be monitored, examined, drugged, or whatever). Staying at home for as long as possible, and remaining active if you can, will help keep interventions in labour to a minimum. If you are in hospital stay as mobile as you can; walk to the toilet often and bring cushions so you can stay comfortably off the bed and upright.

If you are planning to go to hospital, the more established your labour is when you get there, the less likely it is that you will be interfered with. Ante-natally, you will probably be told to come into hospital as soon as you feel a contraction, but this is seldom necessary and you can ignore this advice if you feel you would like to spend more time at home. If you are planning to deliver at home, just get on with what you can, stop and rest when you need to and await events. Some labours, particularly first labours, can be very long and there is seldom any need to panic or seek immediate medical attention at the first sign of a contraction.

Third Stage of Labour
The third stage of labour is the delivery of your placenta. In many hospitals, and even in some home deliveries, the third stage is actively managed by injecting the mother with *syntometrine* as the baby is being born. Syntometrine is an oxytocic drug: a combination of the synthetic hormone syntocinon and ergometrine. The syntocinon element works immediately to separate the placenta from the uterine wall and the ergometrine begins to work five

minutes or so later to cause further sustained contractions which clamp off the uterine blood vessels. *Controlled cord traction* (pulling on the umbilical cord) and *fundal pressure* (pressing hard on the mother's abdomen) are also used, as well as clamping and cutting the cord immediately to prevent the drug reaching the baby. All of these things are unnecessarily violent and are the result of midwives' and doctors' need to 'get it over with' as 'quickly as possible'.

In a natural, physiological third stage, the placenta may take anywhere from five minutes to an hour to be delivered. Although practitioners may worry – and cause the mother to worry – about the possibility of post partum haemorrhage and retained placenta, the medical research is very clear. Syntometrine is very useful in treating post partum haemorrhage, but there is no evidence that its routine use actually prevents it. It can, however, make you feel nauseous, give you headaches, raise your blood pressure, and cause tinnitus, palpitations and cramps in your legs and back. Post partum haemorrhage is many times more likely if your practitioner is pulling on the umbilical cord – risking separating the placenta before the uterine blood vessels have had a chance to close themselves.

There are risks for the baby as well. Syntometrine causes unnaturally strong uterine contractions, forcing a great rush of blood into your baby's system. The risk here is over-transfusion, sometimes involving as much as double the amount of blood which your baby's system is designed to cope with. This puts enormous stress on the baby's vital organs and can cause jaundice. Jaundice is caused by the process of breaking down the excess of red blood cells. During this process, a chemical called bilirubin is produced which has to be excreted by the liver. If the liver is unable to cope with the large amounts, the bilirubin builds up in the blood and turns the baby's skin yellow.

If your labour has been totally altered with the use of drugs to induce or accelerate labour, or if you have had an instrumental or surgical delivery, syntometrine and all the routines which go with it may be unavoidable and even necessary. If not, relax. Give your body a chance to do what it is built to do. Putting your baby to the breast as soon as it is ready will stimulate the release of natural oxytocin into your system, which will help the placenta separate and the blood vessels to close by themselves. If your baby is not interested in suckling, then try gentle nipple stimulation instead. To

prevent blood clotting at the placental site, get yourself mobile –
walk to the toilet, or the bath or the bed – as soon as possible after
the delivery.

Twins

Twins occur in around 1 in every 80 pregnancies. If you are a twin
yourself, or if you have a history of twins in your family, you are
more likely to have a twin pregnancy yourself. *Fraternal twins*
occur when two eggs are fertilised by two sperm; *identical twins*
occur when one egg, fertilised by one sperm, divides into two,
usually after implanting itself in the uterus. Fraternal twins have
separate amniotic sacs and placentas; identical twins have separate
amniotic sacs, but usually share the same placenta.

The birth of twins does not have to be a medical emergency,
though it is often treated as such. Rather than make plans for
elective caesareans or inductions it is often advisable to wait and see
how the pregnancy progresses. The weight of the twins can cause
the cervix to stretch open and there is always the likelihood of the
mother going into labour before 37 weeks. There is no way to
predict which mothers will do this, and there is very little evidence
that bed rest is a good way to prevent it. On the contrary, inactivity
may do more harm than good, restricting blood flow to the babies
and causing considerable stress in a mother who may be worried
about the time she's taking off work, and whether the house is
falling apart around her ears.

The caesarean rate for twins has risen over the last decade or so,
but the rise is not justified by the evidence. Often a mother will be
pressurised to have an elective caesarean. She will be very vulnerable to this suggestion as she will be feeling big, uncomfortable and
very much more tired than a mother carrying a single baby. She may
also be anaemic since her babies will be placing extra demands on
her reserves of vitamins and iron.

However, a caesarean is an aggressive solution with implications
for your and your babies' health, and these problems can be more
effectively dealt with by careful attention to your diet, by taking
extra supplements of natural iron (such as the tonic Floradix, which
you can get on prescription) and making sure you get all the rest
you can handle.

One of the babies may be breech or even transverse (lying across
your abdomen), but with a skilled practitioner this is unlikely to be a

problem. Breech babies can be safely delivered vaginally, even in a twin delivery. If the second twin is high in the uterus, your practitioner may worry about possible cord prolapse. The solution is not to break your waters immediately, and to make sure you are upright and breathing steadily (neither hyperventilating nor holding your breath). Steady breathing will ensure that the second twin is getting enough oxygen. If the second twin persists in a transverse lie, it will have to be delivered by caesarean, under a general anaesthetic.

For a mother, the biggest emergency may be an emotional one. While some women are pleased when they hear they are expecting twins, others feel double the fear and anxiety about pregnancy and labour. Most mothers experience panic about how they will cope with two babies. Mothers of twins are also more likely to experience morning sickness, tiredness and pre-eclampsia to a greater degree than mothers with single babies. It is better to address these things early on in pregnancy, rather than wait until you are too exhausted to cope.

Ultrasound

Many women associate the idea of ultrasound with getting those little pictures, or in some cases videos, of the baby inside them. There is no doubting the thrill of seeing your baby and hearing its heartbeat. For some women it confirms the reality of the baby. However, although ultrasound is one of the most common screening procedures given to pregnant women, it is also one of the most under-evaluated. The social issues which dictate that machinery confirms a pregnancy to a mother, before her own instincts do, are beyond the scope of this book, but are certainly worth pondering before any woman embarks on a course of routine ultrasound scans.

The problem is often not so much to do with the machinery as with the way it is used. Used selectively, in women who may be genuinely having problems in their pregnancy, or whose babies' health may genuinely be at risk, ultrasound can be a useful screening tool. Used routinely, on vast numbers of women every year, it may have implications for our and our babies' health which we are only just beginning to get to grips with.

The use of ultrasound blurs many boundaries in ante-natal screening. Quite often it is referred to as *diagnostic* ultrasound – giving the impression that the mother is receiving a definitive

answer to questions about her baby's health. Ultrasound is not a
diagnostic tool – in other words it cannot produce a definitive
answer. It is a *screening* tool which can provide an educated best
guess about what's going on inside you. Also, because we screen
many women, without indication, ultrasound breaks one of the basic
tenets of screening procedures, which is that you should only screen
for things you can do something about.

Many practitioners have come to rely on ultrasound instead of
their own clinical skills. Some can no longer confirm the presence
of a baby, or of twins, or of a breech or transverse baby without the
aid of this machine. Ultrasound cannot accurately establish a baby's
age or rate of growth after the first three months of pregnancy (when
most women have their first scan). There is even evidence to suggest
that routine screening may actually be a contributing factor to
intrauterine growth retardation (IUGR). The problem is, even if
IUGR is detected, there is not much that can be done about it,
except watch and wait. The same applies to conditions like placenta
praevia.

The newest form of early ultrasound screening is called the
nuchal scan. It has been shown that babies with Down's Syndrome
tend to have a thicker fold of skin at the back of their heads – known
as the nuchal fold. Your practitioner will be looking to see if the
fold, which appears on the screen as a large black space, is greater
than three millimetres. But many babies who do not have Down's
appear to have folds bigger than this. So, while this test can
pinpoint, with around 80 per cent accuracy, the risk of Down's, it
may also give false information.

With transvaginal ultrasound a small probe about six inches long
is inserted into the vagina. This is the latest Doppler ultrasound
gadget. Some practitioners even see it as the future of ultrasound,
but, of course, it has its disadvantages. The probe has to be covered
with a condom and the condoms have been known to break,
increasing the risk of infection. In a normal ultrasound scan your
baby is protected from much of the ultrasonic waves by your own
body fat and your abdominal muscles, but because the transvaginal
probe is inserted in the vagina a greater volume of ultrasonic waves
bounce directly off the baby (which is why this procedure is said to
produce such significantly better pictures). There is also concern
about the highly sexual nature of this form of screening and its use
has coined the phrase 'diagnostic rape'. There have been cases of

practitioners abusing this technology in both America and Australia. If you have this procedure, you should, as a matter of course, have another person in the room with you, and there is no reason why your partner should not be allowed to be there. If your doctor is very keen that you should have this kind of ultrasound, but says partners are 'not allowed', you are in a good position to strike a deal: no partner, no scan. At any rate, your doctor should have a very good reason for wanting to perform this kind of scan.

Much of the accuracy of your scan will depend on the person carrying it out. There have been some shocking stories in the news recently of babies being scheduled for terminations because the scan showed they were dead or abnormal, only for the mother to be told at the last minute, often by pure chance, that the baby was fine. There have also been stories from deeply angered mothers who have given birth to abnormal babies, when the scan told them everything was OK, and there is evidence that many normal babies are aborted on flimsy ultrasound 'evidence'. If you are uncertain of the results of your scan, you can ask for another and not allow yourself to be fobbed off with excuses about ultrasound's accuracy.

It may also be wise to limit the amount of exposure you have to ultrasound, including the ultrasound in hand-held Dopplers or sonic aids. There is mounting research to show that ultrasound alters neurological function. Studies which show that scanned mothers produce more left-handed babies and more babies with learning and speech delays are illustrative of this. What's more, we are only just beginning to explore the ways in which ultrasound may alter immune system function and even cause chromosomal damage.

Vaginal Birth after Caesarean (VBAC)

Many hospitals operate a 'once a caesarean, always a caesarean' policy, citing the possibility of scar rupture as the reason. In medical literature the possibility of scar rupture is a non-issue, since the risk is measured in fractions of a per cent – from .09 to .22 per cent for women who have had a previous lower segment or 'bikini line' cut. Some scars do rupture, but without any symptoms such as bleeding or pain. These are minor ruptures which cause no problems to mother or baby and heal by themselves.

You may find that at first your hospital says there is no problem about you having a 'trial of labour', but as your pregnancy progresses more and more pressure is brought to bear on you to have another caesarean. It might be a good idea, early on, to find out your hospital's statistics for VBACs, since the figures often tell a different story from the consultant.

Mothers who had their first caesarean because the baby was breech have the highest chance (90 per cent success rate) of delivering normally next time around. Those whose operation was performed because of 'fetal distress', 'failure to progress' or cephalo-pelvic disproportion still have as high as a 75 per cent chance of delivering vaginally. When hospitals boast their VBAC rates, be aware that these will have been culled from a highly select group of women. Often hospitals require mothers to satisfy a laundry list of (usually arbitrary) pre-conditions before they will 'allow' them to have a VBAC. Even if you don't meet the criteria, you can still insist on a VBAC, either in hospital or at home.

Be aware that with a VBAC your body will perform in the same way as if this were a first birth. This means that your labour is likely to take longer. It's important that you have a midwife who understands this, and does not try to apply *any* time limits to your labour, let alone those which are considered appropriate to second and subsequent labours (these are invariably shorter than for first labours). It is also important to try and avoid routine interventions, such as induction or acceleration, since many mothers find that these things begin a cascade of interventions which they cannot control. Also, if you have an induction or have acceleration, you are increasing any risk of scar rupture since the powerful contractions produced by induction place greater strain on your uterus.

If you are planning a VBAC, and particularly if it's a home delivery, it is especially important that you find a midwife who feels confident in her skills, since her fear can interfere with your own confidence and lead to unnecessary interventions which can push you closer to a repeat caesarean. It is true that VBAC mothers usually have a lot of feelings of 'failure' to work through. The caesarean (or in some cases caesareans) may have totally shattered their confidence in their body's ability to give birth. In some cases, help, information and support are all that is required. In other cases, counselling may help to work through any issues which you feel may have affected your ability to give birth before.

There are many groups which support women who want to have VBACs, providing information and encouragement.

Water Birth

Women use water during labour and birth in many different ways. Some like to sit in warm baths or stand under showers, others run taps or flush toilets, some spray themselves with mixtures of water and essential oils or play tapes of rivers and oceans. Even sipping iced water or sucking ice cubes puts you in touch with the versatility and magic of water.

The greatest body of evidence shows that water can be very beneficial at taking the edge off contractions in labour. It is not a form of treatment like a drug or piece of equipment and many women appreciate the difference. It is women's interest in, and demand for, this form of relief which has led to a boom in the private rental of birthing pools, and to some hospitals establishing rooms with integrated birth pools, or where mothers can, at the very least, bring their own hired pools in to use.

Because, until recently, much of the medical establishment has considered labour and birth in water a bit of a joke, there has been very little formal evaluation of its uses and safety. Nor has there been much attention paid to making sure that staff are adequately trained in helping women labour and give birth in the water. For a long time we have had to rely on the anecdotal evidence of a handful of motivated practitioners – mostly midwives. Now, however, more and more evaluation of the safety and efficacy of labour and birth in water is emerging.

What we do know about labour in water is that, on the whole, it results in less pain and quicker labours, it lowers blood pressure and softens the perineum so that tears are less likely. Mothers labouring in water are less likely to be on the receiving end of a whole variety of interventions, including drugs and episiotomies, which means that they and their babies recover more quickly from birth.

Now that water is increasingly becoming such a part of the fabric of labour and birth, guidelines have been developed in an attempt to standardise practice and assure safety. For instance, it is recommended that the water be body temperature for delivery and only a few degrees either side of this for labour. Some misinformed parents and practitioners have delayed bringing the baby to the surface after it is born, in the mistaken belief that they were making its transition from water to air more gently. The only safe advice, however, is to bring the baby calmly to the surface *immediately* after it is born. Artificially delaying the emergence into the air can result in death or brain damage.

There are even guidelines for when to get into the pool. Some water birth experts say that women shouldn't get into the pool until they are five or six centimetres dilated. They believe that this is the time when the pool will be most effective at taking the edge off contractions and, because labour is well established, the altered gravity experienced in water will not interfere with its progress. There is some merit to this point of view, however it is important not to be prescriptive. Many women enjoy being in the water in early or pre-labour. You should get in and out as your inclinations dictate.

There are very few restrictions on which women can or cannot give birth in the water. Only those who start labour before 37 weeks are not suitable. If you want a water birth, but your midwife is reluctant, don't change your plans. Get a new midwife instead. Your hospital has an obligation to provide you with someone who is skilled and experienced in this form of birth.

What Is AIMS?

In 1960 AIMS' founder, Sally Willington, wrote to a national newspaper about her own ante-natal and birth experience. A deluge of sympathetic letters from other women followed and the Association for Improvements in the Maternity Services was born.

Since that time AIMS has been at the forefront of the maternity care movement in Britain, has provided much of the dynamism for changes in the way professionals perceive and relate to pregnant and labouring women, and has paved the way for changes in the way in which routine procedures are used. AIMS has consistently supported midwives as practitioners in their own right, who, in most cases, should undertake the care of mothers and babies throughout pregnancy, birth and afterwards.

AIMS members – parents, midwives, doctors and other health professionals – are drawn from all over Britain and Ireland, as well as from abroad (there is an AIMS America and Australian AIMS). There are AIMS contacts throughout the country who support each other and campaign on national and local issues.

AIMS publishes a well-respected and widely read quarterly journal which focuses on current issues in maternity care, gives news about ongoing campaigns and analyses the latest research. It also includes readers' views and stories, book and video reviews and conference reports from around the country. The *Journal* spearheads lively and informed discussion about change and development in the maternity services. Parents and professionals alike find it an excellent source of information.

Finally, and most importantly, AIMS receives thousands of letters and phone calls each year from individual women and couples seeking advice and guidance, and provides emotional support and encouragement as well as information about choices and rights.

As part of AIMS' ongoing campaign to improve all aspects of

maternity care, data is collected and published in a wide range of leaflets and booklets which enable parents to make informed decisions about their care.

If you would like to know more about AIMS, or take out a membership, please contact:

Sandar Warshal
Hon. Secretary
AIMS
40 Kingswood Avenue
London NW6 6LS
(0181) 960 5585

Useful Contacts

AIMS (Association for Improvements in the Maternity Services)
40 Kingswood Avenue
London NW6 6LS
(0181) 960 5585

In Scotland:
40 Leamington Terrace
Edinburgh EH10 4JL
(0131) 229 6259

In Northern Ireland:
23 Station Mews
Todd's Hill
Saitfield
Co Down
(01238) 511786
Support and information about parents' rights and choices and advice about complaints procedures. Produces a quarterly journal and booklets covering current issues in maternity care.

Action For Sick Children
Argyle House
29–31 Euston Road
London NW1 2SD
(0171) 833 2041
For parents who have children with special needs.

Action for Victims of Medical Accidents (AVMA)
Bank Chambers
1 London Road
Forest Hill
London SE23 3TP
(0181) 291 2793
Help and advice for parents who wish to take legal action.

Action on Pre-Eclampsia
31–33 College Road
Harrow
Middlesex
HA1 1EJ
(0181) 863 3271
Advice for mothers suffering from pre-eclampsia.

Active Birth Centre
25 Bickerton Road
London N19 5JT
(0171) 561 9006
Classes for mothers interested in active, physiological birth. Can put you in touch with local groups and supply birth pools.

Association of Breastfeeding Mothers
26 Herschell Close
London SE26 4TH
(0181) 778 4769
Telephone advice and support groups for breastfeeding mothers.

Association of Radical Midwives
62 Greetby Hill
Ormskirk
Lancs L39 2DT
(01695) 572776
Professional group which supports excellence and autonomy in midwifery practice.

Alcoholics Anonymous (AA)
AA General Service Office
PO Box 1
Stonebow House
Stonebow
York YO1 2NJ
(01904) 644026
Network of independent self-help groups. Find your local group in the phone book or by contacting the number above.

Avon Episiotomy Support Group
PO Box 130
Weston-super-Mare
Avon BS23 4YJ
Self-help advice and a national network of support for women who have torn or had episiotomies. Please send SAE with enquiry.

BLISS
17–21 Emerald Street
London WC1N 3QL
(0171) 831 9393
Practical and emotional support for parents whose babies need intensive care or special support.

Caesarean Support Network
c/o Sheila Tunstall
2 Hurst Park Drive
Huyton
Liverpool L36 1TF
(0151) 480 1184
Emotional support and practical advice for women who have had or may need a caesarean delivery.

Community Health Council
In Scotland CHCs are called Local Health Councils.
In Northern Ireland they are called Health and Social Services Councils.
Look in your phone book under your local health board.

Consumers for Ethics in Research (CERES)
PO Box 1365
London N16 0BW
(01732) 458021
User group concerned about ethics in medical research.

CRY-SIS
BM CRY-SIS
London WC1N 3XX
(0171) 404 5011

*Support for parents of babies
who cry excessively or those
who have difficulty sleeping.*

District Health Authority
In Scotland the DHA is known
as the Health District.
In Northern Ireland it is called
the Health and Social Services
District.
*Look in your phone book under
your local health board.*

Down's Syndrome Association
155 Mitcham Road
Tooting
London SW17 9PG
(0181) 682 4001
*Advice for parents of Down's
children.*

Family Health Services
   ## Authority (FHSA)
*The address of your FHSA will
be on your medical card and in
the phone book. Can help you
change doctors, and deals with
complaints at the local level.*

Foresight
28 The Paddock
Godalming
Surrey GU7 1XD
(01483) 427839
*Information on preconceptual
care and nutrition during
pregnancy. Please send
SAE.*

Gingerbread
35 Wellington Street
London WC2E 7BN
(0171) 240 0953
Self-help for one-parent families.

Health Information Service
(0800) 665541
*Freephone line for information
about NHS services, including
complaints procedures.*

Independent Midwives
   ## Association
94 Auckland Road
London SE19 2DB
(0181) 406 3172
*Can supply a list of
independent midwives in your
area experienced in home birth.*

Informed Parent Network
PO Box 870
Harrow
Middlesex HA3 7UW
(0181) 861 1022
*Support and information for
your vaccination decision.
Please send an SAE with
enquiry.*

JABS
1 Gawsworth Road
Golborne
Nr Warrington
Cheshire WA3 3RF
(01942) 713565
*Information, support and legal
advice for parents whose
children have been adversely
affected by vaccinations.*

Kith & Kids
404 Camden Road
London N7 0SJ
(0171) 700 2755
*Advice and support for parents
of handicapped children.*

**La Leche League (Great
    Britain)**
BM 3424
London WC1N 3XX
(0171) 242 1278 (24 hour
answerphone)
*Breast-feeding support and
counselling. Groups meet
locally throughout the UK.*

Maternity Alliance
45 Beech Street
5th Floor
London EC2P 2LX
(0171) 588 8582
*Information on all aspects of
maternity services, rights at
work and benefits. Send an A5
SAE with enquiry.*

**Meet-a-Mum Association
    (MAMA)**
c/o Briony Hallam
58 Malden Avenue
S Norwood
London SE25 4HS
(0181) 656 7318
*Support for mothers who feel
lonely, isolated or depressed.
Can put you in touch with other
mothers in a similar situation
and/or support groups.*

**Midwives Information and
    Resource Service (MIDIRS)**
9 Elmdale Road
Clifton
Bristol BS8 1SL
(0117) 925 1791
*Information service primarily
for midwives but non-members
may also purchase copies of
research papers concerned with
pregnancy and birth.*

Miscarriage Association
c/o Clayton Hospital
Northgate
Wakefield
West Yorks WF1 3JS
(01924) 200799
*Advice and support for mothers
who have experienced
miscarriage. Also information
on cervical stitches and ectopic
pregnancies.*

Narcotics Anonymous
PO Box 417
London SW10 0DP
(0171) 498 9005
*Self-help organisation whose
members help each other to
stay off drugs. Write or phone
between noon and 8pm for
advice and details of local
groups.*

**National Childbirth Trust
    (NCT)**
Alexandra House
Oldham Terrace
London W3 6NH
(0181) 992 8637

*Information and support for all
aspects of pregnancy and birth.
Ante-natal classes and
breast-feeding support. Local
groups meet informally all over
the country.*

**National Childminding
   Association**
c/o Veronica Day
8 Masons Hill
Bromley
Kent BR2 9EY
*Can supply a list of
childminders in your area.
Please send an A5 SAE on
application.*

**National Information for
   Parents of Prematures –
   Education, Resources and
   Support (NIPPERS)**
28 Swyncombe Avenue
London W5
(0181) 847 4721
*Information and support for
parents whose children have
been born prematurely.*

New Ways To Work
309 Upper Street
London N1 2TY
(0171) 226 4026
*An independent organisation
which promotes job sharing and
other flexible ways of working.
Produces many useful books.*

**Ombudsman (Health Service
   Commissioner for
   England)**
Church House
Great Smith Street
London SW1P 3BW
(0171) 276 2035
*For complaints about the
administrative aspects of care
or the way a complaint has
been handled.*

Parents At Work
45 Beech Street
London EC2Y 8AB
(0171) 628 3578
*Can advise on women's
rights and options in the
workplace.*

Parents of Prems
122 Tyndale Close
Great Barr
Birmingham B43 7NR
(0121) 360 6668
*Telephone and one-to-one
support for parents of
premature babies.*

Patients' Association
18 Victoria Square
London E2 9PF
(0181) 981 5676
*Campaigns on behalf of NHS
patients. Can give information
and advice about making
complaints.*

**Pre-Eclamptic Toxaemia
  Society (PETS)**
17 South Avenue
Holdbridge
Essex SS5 6HA
(01702) 232533
*Self-help and sound advice for
women with pre-eclampsia.*

Quit
102 Gloucester Place
London W1H 3DA
(0171) 487 3000 (helpline –
phone between 9.30am and
5.30pm)
*Advice on how to stop smoking
and details of local support
services. Recorded message
played outside office hours.*

Regional Health Authority
In Scotland the RHA is known
as the Health Board.
In Northern Ireland it is the
Health and Social Services
Board.
*Look in your phone book under
your local health board.*

Relate: Marriage Guidance
Herbert Gray Cottage
Little Church Street
Rugby CV21 3AP
(01788) 573241
*Confidential counselling for
relationship problems. Look in
the phone book under 'Relate'
for local branches.*

**Society of Teachers of the
  Alexander Technique
  (STAT)**
20 London House
264 Fulham Road
London SW10 9EL
(0171) 351 0828
*Can put you in touch with a
teacher/group in your area.*

**Support Around Termination
  for Abnormality (SATFA)**
73-75 Charlotte Street
London W1P 1LB
(0171) 631 0285 (helpline)
(0171) 631 0280
(administration)
*Self-help charity. Support is
given by parents who have had
similar experiences.*

Splash Down Birth Pools
17 Wellington Terrace
Harrow-on-the-Hill
Middlesex
(0181) 422 9308
*Supplies birthing pools
nationwide.*

**Stillbirth and Neonatal Death
  Society (SANDS)**
28 Portland Place
London W1N 4DL
(0171) 436 5881
*Information and a nationwide
network of support groups for
bereaved parents.*

Society to Support Home Confinements
'Lydgate'
Wolsingham
Co Durham DL13 3HA
(01388) 528044 (preferably after 6pm)
Telephone support for women who are experiencing difficulties obtaining a home birth.

Twins and Multiple Births Association (TAMBA)
PO Box 30
Little Sutton
S Wirral L66 1TH
(0151) 348 0020
(01732) 868000 (helpline 6–11pm weekdays; 8am–11pm weekends)
Self-help organisation to encourage and support parents of twins or more. Can advise on local support groups.

United Kingdom Central Council (UKCC)
23 Portland Place
London W1M 3AF
(0171) 637 7181
Governing body for nurses, midwives and health visitors.

VBAC Information and Support
c/o Gina Lowdon
Park View
Mill Corner
North Warnborough
Hook
Hampshire RG29 1HB
(01256) 704871
Information and support for women who wish to avoid a repeat caesarean.

What Doctors Don't Tell You
4 Wallace Road
London N1 2PG
(0171) 354 4592
Leading edge newsletter on all aspects of medicine and health. Also publishes Mothers Know Best *and* Proof! *as well as many booklets.*

Working for Childcare
727 Holloway Road
London N7 8JZ
(0171) 700 0281
Helps advise groups or individuals wishing to persuade an employer of the benefits of setting up a workplace nursery or creche.

Suggested Reading

Pregnancy and Birth (general)

Janet Balaskas,
  The Active Birth Partners Handbook (Sidgwick & Jackson)
  Natural Pregnancy (Sidgwick & Jackson)
  The New Active Birth (Unwin)
  Preparing for Birth with Yoga (Element)
Janet Balaska, Yehudi Gordon,
    Water Birth (Unwin)
    Encyclopedia of Pregnancy and Birth (MacDonald Orbis)
Andrea Frank Henkart,
    Trust Your Body! Trust Your Baby (Bergin & Garvey)
Deborah Jackson,
    Three in a Bed (Bloomsbury)
    Do Not Disturb (Bloomsbury)
Sheila Kitzinger,
    The Crying Baby (Penguin)
    The Experience of Childbirth (Penguin)
    The Experience of Breastfeeding (Penguin)
    Home Birth (Dorling Kindersley)
    Ourselves as Mothers (Bantam)
    Freedom and Choice in Childbirth (Penguin)
Judith Laskar, Susan Borg,
    In Search of Parenthood (Pandora)
Ann Oakley, Ann McPherson, Helen Roberts,
    Miscarriage (Penguin)
Michel Odent,
    Birth Reborn (Souvenir Press)
    The Nature of Birth and Breastfeeding (Bergin & Garvey)
    Water & Sexuality (Arkana)

Pat Thomas,
    Every Woman's BirthRights (Thorsons)
Jacquiline Vincent Priya,
    Birth Traditions and Modern Pregnancy Care (Element)

Medical Research and Information

Books:
Beverley Lawrence Beech (ed), *Waterbirth Unplugged* (Books for Midwives)
Murray Enkin, et al, *A Guide To Effective Care in Pregnancy and Childbirth* (Oxford University Press)
Colin Francombe, et al, *Caesarean Birth in Britain* (Middlesex University Press/NCT)
Henci Goer, *Obstetric Myths and Research Realities* (Bergin & Garvey)
Alison Macfarlane, Rhona Campbell, *Where To Be Born – The Debate and the Evidence* (National Perinatal Epidemiology Unit, Oxford)
Marjorie Tew, *Safer Childbirth? – A Critical History of Maternity Care* (Chapman & Hall)
Marsden Wagner, *Pursuing the Birth Machine – The Search for Appropriate Birth Technology* (ACE Graphics)

Booklets (These can be ordered direct from the publishers – see 'Useful Contacts'.)

Available from AIMS:
    Birthing Your Baby – The Second Stage
    Childbirth Care – Users' Views
    Choosing a Home Birth
    Choosing a Waterbirth
    Delivering Your Placenta – The Third Stage
    Safety in Childbirth
    Ultrasound? Unsound!
    Vitamin K in Relation to Haemorrhagic Disease of the Newborn

Available from What Doctors Don't Tell You:
    Guide to Patients' Rights
    Guide to Women's Screening Tests
    Hospital Survival Guide

My Healthy Child
Vaccination Handbook

Complementary and Alternative Therapies

Kitty Campion, *Holistic Herbal for Mother and Baby* (Bloomsbury)

Phillip M. Chancellor, *Bach Flower Essences* (Daniel)

David Hoffman, *New Holistic Herbal* (Element)

Dr Andrew Lockie, *A Woman's Guide to Homeopathy* (Hamish Hamilton)

Carol Rogers, *Woman's Guide to Herbal Medicine* (Hamish Hamilton)

Denise Tiran, Sue Mack, *Complementary Therapies For Pregnancy and Childbirth* (Balliere Tindall)

Robert Tisserand, *The Art of Aromatherapy* (Daniel)

Henrietta Wells, *Homeopathy for Children* (Element)

Index